25 YEARS
AND COUNTING
CANCER FREE

KAREN CAMPBELL

25 YEARS
AND COUNTING
CANCER FREE

KAREN CAMPBELL

With Over 25 Chapters of What They're Not
Telling You and What I Have Learned
That Has Saved My Life

Sign the petition NOW, lives are counting on us!
"Tell us why we're dying!"®

TELLUSWHYWEREDYING.COM

25 Years and Counting Cancer Free

First Edition
ISBN 978-1-7356054-1-8

"Tell us why we're dying!"® and If only 25% of breast cancer is genetic then what in the environment is giving 75% of us cancer?® are registered trademarks of Karen Campbell. Logo on book cover is trademarked to Karen Campbell. Book written solely and entirely by Karen Campbell.

Sign the petition at telluswhyweredying.com.

For more information or to contact the author, please go to:
twentyfiveyearsandcountingcancerfree.com
karen@twentyfiveyearsandcountingcancerfree.com

Some names and identifying details have been changed to protect the privacy of individuals.

All content found in this book including text, images, audio, or other formats, are provided for informational purposes only. The content is not intended to be a substitute for professional medical advice, diagnosis, or treatment. Always seek the advice of your physician or other qualified health provider with any questions you may have regarding a medical condition. Never disregard professional medical advice or delay in seeking it because of something you have read in this book. Links and references to educational content not created by the author are taken at your own risk. The author is not responsible for claims made by any external websites and education companies.

Brief news excerpts, public statements, and images by individuals or companies other than the author are used under section 107 of the Copyright Act of 1976, allowance is made for "fair use" for purposes such as criticism, commentary, news reporting, teaching, scholarship, and research.

*This book is dedicated to all the women I have loved and known
who have died of cancer.
I watched you fight so hard to stay here with your loved ones.
We, the women left behind, will join together to fight to know the real truth.*

Contents

Be Prepared, Get Organized, Know Your Rights

Introduction

I HAVE BEEN CANCER-FREE for 25 years and counting. I went against recommended medical protocols; partly because other people in my family have not been as fortunate taking that route and partly because I am the type of person who likes to do things differently, as evidenced by my career in holistic medicine. I owned a business working as an independent consultant to holistic centers for 25 years. I have been very fortunate to work with some of the top healers in the county.

That work gave me a chance to see holistic practices healing many health issues after medical doctors said there was nothing they could do. I helped train staff and set up policies in 40 clinics across the country that allow holistic practitioners to treat patients free of worry so they can concentrate solely on healing. The results have been incredible.

I took this knowledge and my personal experience and studies to design my own care regimen that I would use to battle cancer. With the help of prayer—and my spiritual knowledge—I knew I could win the battle with cancer.

As the years from my original diagnosis in 1994 went by, I was often asked what specifically I had done differently and what I was doing now to stay cancer-free. When I explained my approach, nearly everyone remarked, "I wish you would write a book. It would be so much easier than trying to remember everything you just said!"

Initially, I dismissed any notion of the idea. I am not a writer and didn't know how to approach such an undertaking. But as more people expressed interest in my methods, I decided I would take the next steps and this book is the culmination of my research and experiences.

Starting the process of putting this book together has been a journey of its own. I felt it was important not to only give my opinions; I wanted to make sure my beliefs where factual. I spent countless hours doing online research to find proof of my thesis. As I studied, I became more upset as I discovered information cancer patients are not being told, especially how we can better our chances in our desire to finally defeat cancer. I realized we were not being told how to stay alive.

I began to ask myself some critical questions. Was I biased because I overcame cancer so long ago? Had I found some sort of secret? I informally quizzed new cancer patients and they confirmed my hypothesis: they were not being told about treatments I had found 25 years ago. This was a wake-up call for me to get into action. If what I know can help my chances of not getting cancer again then I want others to have this information. I want patients to know why medical professionals are not giving them this information in the first place.

I gathered all the opinions together based on what I would want to know in order to make my own decisions about critical issues such as changes in diet, the truth about testing, what helps cancer grow, and what the body needs to repair cancer cells. I wanted this information to be easy for me to understand so I can make choices. If the research is not complete, explain why or finish it, so I can make a decision based on all the facts available, not on just what you want to tell me.

We want to know how to save ourselves from cancer and save our loved ones from getting cancer. We do not want to accept that cancer has no end. When you think of eight women you know and consider that one of them will get cancer, perhaps it is because no one is asking the right questions. If only 25 percent of cancers are genetic, shouldn't we demand to know where the other 75 percent is coming from? Could it be that we are all doing the same thing that is giving us this deadly disease?

When I discovered the things that cancer patients are not being told, I was heartbroken. And when I shared what I'd found with others, they were angry. "I can't believe that," they'd say. "Why didn't anyone tell us?" I didn't know the answer. But when they insisted, "Why aren't you telling the world?" I realized I have a part in helping.

Knowledge is power. We need to arm ourselves and fight for the right to live cancer-free forever. This book will help you to ask questions along with me. Together we can become one voice, one loud voice breaking through the secrecy, as we demand:

"Tell us why we're dying!"®

Enough is enough.

Karen's Amazing Story: How She Fought to Win the Battle of Cancer on Her Terms

I'm 36 years old and that's way too young to have cancer. My mom had cancer, which didn't show up until she was 50, so don't I have more time? I'm so scared I can barely breathe. I've had little lumps in my chest before so this shouldn't be anything to worry about. I was told as a younger adult these were from drinking too much coffee. They were just little fatty cysts, right?

My God, my daughter Kasondra is only two years old. What will happen to her if this is something scary? I'm not going to think like that and think positively instead. Don't scare yourself until there is something to scare yourself about. The first thing I need to do is get to the doctor. I don't really like doctors and only consult them if there's nothing I can do myself. But I need to call my primary care doctor.

THOSE WERE THE THOUGHTS I had before I showed up at my primary care doctor's office to tell him I had found a lump in my left breast. I also found lumps in my right breast. But the one in my left breast was the biggest, about the size of a nickel, and it was hard when I touched it.

The year was 1994, and I had no information about cancer. I called my mother and told her I was being tested for breast cancer. I knew she had gone through it herself and I wanted to tell her what was happening with me. We never talked about her cancer and all she went through. She had cancer so long ago, when I was in college and living in Los Angeles.

My dad called me and said, "Your mom had cancer, she had surgery, everything went well and she is fine now." *What?*

And that was the end of the discussion. We never went into detail about the family history of cancer. It was like a secret no one wanted to talk about.

On the call to my mom to tell her my news, she finally told me about all the cancer we had in the family. Did I hear about this before and never put it all together? I'm not sure, but now that it was happening to me, I started asking questions.

I found out my mom's sister had cervical cancer and died, her daughter (my cousin) had breast cancer, went through chemotherapy and the cancer returned. She lived but had a double mastectomy to save her life. And finally, her mother had a brain tumor and died. *What?!*

My mother told me she only had one breast removed. I didn't know if that was a good idea now, since cancer can spread to the other breast tissue quickly. Finding out about our history—with all this working against me—what were my chances? I explained everything I had found out to my primary care doctor, added it to my medical paperwork and went over it with him.

He examined my breasts thoroughly, feeling and charting every lump and location. I had a PacifiCare HMO insurance plan, which meant for me to have any kind of testing done, my primary care doctor would need to request in writing to ask for the testing that I wanted. He wrote a report requesting a mammogram.

Once approved, I showed up at a radiologist's office, one of the largest radiology buildings in Encinitas, to have a mammogram. On the intake forms I described where I found the lumps on both sides of my breasts. I also wrote on the forms that my mother had breast cancer. My aunt had cervical cancer and passed away. My first cousin had breast cancer, which came back a second time after chemotherapy treatments. Other cancers ran in my family. My mother's mother had a brain tumor, which was cancerous.

I wanted to make sure everyone at the clinic knew there was a lot of cancer in my family. I wanted to make sure that they understood how important these x-rays were going to be for me. On the intake forms, I wrote "bilateral lumps" to make sure they knew I had lumps on both sides of my chest. I also made an X on the chart to show where all the lumps were on the body diagram. Looking at all the Xs just made me more scared, and the size of the one on my left was so big! I didn't want to leave anything to chance because of my daughter. I knew my chances of having cancer were high. The only thing that was keeping me from being out of control was that I was only 35 and that was way too young to have cancer, right?

I tried to watch the technician's face to see if she would let on if she thought it was cancer or not. There was no sign from her one way or the other so I decided to ask her straight out. Do you think it is cancer? She told me to ask my doctor. When I was finished, she explained that the results will be sent to my primary care doctor and she could not explain anything to me because she was only the technician.

I made a follow-up visit with my primary care doctor to go over the results of the mammogram. He told me during that appointment that we should just watch all the lumps. The lumps didn't seem to be anything serious as far as the mammogram showed. He told me they didn't have the characteristics of cancer, and that cancerous lumps usually weren't hard like mine were. He said that they didn't feel like tumors. The radiologist report indicated they had the consistency of fatty cysts. I never looked at the report myself. I trusted my primary care doctor since he knew my family's cancer history and I thought he would take the reports seriously.

He also kept telling me not to worry, that I was only 35, and that was way too young to have cancer. But having lumps in my breasts bothered me and I really did not know or understand what they were. I decided to ask an Ob/Gyn to get another opinion. Dr. Kristin Pearl was very popular in town and I heard everyone say she was a great doctor. The only problem with being popular is that it takes months to get an appointment to see her. I left a voicemail message with her office explaining that I'd found lumps and wanted a second opinion because my primary care doctor had advised me to simply watch the lumps because of my family history of cancer, which made me nervous. I told her I wanted the lumps taken out. Surprisingly, she called me back to talk things over, which was very sweet, since technically I wasn't her patient yet.

After I told her everything that was going on, she said something that changed my thinking. "You cannot see what's growing underneath the lumps. If I were you, with your family background, I would have them taken out right away." I never thought of it that way—there could be something growing underneath, especially under the big mass on my left. How could you see underneath them if they're solid?

I had to be sure for myself and for my daughter. *If no one else is going to fight for me, I'm going to fight for myself and for my daughter to have a mother for as long as God permits.*

About a month later, I went back to my primary care doctor. This was the first of many more times I would fight medical professionals to get what I wanted. I explained that my Ob/Gyn told me that we couldn't see what was underneath these fatty cysts, and that I wanted them out, now.

He told me I'd need an ultrasound test to see if the tumors had the characteristics of cancer or not. He sent me back to the mammogram place and they did an ultrasound on all the lumps. At every stage I was so scared. I can't describe to you the fear I had but I wasn't going to let these lumps of tissue continue to grow in my body. I needed to know… I was pushing to know.

The lab did an ultrasound of all the lumps in both breasts. On my return visit to my primary care doctor to go over the test results, he told me he had reviewed the report and the lumps did not look cancerous, they were only fatty cysts as he had originally thought after seeing the mammogram. I stressed the point to him again. "But you can't see under them, aren't you wondering if something is growing underneath the cysts?"

I still couldn't accept that there weren't any conclusive results that would make sure that I would stay alive for my daughter. I told him I needed to know for sure that this wasn't cancer. "Isn't there any way we can know for sure?"

"Yes," he said. "The next step is to do a biopsy of the tumor." He explained the procedure and how they go into the tumor with a needle to extract some tissue to study it microscopically and to determine if the cells are cancerous or not. I agreed that if this is the best way for me to know for sure, let's do that.

His office scheduled the appointment with the biopsy clinic. I filled out a new form and shared all the paperwork again making everyone was aware of all the cancer that was in my family. I just wanted to make sure that these people didn't take my case lightly. I wanted everyone to know the odds that were stacked up against me.

They didn't seem to be shocked when I told them about all the cancer in my family. They didn't seem to really care either way. This made me even more frightened. Why weren't they reacting like, "Crap, that is a lot of cancer." I thought it could be because they've seen so much cancer that nothing really shocks them anymore. But maybe this wasn't shocking them because they weren't really paying attention. *Hey, this is my life were talking about! Don't they care that my daughter could have a life without a mother?*

As the procedure got underway, they told me they were going to take a needle and stick it in the tumor. They smeared some numbing cream on my chest. *This is so insane*, I thought. *Why won't they just take them out right now?* The needle was inserted and then the technician said she missed the tumor since the needle never stopped and went in too far. *What the Hell? Isn't this like a big tumor?* "Let me try this again," she announced. This time as she tried, blood started to come into the syringe. As I am watching she says, "Oh, I hit a blood vessel, not the tumor."

My immediate thought was wondering if God was trying to protect me. *If they were this bad at finding a large tumor, how bad would they be in reporting on what they found?* I knew I had to stick up for myself. "I'm just going to have them cut out," I told her, indicating I wanted her to stop.

"No, no, no—that's not necessary, we can get it—just give us a couple more tries," she said.

"No, I'm done. I just want to leave. This is enough of this, you are scaring me," I insisted. They let me get dressed and I left in tears.

When I saw my primary care doctor again, I told him they couldn't find the tumors to take a biopsy. I explained the entire ordeal and finally I cried out, "I have holes all over my chest!" I wasn't willing to go through that again.

"Without the biopsy we will have to go on the ultrasound findings, he explained." He told me that the radiologist definitely thinks that there is nothing to be worried about.

I left even more confused about what to do. I knew I wanted a second opinion and Dr. Pearl's words kept coming back to me… *what's underneath?*

I was being told that my primary care doctor had this under control but that wasn't good enough for me. I thought, *No, I want to go to a breast cancer expert.* I needed to know exactly what was going on. And if he wasn't going to let me have my second opinion, I would get it myself.

Luckily for me, I had worked as an insurance consultant for doctors' offices for 20 years. I knew what to say and do to get around the limitations. I knew HMO doctors were directed to limit unneeded tests. And my primary care doctor thought he had all the tests he needed. *Well, he is wrong. It is my life, not his. I needed more tests.*

I called my insurance company and said I wanted a second opinion. Right away, they started to explain that my doctor was going to have to request this in writing. I told them he wasn't going to write a report for me as he didn't think that I needed a second opinion. And they told me that I wasn't going to get one. But in my heart, I knew I had to have one.

There were so many things leading me to that second opinion that I wasn't going to let it go. I asked for a supervisor at the insurance company and I told her that I wanted a second opinion. She also said no, not without your primary care doctor's prescription for one.

I still wasn't going to let it go. I asked the supervisor for her fax number and her supervisor's fax number. I wrote a letter to the insurance company, explaining my family background with cancer, how large the tumors were, and that they were growing. I explained what Dr. Pearl told me. I wrote that I was formally asking for a second opinion and that I wanted a second opinion. I stated that if I died and my daughter didn't have a mother, I wanted this letter to be added to my permanent record to prove that I requested a second opinion and was denied one. I told that supervisor that her name and her supervisor's name would be noted so the lawyer who was going to sue the insurance company would have that information included for the suit. I faxed them my letter, with a cover note asking them to put the document in my permanent file.

Next, I returned to my primary care doctor's office, handed him my insurance company letter, and asked him to sign and date it to acknowledge that I had given him the letter. I asked a nurse to witness his signature and to sign and date the letter as well and to put a copy into my permanent file. I also asked him to sign and date a letter I had addressed to him, confirming that I had requested a second opinion but he had denied me.

Within a week, PacifiCare was allowing me to go to get my second opinion. Thank God for PacifiCare, because they didn't make me fight any more than I had already. I think any other insurance company would have given me the runaround for months and months. PacifiCare gave me what I wanted, like a gold card, to go for a second opinion.

Now what do I do? Since my primary care doctor was mad at me because I went around him, he was not really willing to help me anymore, but that was a risk I was willing to take in order to save my own life.

I started researching who was the best breast cancer doctor in my area. I left a message for Dr. Pearl asking if she could tell me where I should go. Later, she called me personally to tell me the best doctor that she knew for breast cancer was Dr. Mary Watkins. She also told me she was proud of me for fighting for what I wanted. Her office told me to gather all my records, my ultrasound and my mammogram, and the radiologist reports from my primary care doctor's office, and bring them to the appointment with Dr. Watkins. Remember, Dr. Pearl is a doctor who has never seen me as a patient. She was a doctor who just cared about me as a person, as a mother, as a woman. Every time I talked with her, I started crying—and I am not a crying person. I was scared, and at the same time, so blessed that God had brought her into my life at this time. I knew she could help me save my life.

It took me a while to get an appointment with Dr. Watkins. It took even longer to get my x-rays and copies of my medical records from my primary care doctor before the appointment. I had to go and say I am not leaving until you give me the reports. I sat in the waiting room for an hour. Apparently, when you start going outside a doctor's sphere, they don't necessarily want to help you so quickly anymore. But I persisted.

Finally, I was armed with courage and ready to take my information to Dr. Watkins to really see what was going on. Nearly three months had gone by as all this was happening and I could feel the big tumor on the left getting bigger and bigger; it went from the size of a nickel to the size of a fifty-cent piece. The three smaller tumors on the right stayed the same. This scared me even more. *Why was one of them growing?*

I loved Dr. Watkins from the minute I met her. She had this sense of peace around her. She walked in, shook hands with me and my husband, and said, "Okay. Let's look over what you brought me." She put the mammogram film up on a light box, examined it quickly, and turned back around to look at me with that look. I sensed from her face that this was not good news. I don't know how to convey in words how utterly frightened I was when she looked at me with that look. Think about the scariest thing in your life and then multiply that by thousands. I had a two-year-old daughter. I could only think of all the things Dr. Watkins' look meant and I tuned-out everything else.

How is my husband going to raise my child and work at the same time? Does this mean someone else could be raising my child? She is only two, will she remember me? And then faith kicked in. *You're a fighter, Karen. You are in front of Dr. Watkins and she is going to take care of you, you just have to believe that!*

My thoughts finally came back to the room when Dr. Watkins asked me, "How long has this been going on?"

"Months," I answered, wondering why was she asking. She examined me and asked how much the lump on the left had grown since it looked much smaller in the mammogram. I told her it had grown a lot since I discovered it a few months ago. I explained this was an old mammogram she was looking at, but only a few months had passed. She told me the big tumor on the left had doubled in size since then.

She was as reassuring as she could be. "Let me take a look at all the information you have given me and we will go over it tomorrow together," she said.

I came back to meet with Dr. Watkins the next day. She had been through the notes from the radiologist who had prepared the report on the mammogram and discovered he'd only reported on my right breast. He'd never done a report on my left breast, even though x-rays were taken on both. In all of my intake information, I stated I had lumps on both breasts. And I drew a picture on the form to indicate that the largest lump was on my left breast. My primary care doctor did not catch that the radiologist had only done a report on my right breast.

That meant for all these months, my tumor was growing unchecked because no one had truly studied the reports until Dr. Watkins came into the picture. My primary care doctor never cross-checked the mammogram findings against his personal findings or my intake forms putting my life at risk this entire time.

Dr. Watkins told me that based on the information at hand, she recommended removing the tumor right away so she could see what she is dealing with. The best way of doing that was to do exactly what I had been fighting for: *take it out.*

She went on to explain that based on how large the left-side tumor was now, there was going to be a huge hole in my chest after the removal, but that would be repaired later. She would not take any lymph nodes yet. "Okay," I said. I wasn't sure what this all meant yet.

What I found out was that I was in an urgent situation and I needed to be ready anytime the hospital had an opening. While she never said we were dealing with cancer, at the pace things were moving, I knew she thought it *was cancer.*

I would be going to Scripps Memorial Hospital in La Jolla, California and soon enough, I had all my pre-op instructions. Blood work and other tests had to be okayed in advance by PacifiCare plus I had to use doctors who were associated with PacifiCare. Luckily for me, all the doctors Dr. Watkins wanted were part of the PacifiCare system.

Over the next few days, things started falling into place and she was ready to do the lumpectomy. I tried to stay in good spirits for my two-year-old daughter, but I was scared every day. *Please don't let me die* was the constant plea with God. *Has it spread? I know its cancer, but where could it be now? You are going to have to fight to stay alive now, so get ready.*

I was ready for surgery. I wanted this over and to get onto whatever was next. However, I was not ready for the going-to-sleep part. How do they keep you close to death and not let you go all the way to death? I had several surgeries before for a wrist problem and I threw up for hours afterwards. Anesthesia and I do not get along well at all. I told Dr. Watkins about the problem and she said I could talk to the doctor who would be putting me to sleep beforehand to tell him what I was scared about.

In walks Dr. David Ross, the anesthesiologist, who I later nicknamed Dr. Night-Night. *Okay, is this a joke? Really? This man is a model for a magazine, right?*

With the biggest smile, he introduces himself and says, "I hear you have some questions."

I am thinking, *wow, he is a nice thing to look at before I go to sleep.* He had perfectly dark, wavy hair peeking out from a colorful hair cap. *This guy looks like a "Mash" doctor. Thank you, God, for the distraction and the moment of fear-removal.*

"Yes," I responded. "I throw up after anesthesia."

"Okay," he assures me. "Don't worry. I will make sure that never happens. I can make a mixture that will keep you from doing that."

"I am scared to death of you putting me to sleep."

"What scares you?"

"Not waking up for my daughter. What if something goes wrong?"

"I would never let that happen. You need to trust me."

"Are you sure you won't let me die?"

"Yes, I promise you will see her soon. This is a short surgery and you will wake up before you know it." He looked at me as though he knew I was praying.

God, please hear my prayers. I am so scared, not just about this surgery but about what they are going to find once it is over. Please, Lord, help me. Give me the strength to hold myself together. Surround me with your white light and protect me. Help the doctors do as they were trained to do. Amen.

I woke up from the lumpectomy surgery about three hours later. At first, I was waiting to throw up but it never came. He was right, I did not get sick on his watch. I did not get sick at all.

Dr. Watkins came in during recovery and told me she took the giant tumor out of my left breast and three smaller tumors on the right. The giant tumor was so large that in order to take it all and have clean margins around it, she had to remove one-third of my chest. Now I had a giant hole where my chest used to be on the left and three smaller holes on the right side.

I was in a lot of pain, but all I cared about was if I was going to live. When I asked her what she thought, her eyes started to fill with tears. She said she wasn't sure and didn't want to say anything until the biopsy results came back. I will have my staff call you as soon as the biopsies come back from the lab to schedule an appointment. The one good thing she told me was that the large tumor was still intact and that it had not broken open or spread as far as she could tell. She remarked that she had *never* seen such a large tumor stay that way. It sat in her hand like an egg.

⤛

Now comes the waiting game. You know in your heart that there's something wrong but you have to wait. And the whole time you're waiting, everything around you becomes more precious. Every giggle and every hug from my daughter meant so much more. Every time God gave me these precious moments with her, or even the sight of a beautiful tree or an incredible flower, I would pray, *thank you, Lord.*

I also felt concerned that my daughter couldn't really understand why I wanted to hold her all the time. But my chest hurt so badly that I could barely stand picking her up. I tried to frame my hugs in a way that so I wouldn't scream out in pain. Since I don't like taking heavy pain medications for what they do to my body and the way they make my brain foggy, I managed with over-the-counter drugs and stuck to extra-strength Tylenol.

My main support system was my husband and he had to work. My sister and one brother lived in Oregon and my other brother lived in Arizona. Fortunately, before this all started happening, we had found a great daycare center for my daughter that she was attending two days a week. Now, we had her going four days a week. Another blessing is that she loves going to daycare. The hard part was that with her gone and my husband off at work, I was left by myself with my thoughts and waiting to see Dr. Watkins again. I was not sleeping. I was crying a lot, talking to myself, and talking to God.

I had always attended church, and it's true that when something this terrible comes around, most people get closer to God. I think this is because when you have done everything you can possibly do and there's nothing else to do, there is no choice but to leave everything to God. I had prayed to God before but now I experienced an entirely new meaning of prayer. I was having conversations with God. I started calling him Father instead of God. All day long, we talked. I was never afraid of dying to be with God. I was more afraid of leaving my daughter behind.

Father, I ask you: please keep me alive for my daughter.

The time came for my appointment Dr. Watkins. I was ready to know the results one way or the other. I had reached the point to where I really didn't care if it was bad news, I just wanted to know what the news was. As the nurse led us to the doctor's office, I told my husband that I couldn't breathe out of fear but it was time to fight. I had all my conversations with God and I was ready. Whatever news there was, I was ready.

Dr. Watkins walked into the room. She looked at me and then she looked at my husband. Tears welled up in her eyes. "It's cancer," she said. She got very emotional as she went on to explain. "This is not good news. This is the worst kind of cancer you can possibly have. This is stage 3 breast cancer, with a 5-centimeter tumor."

I started to cry. In my mind, I was prepared to hear I had cancer, but I wasn't ready to hear how bad or how dangerous it was. My chest hurt badly; not from the pain of the surgery, but from the fear welling up inside my body. I took a breath. I asked the question that was just sitting there in the room waiting to be asked. "Am I going to die?"

What she said next was nothing short of a miracle from God. "When I took the tumor out of your chest, it rolled around in my hand like an egg. I've never seen anything like it. It had encapsulated itself three times. And when they cut it open to see what kind of cancer it was in the internal part of the tumor, it started to change. They have never seen anything like it. With that much cancer and that stage of cancer you should be dead. But something in your body saved you. Something kept the cancer encapsulated and did not let it break out. If you had not had the surgery this type of stage 3 breast cancer—which is an estrogen-based cancer and one of the fastest-growing cancers—would've killed you in a matter of months."

I couldn't stop crying and I could barely breathe. What a gift from God. I kept saying, "Thank you, God." We were all going to pieces and finally, once we composed ourselves, I asked the next question that was waiting in the room. "Now what do we do?"

Now was the decision-making time as to what I was going to do with my body, the body that just saved me. Did I want to save my chest while I tried to stop the cancer with chemotherapy and radiation? If I wanted to keep my breasts, I would need to see a plastic surgeon because the holes in my chest from where Dr. Watkins took out the tumors had made my chest uneven. This was not a pretty sight. If I decided not to keep my breasts, I would still need to see a plastic surgeon so they could explain what was possible in terms of making me a new chest.

Dr. Watkins suggested a plastic surgeon she loved to work with, Dr. Stephen Crane. I told her, "I trust you with my life, Dr. Watkins. I will go wherever you want me to go." But first, there were more details to work out.

"There's one thing, Karen," she started. "If you decide on a mastectomy, the team I usually work with on mastectomies are getting ready to go on vacation. So, if you want my normal team, you have 48 hours to decide if you want to have a mastectomy or not so we can schedule it and get it done."

We left for home and talked about figuring out the safest way for me to proceed in what could be my best chance to live. At this point, none of my lymph nodes had been biopsied or removed, so we weren't sure if the cancer had spread to my lymph nodes or not. We were just dealing with the enormous tumors at this point. But the way the cancer had been encapsulated and removed with the tumor, Dr. Watkins did not think she would find cancer in the lymph nodes.

When I returned to see Dr. Watkins, I said I wanted a double mastectomy. I did not ever want to worry about cancer again. I wanted this over with and behind me so I could be ready for whatever came next. Dr. Watkins told me she thought I'd made a great decision, adding, "Your body saved you once, but it may not do it again."

She then proceeded to explain to me that a double mastectomy meant she was going to remove my chest including the nipples. I was no longer going to have a chest at all. In order to be cancer-free and remove the worry about cancer returning, I had to know that the easiest place for cancer to grow was in breast tissue. Without any breast tissue, my odds of getting cancer again would be much less. I didn't want to worry about cancer all the time; constantly checking my chest. So, I agreed. But I wasn't ready to hear all that would have to happen. She went on explaining the procedure. My head was spinning. I knew I had to pay attention. *Keep focused*, I kept telling myself. Eventually, I asked her to tell me everything again.

This was the process: both of my breasts and the lymph nodes would be removed. Once that healed, a plastic surgeon would put in what they called expanding implants to make my new chest. I needed to go to Dr. Crane's office to pick out what implants I wanted. Basically, I needed to pick out my new chest. *My new chest.* I could not imagine what that appointment would be like but I knew this is what I had to do to save my life.

My body and God saved me once; it was my turn to save myself.

On my first appointment with Dr. Crane, I didn't know what to expect. How can I describe Dr. Crane? By comparison, Dr. Watkins is sweet and she cried right along with me. When I first met her, I felt a kind of emotional connection. I know that sounds weird, but I knew right away that she truly cared about me. She is like a teammate who is always on your side. Dr. Stephen Crane is all "doctor." His aura is, "I am the doctor," and he lets you know that every time he enters the room. He is scary and intimidating at the same time. How was I going to work with him? I am an "ask questions" kind of person. I can't make decisions without asking questions. It wasn't easy for me to ask questions of someone I felt scared of, so at our first session, I sat there for a while listening. Or was I listening? My attention kept wandering in and out of the room and I had to keep reminding myself to stay focused.

Then I heard him ask, "Do you want a round or football shape? What size are your breasts now? Do you like that size?" He showed me a book with pictures of other breasts he had formed.

What the Hell? Do you think this is helping? I wanted to scream. Something he said next jerked me back into action. "You mean this can get screwed up?" *Okay, I am all in now; I don't give a crap how scary he is, he better be ready for a lot of questions.*

Dr. Crane explained that once I am healed from the first operation, and depending on the chemotherapy I'm prescribed, he can start with my chest reconstruction. Since I had a very serious cancer, the protocol was for extensive chemo immediately following surgery. And this treatment can also make me sick and slow the healing process.

Okay, Karen, let that go by and stay focused on the process.

"What is the process?" I asked, finding my voice.

"We will open you back up after you have healed and put in stretching implants. The implants go underneath the muscles of your chest where your breasts were. These muscles are on top of your ribs. We will peel them from your ribs and place the implants underneath them. The implants have an opening." He shows me one of them. "On the top here, I will be sticking a needle into them to fill them with water. They will stretch the muscles in the size of the implant, making a hole for me to later put in your permanent implants."

What the Hell? Okay, doctor, get ready.

I flooded him with questions. How long does it take to get them full? Does it hurt when you fill them? How long will the initial procedure take? How many surgeries is this going to take? How many months is it going to take to fill them up?

When I had enough information for the time being, I needed to process what I had just heard. The pictures were still in my mind. I guess that is when everything became real for me—when I saw the pictures of the other patients' breasts. I wasn't going to have a chest anymore. Before, my main thoughts had been about staying alive for my daughter, but now I realized I wasn't going to have a chest anymore.

I didn't get a chance to mourn. I had too many decisions to make. We had decided that my breast cup was a size C and that would look the best for my body size. We could wait until they were stretched to decide on the shape.

I am picking out a shape for my chest.

"After the permanent implants are in place, we will make your nipples," Dr. Crane said matter-of-factly.

"I'm not going to have nipples?"

"No. Nipples have breast tissue. You don't have to have nipples. A lot of patients don't."

"No wait," I insisted. "I want them to look normal for Kasondra. I don't want to have to cover up every time she comes around me."

"We can tattoo them on, or we can graft them from skin taken from the inside of your leg," he offered. Then, out came the pictures again.

"Why from the inside of leg?" I asked, as though the idea was completely crazy.

"Because it has darker skin and they will look real that way. The tattooing can fade."

"Well, I want them to look real. That's crazy but, yes. Let's do the grafting," I decided.

"I need to tell you the risks," Dr. Crane warned me. "If we graft them from the skin on your thighs, there is a possibility it may not take. Your body may reject the graft, and then I am done. I cannot make a nipple."

Even with the risk, I still wanted to try. I wanted to look normal as possible.

I knew that information would be the key to this whole thing. I turned to the Internet to search for options. In the meantime, I was still being a mom to my two-year-old daughter, Kasondra. I was taking care of the house, our dog, I had clients in Los Angeles and Orange County, and was trying to keep my business going. Dr. Crane was waiting on my decision. I had limited time to decide.

I felt that I now had to be in complete charge of my case. The power had to belong to me, the patient. The problem with Internet information is that much of it is not there (in 1994) to truly help the patient. In-depth studies seemed tailored to healthcare providers with information that is not very practical for patients. I had also asked Dr. Watkins' office for pamphlets but they did not tell me what I wanted. There was no step-by-step brochure or document. I am a step-by-step person. Without it, there is no order. And for me, without order, there is cause for fear.

Okay, stay calm, just write down all your fears and ask the doctors for the answers.

I also realized how most medical advice was dominated by Western-medicine doctors. I spent more than 20 years with Eastern-thought and holistic doctors who stayed away from Western medicine. My daughter had the same vaccinations I had as a child and no more. She had not been to a doctor since she was a year old. Where was I going to get my information?

I had a follow-up visit with Dr. Watkins scheduled before the mastectomy, and I was coming in with tons of questions. There were so many, in fact, I called to ask if I could have more time with her to go over them all. Here was my list:

- » How many of these had she done?

- » Were all the surgeries successful?

- » How long is the recovery?

- » How long was someone going to have to take care of Kasondra while I was recovering?

- » How much pain could I expect?

- » How many days would I be in the hospital?

- » When could I go back to work? (We were living paycheck-to-paycheck at the time.)

- » **Why does there have to be two surgeries?** (I marked this as important.)

» Why did I have to heal and then re-injure my body again with another surgery with Dr. Crane? Why not do them both at the same time?

The lovely Dr. Watkins answered all my questions. She had done hundreds of these surgeries and all of them had been successful. She told me it would take months before I would be totally healed.

As far as taking care of Kasondra, I would not be allowed to pick up anything in order for my chest to heal. Did the doctor tell me that? No. I just figured it out by myself. The way I looked at it was like this: if my elbows are attached to my side, once I lift my arms up above that, I am involving the use of my pectoral muscles. If I use my pecs, then I am moving the implant around, and if I move the implant around, it won't heal. And I wanted to heal as fast as I could in order to get back to my normal, healthy self.

Why do they do two surgeries? They have always done two surgeries, she said. That made no sense to me. Why not let the body heal one time? I told her I only wanted one surgery. One surgery to take my old chest off and to put the expanding implants in at the same time.

"We have never done that before," Dr. Watkins said.

"Remember that I don't do well with anesthesia plus I do not want to go under multiple surgeries over months of time. I want my body to heal once," I pressed.

Dr. Watkins said she would check with the team to see how they felt. I volunteered to be their guinea pig and we could all see how it works out.

"I'm not sure how we could arrange for the different teams to come in at the same time," she explained, but added, "Let me talk to the doctors and see what we can do."

I was hoping she would just say they would do it, but I was also wondering what risks were involved? *What will my insistence on doing everything together do to me?*

While Dr. Watkins talked to the doctors, I had an appointment with an oncologist to see what the next steps would be after the surgeries.

This appointment scared me more than the others where we were talking about surgery. Now I am going to be talking about drugs so powerful they could bring me closer to death. Chemo and radiation would bring my immune system down. My low white blood cell count would mean it would be hard to fight off even a common cold. And I have a two year old going to daycare every day who will be bringing home who knows what.

I watched my mom go through chemo and she was so sick. She lost all of her hair and she threw up so much. Her body was never the same. She was always tired, and I knew this was not the life I wanted for myself.

As I sat in the waiting room with other patients, I thought how we all looked so scared. Some looked so sick, too. We were all looking at one another, trying to figure out what stage everyone was in and comparing that stage to our own. The room seemed emotionless and the more I looked around, the more scared I became. When I am scared, I start talking. But here, I didn't want to open up a conversation. I was scared someone might say they were dying. I thought I might cry so I went into the bathroom.

Father God, please help me. I am so scared. Please help me to not cry out there. Please compose my mind so I can ask the questions I want to ask. I know the doctor is going to tell me so many things that are going to frighten me. Help me, my God, please help me.

Okay, you're ready, go back out there....

During the appointment, the doctor confirmed that I had the fastest-growing type of breast cancer, which was a stage 3, estrogen-based cancer. In the breast cancer world, there is a scale of 1 to 4 for things you do not want your cancer to have. I had three of them. Really, I missed one.

The usual procedure is to start chemotherapy right after surgery to kill any cancer that might be spreading anywhere else in the body. Since I was having a double mastectomy, I would only need chemo and thankfully, not any radiation treatments along with it. My thoughts kept coming back to who was going to take care of Kasondra if I was throwing up all of the time. How was I going to explain to my two year old why I am always sick?

Then, I remembered that Dr. Watkins said she rolled the tumor around in her hand as if it was an egg. Cancer had not broken out at all.

I told the doctor that the cancerous cells had encapsulated themselves numerous times. They did not seem to have broken out, the cancer seemed to stay inside the tumor "egg."

So, I asked him, "Why should I do chemo? My body saved me. Why torture it? Let it keep saving me." I thought he was going to fall off his chair.

"Karen, I know you are in shock with all of this, but without chemotherapy, you will probably die. This cancer will come back. Do you understand what I have said to you so far?"

"Yes," I responded. "I fully understand what you have said but it makes no sense to me. Doctor, I am a "stats" person from what I do for a living. What are the stats that cancer will come back? What are my chances it will come back if I do nothing?" I continued, "For that matter, what better chances of not dying is chemo going to give me?"

"Chemo will give you a **10 percent** better chance of the cancer not coming back," he told me.

"Hold on, what?" I exclaimed. "Ten percent is all you're giving me with chemo? You're going to destroy my body for a 10 percent better chance of living? That makes no sense to me. Why bring my body next to death when it just saved me? God just saved me, and now you want me to slowly kill my body for a 10 percent better chance?"

And then I asked him a key question. "What if I helped my body with a 10 percent lifestyle change?"

He responded with the "I am a doctor" look, the "you are crazy" look, and the "I don't think you understand what we have been talking about and how close you came to death" look.

Then he became very serious and said, "There is no reason you are alive right now. This type of cancer should have killed you. It will kill you fast if it comes back, we have to get in front of it and stop it before it starts. We need to get you on the schedule so we can start this treatment right away."

"Wait. Wait. Wait," I protested. "How am I going to heal properly from the upcoming surgery if you kill off my immune system that helps me heal? I will have no white blood cells to heal me."

"We can't wait. I am trying to save your life. The protocol is to start this right away, right after the surgery."

"Why?" I asked. "Because statistics show it gives you a better chance to live? What are the statistics that if you wait until after the surgery to start chemo? How much does it hurt my chances if I wait?"

"We don't have a statistic for that. I can't give you any advice if you wait. Who can? No one that I know of with your kind of cancer has ever waited that I have kept track of. We have no studies of people who have waited."

"How do you know then it will hurt me to wait?" I was not budging. "I need both sides to figure out what I am going to do," I told him. "You're asking me to decide with only one side of the information. Where can I study the other information? Who can I talk to about that information? You say there are no studies, so there is nowhere to go? There is no one you can send me to? It is your way or I am alone? None of this makes sense. I am more confused than before I came here."

He was not pleased with my line of inquiry. "I have to study this. I will let you know what I have decided. If you are not going to take the recommended course of therapy today, you will have to sign a document that says I told you about all the risks and you are declining the treatment."

Oh, okay. If that is a scare tactic then it really worked. Okay, don't start crying.

I signed and left.

I always talk to myself when I am processing things and then I pray a lot. As I processed this out in my mind, I couldn't understand why it all felt so robotic. It was weird. You have cancer and this is what you do. Period.

I was mad that he turned off after I started asking questions. Patients should be able to ask questions. *How dare he scare me with dying. Okay, refocus. You have to focus on the surgery—and your life—right now.*

I needed to call my clients to let them know what I was doing and to explain how long I was going to be away and unable to work for them. I knew they would want to know exactly when I'd be ready to come back to manage their clinics. I hadn't told them anything up to this point because I didn't know what was going on myself. But now, I wasn't sure what to say. "I have been with you for years but I have cancer now; they think I may die." That didn't seem do-able. I am also friends with my clients and this was the first time I thought about how I would tell everyone I have deadly cancer. I wondered how people were going to react.

Only my immediate family knew about my diagnosis. I had not told anyone else. I told myself it's going to be okay. *I have friends. I know they will be there for me.* And then the most nagging of thoughts returned. *Who's going to take care of Kasondra?* I decided I'd wait until I heard from Dr. Watkins about what was going to happen so I had the correct information to share.

The appointment with Dr. Watkins finally arrived and I'd find out if she and her teams were willing to do everything during one surgery.

Dr. Watkins walked in with a smile on her face. "Yes, we are going to try to do it together in one surgery," she said. "We have worked it out. I will go in and remove your chest and your lymph nodes while Dr. Crane's team stands by. When I am done, his team will put the expanders in that will stretch out your muscles for your new chest."

She continued, "Karen, you understand you will be under anesthesia for what we think will be up to 8 hours. We are not exactly sure how long this will take, since we have never done this before."

"Yes, I understand," I responded.

"There is a large risk factor the longer you are under anesthesia," she added.

"Yes, I understand," I replied. "But there is also a risk of infection the more times you open me up. And all the work you'll be doing is close to my heart and lungs. An infection can easily spread to those organs and kill me. If you keep shocking my body every time you open me up as a new injury, my body does not understand all this trauma. It needs to start the healing process over and over, putting a strain on my body each time. This way, it will have months to heal before you shock it again with another surgery. It will be totally healed from this major surgery before you do a small surgery to switch out the stretching implants for my forever implants."

I continued, "That would be about a two-hour surgery to switch them out, and then I am done being opened up. They will put on my nipples at the same time. What was originally four surgeries planned close together is now only two surgeries with months in-between for my body to heal and rest. I think that is a better plan for me and my body."

Dr. Watkins looked at me and agreed that this plan made sense. Dr. Watkins is a doctor who listens to her patients and agrees to try new things!

She then asked me about the chemotherapy appointment. "I know you told me you didn't want to go. Did you go?"

"Yes, I promised you I would go," I said.

"And what have you decided?"

"I am not going to do the chemotherapy."

"Karen, this is off the record, but good for you. I don't think you need to. I don't think the cancer spread anywhere. I could not believe it when I took out the tumor and it didn't appear to have opened. I have never seen anything like it. We will not know for sure until I take your lymph nodes out, but we will make sure," she explained.

✂

Now, the entire process ahead of me started to move quickly. Or maybe I was so scared it just seemed like everything was moving fast.

I had to get the new surgical process approved by the insurance company. The doctors had to write reports and I had to write a statement about my problems with anesthesia.

Next, I began to think about what I needed to heal myself after the surgery. I knew that in order to heal, the body needs uninterrupted rest. I needed to treat my chest like an open wound that needed to heal. The muscles could not be moved much so they could heal. That meant my pecs needed to stay still as much as possible so everything could rebuild.

I needed a hospital bed at home so I could raise myself up without involving my pecs. When I called my insurance company, they did not understand why I would need this at all. What I needed was a doctor's report to get this pushed through, I would ask Dr. Watkins the next time I saw her if she would write a report. Okay, what's next.

And who was going to take care of Kasondra while I was in surgery? She could not come to the hospital for at least eight hours while I was having surgery. I called my sister in Oregon, but she had a family of her own and wasn't able to come. It was time to tell my friends and clients that I had cancer, just how bad it was, and what was ahead for me. Of course, when I made those calls, they could not believe what was happening. I told them I didn't know when—or even if—I would be able to come back to work.

One of my favorite clients, who I had helped build their clinic from scratch, Dr. David Tann and his office manager, Pam, were so kind. "Just tell us what you need and we will do it," they said. Dr. Mathew Heck, an acupuncturist from that clinic, worked with me over the phone to advise on what herbs to take and what oils to use to heal from the surgery.

Then came the reality check as the other clinic owners called me back. "Good luck, Karen, we will miss you. Do you know anyone else who can manage our clinics?"

Wait, what?

"Our business must move on but check in with us and let us know what happens," the explanations went.

I was crying after every call. *I gave my all to them, even worked when I was eight months pregnant with Kasondra. I am so hurt right now.* I wanted to scream, "I might die…"

I called one of my best friends who lived in Los Angeles. "I need someone to stay home with Kasondra while I have surgery, will you come here and stay with her?" I asked. "I need to have someone I trust with her so I can go into surgery clear-minded."

"Can't your sister stay with her?" came the answer.

Wait, what?

"I don't know what to do with kids, I don't have any kids. I don't feel comfortable staying with her," the excuses went on.

"You are my best friend. You were in my wedding and you can't do this?" I was shocked. What is happening? None of my friends were willing to help? Who were these people I thought I knew? I had figured, okay, this will be easy. All of my friends will jump in to help. Never in a million years did I think I would be crying about *this*. Now, not only did I need someone to stay with Kasondra, but who was going to help me after the surgery?

Luckily, I had found a daycare Kasondra loved. I called the director who said my daughter could attend full time while I was sick. But full time was only until 2:00 p.m., Monday through Friday. How would I get her there and bring her home? My husband would need to return to work right after the surgery. That meant I'd be by myself. How was I going to get to my appointments? How would I keep up with the housework? Could I make life seem normal for Kasondra? Who would bring me the food and the things I needed to heal?

I called the insurance company but all my "favors" were used up. As an HMO, they didn't provide home care of any kind. I called my dad and told him what was going on.

"Your mom and I will pay for a nurse to come stay with you for while your husband is at work to help with Kasondra."

I was so blessed by this gift. I was taken care of. Some of the fear started to fade away. This help would be incredible, but I still needed someone to stay with Kasondra while I was in surgery.

I called Dr. Tann and I started to cry. "I just need to know she is safe while I go into surgery."

"Don't worry, Karen. I will close the office and Pam, the office manager, and I will come down to stay with Kasondra," he insisted. Finally, I could put my mind at ease, she was safe.

This was a blessing for a day, but what about for the rest of her life? A new reality set in for me and my fear increased.

If I die, what will happen to Kasondra? I need to look over my will now. I need to update my will. I want everything all planned out so if I die, everything will be taken care of for Kasondra.

I had a life insurance policy, but was that enough? What do you do after that money runs out? My dad's will had all of his stipulations spelled out, so I knew that's where I needed to start. He made an appointment for me to meet with his attorney and he helped me design a living trust and a will.

The control freak came out in me, the poor attorney. She started asking questions that prompted answers that surprised her. Our conversation went something like this:

"How many years will she be able to go to school? You don't want her to become a stay-in-school-for-the-money child," she said.

"What? Kids do that?" I asked.

"You need to protect her against men marrying her for her money. They can prey on her and stay married to her long enough to get all the money. Your husband can remarry and she will get all the money." My head was spinning.

"We need to protect Kasondra at all costs. If I am not here, she needs to have the best life I can give her," I said. I then explained what I wanted to give her.

I wanted a full-time nanny for her, our house paid-off so she will never have to move and a set amount of money so my husband doesn't have to work all the time. My income went to paying half the bills and I wanted that covered. I wanted her college paid for so she could have the best education I could provide. I wanted her to drive a safe car, have regular vacations, I wanted to give her everything I could think of. I had a life insurance policy and I wanted to make sure it was used only for her.

This poor attorney grappled with seven pages of my wants. I don't think I left anything out.

Loving mother and control freak have a very fine line in-between them. I convinced myself I was doing it for the love of my daughter, but was that really true? I hope she never has to find out.

Now that the dying part was covered, my next step was planning for living. I had to plan for my life after surgery. What did I need the nurse my dad was paying for to do? Facing a major surgery, I had to plan around all the aspects of my life.

I researched the fastest ways to get my body healed in the shortest amount of time. One problem was that few people, if anyone, had both surgeries at the same time. How was I going to find any research when I am living the research?

I started with what I know about the body based on more than 20 years of working with holistic centers. The best way to heal is to make sure the part that is healing does not move, right? So, I have to make sure my chest does not move to the point where I am interrupting the healing process. I would need to treat my chest as an open wound and my pec muscles need to stay as still as possible. What types of things make me engage my pecs?

I owned an aerobics center years ago and trained people to understand what muscles are used in various exercises. My idea was to pretend that my elbows were permanently attached to my sides so I could not use my pecs to do anything. Once I tried practicing that, I could see how much I used those muscles.

Wow, I am really going to need help, I thought. *I am going to be severely limited in picking up Kasondra, doing laundry, vacuuming, pulling up sheets on the bed.*

Speaking of beds, I didn't realize how much we use our arms to get out of bed! Your pecs are the main muscles used to push your body up and out of bed. I also couldn't carry much of anything at all. If I wanted to heal fast, I'd need to put the least amount of stress on my body. It's true that stress causes cancer and my body was going to have to deal with a lot of stress. A new fear came over me.

Wait, there are more than just these limitations. I will be practically defenseless when I am home alone. What if something happened to me? Who was going to be there to help me? And worse, who could help Kasondra if something happened to her?

I sure needed a nurse and I felt so blessed my father was helping me to have one. Otherwise, I would be using credit cards. He said he could pay the costs to cover a few days, but would that be enough? I had no idea. More questions came flooding in.

I was going to be laying down to rest; who was going to help me get out of bed? What if I needed to go to the bathroom in the middle of the night? Was I supposed to wake my husband every time? It is so hard not knowing what to expect and there is no one to talk to since this double-surgery-in-one-go had never been done before. How much pain am I going to be in? How much pain can I stand or handle? I have never been in really bad pain before, at least not pain that lasted for hours, days, weeks?

Okay, Karen. Change your thoughts away from the pain or you are going to get scared. I need a plan to get healed as fast as I can. I need to focus on the healing—the faster I heal, the faster I'll be out of pain, and the faster I'll get my life back.

I knew I'd do just about anything to get back to normal and on the other side of healing. Don't forget the hospital bed so I could raise myself up without involving my pecs. The insurance company was not going to approve this so I knew the only way to change that was to show them the danger I would be in *without* a hospital bed and to explain the risks of me getting hurt while being alone during my recovery. I also knew that the only person who could convey that was my doctor.

I asked Dr. Watkins if she would help me get a hospital bed. I needed her to write a report explaining I would be in danger of hurting myself while I am alone without a hospital bed. Thankfully, Dr. Watkins is willing to ask for anything to help her patients. "Of course, Karen, I'll write the report, consider it done, one less thing to worry about.

Now I needed to find a nurse. Where do you find someone you can trust with your life? And not only my life, but Kasondra's life, too. She is two years old. She doesn't know yet if someone is doing something wrong to her. I didn't want to be completely vulnerable and unable to defend Kasondra or myself. I asked around to see where I could find a nurse. A friend told me about a nurse-staffing center in Carlsbad. I called and asked for pricing.

While talking to the owner, I found out that her brother had been a friend of our family's years ago. Her family had lived on the street where I grew up and I had known them for years. Out of all the staffing centers I could have called this one knew my family. *Was God leading me again?* Everywhere I turned, things were being handled for me. My parents were going to pay for three days. I had no idea how long I would actually need extra help but I scheduled nursing care for three days.

It was time to wait until the day of the surgery. *Okay, take one thing at a time; surgery and then whatever comes next.*

Everything I could think of was in place. I was as ready as I could be. I went to the post-op consultation with my husband. They went over the expenses with us and I could see how blessed I was to have insurance. I was so glad to have the HMO plan but we still could not afford the copays. We set up a payment plan to pay all the things insurance would not cover.

I had blood work and started getting ready for the surgery. Doubt was coming out of me but I couldn't turn back.

This cancer could be growing in me like a time bomb. Who knows, it might be everywhere? Maybe there was a little hole she missed and it has spread. Until surgery and examination of the lymph nodes, we won't know for sure.

On the day of the surgery, I'd be checked into the hospital and all the plans we've made would be underway. I had everything in place for after the surgery and all the players were ready. I was ready. I thanked God for Kasondra and knew I was blessed every day. Because I'd be under for possibly as long as 8 hours, I was more afraid of not waking up than the surgery itself.

How do they keep you so close to death but not let you cross over to death?

I searched for an anchor to keep me here; something that would remind me of all I have. My jewelry would be removed and I would be stripped bare. I decided to made a knot anklet with Kasondra to have her with me. I bought some colored string and taught her how to tie knots.

Karen, don't cry as you are doing this. Good job, Kasondra! Pull the string… look! A knot. Wow, you're so good at this! Don't cry. Multi-color string with small knots, it's all-strange with no pattern… let's tie this on Mommy, so pretty. Okay, pull the string, perfect….

This was my anchor to this world as my daughter was tying one knot at a time, so I would be connected to this world and her. I was ready.

Kissing my daughter that night had a new meaning for me. Was this the last time I would see her? I knew it was up to God as to what would happen next. For a controlling person, this mindset was so out of control.

In my hospital room, my husband and I wait for them to come get me.

Don't cry. My God, I am so scared. Not of the pain or even the results, only if you have plans for me not to be here. Does negotiating with God work? If it does, I promise you anything right now. Please, God, don't let me die. Breathe, Karen. Keep breathing.

In walks Dr. Ross. "I just wanted to say I am here and I am ready. Everything is going to be fine." Next, Dr. Watkins arrives and finally, Dr. Crane. They were all ready. Was I?

It is time to go now. The hospital has a schedule, and I am on it for today.

God, please, please don't let me die... Karen, you have two surgical teams waiting for you... get in control of yourself... Dr. Watkins won't let you die... you trust her, right? But more than that, God is waiting for you in surgery. The angels you have felt around you for your entire life are there... how else could so many things fall into place without God?

They wheel me down to the operating room. I keep praying and tell myself not to stop until I am asleep and truly in God's hands. We arrive in the operating room and fear hits me again.

All the doctors start coming in to the pre-operating room to go over what they will be doing during the surgery and to let me know they are here and ready to go.

Did I make the right decision? It's too late now....

"Can you please get off the gurney and get to the operating table now?" I hear a voice instruct me.

Looking around the room, I felt like I was in a TV show with equipment everywhere. It made me realize just how real this all was and the depth of the surgery they were about to do on me. There where so many people in scrubs and masks, all looking at me, I could not tell who was who anymore, were my doctors here, I could not tell.

"Hi, Karen. I am the lead nurse and you're going to be okay; we are going to start getting you ready for the surgery now. We are going to lay you down; we have to put your arms out here," (like a cross) "so we can get to them if we need to start an IV line."

I am raised off the gurney in a sling to take the pressure off my body.

"Oh, my God. I can't breathe," I cry.

"No, you are fine. We can see the oxygen levels and your heart rate. You are fine," came a reassuring voice.

"I have to go to the bathroom and I don't want to have to go during the operation," I tell her.

"It really doesn't matter. People do it all the time, we have a pad underneath, so you just pee."

"I don't want to. I can't." I start to get very anxious and upset. I begin to cry.

Dr. Crane steps in. "What is going on?" he asks me.

"I really need to pee, please, I just want to go to the bathroom, please…"

Dr. Crane says, "Let her down and let her go to the bathroom."

The head nurse was not so giving. "We need to keep to schedule and she is already nearly set-up for the surgery."

"I said, 'Let her go to the bathroom,'" Dr. Crane's voice is one that makes the world stop and listen.

They lowered me and helped me off the gurney. My feet never felt so good on the floor. I ask where the bathroom is and they lead me to the hall to show me. I walk into the bathroom by myself, step inside and immediately start to cry.

I have never been so scared God, am I doing the right thing? I don't want to die. Who will raise Kasondra? I love her so much. I have just started to be her mother, please; I beg you… give me the strength to finish what I have started. I will cherish the life you give me if you let me live.…

Please, God… I know you are here. I can feel you. Please stay with me, let me wake up. Amen.

Walking back into the operating room, I lay on the gurney again. People are moving around me in a rush. Then I see her. Like a beacon of reassurance, Dr. Watkins comes in.

"Hi, Karen, it's me, Dr. Watkins," she says. "First, they are going to get you ready then my team will come in to remove your breasts. When we are done, Dr. Crane and his team will put in your stretching implants. Do you understand what is going to happen to you?"

"Yes, I understand."

"Everything is going to be okay."

I am going to let them do their work and get ready.

The nurses are moving quickly around me, hooking me up to things I don't understand but they need for the surgery. As they start to strap me down, a nurse sees my knot anklet.

"You can't have any jewelry on in surgery so we have to take this off."

I start to cry. "No, you can't take this off. I need it on, please."

"It is not sanitary to have that on during surgery," she insists.

"No, please..." I am crying so hard I can barely breathe.

Dr. Crane asks, "What is going on? Who is getting her so upset?"

She shows him the anklet and I start begging, "They want to cut it off. My daughter tied it on me. Please, I really need to keep this on. I need to feel her with me, please."

"You can't have it on," argues the nurse. "This is the hospital's rule! If we need your legs for an IV this is not sanitary."

"I can cut it off in an instant if need be," Dr. Crane tells her. "Tape it all the way around to seal it to her leg."

"But doctor..."

"I take full responsibility. Leave it on her leg."

"Okay, fine. It stays," the nurse gives in.

"Karen, it's okay, don't cry," Dr. Crane assures me.

Dr. Night-Night has now arrived. He has a portable stereo under his arm and a multi-colored surgical cap on his head. He looks so handsome; I almost forget how scared I am. Almost.

"What kind of music do you want to listen to as I put you to sleep?" he asks.

I couldn't speak, I just looked at him with fear in my eyes. All I could see was his eyes above his mask, he looked back with reassurance and an eye smile as to say it's going to be okay.

"I'll find something fun for you," he says. I take a long sigh. "I have to get all your IVs in now so we don't get behind. It is all going to be okay, Karen. Like I promised you before, I will make sure you wake up. You have my word."

All I see all around me is a sea of doctors' scrubs. I am not sure who is who now.

"All the IVs are in and we are ready to go, Karen," Dr. Night-Night tells me.

I see beautiful bright blue eyes. "It's Dr. Watkins, Karen. We are going to put you to sleep now so we can start the procedure." She grabs my hand and gives it a squeeze.

A nurse wearing glasses walks up to my bedside. "We are going to start to put you under."

"Wait, wait!" I say it so loud the room stops. "Please, wait! I want to pray God into the room first." The room grew silent.

Our Father, who art in Heaven,
Hallowed be thy Name;
Thy kingdom come;
Thy will be done
on earth, as it is in Heaven.
Give us this day our daily bread;
And forgive us our trespasses,

as we forgive those who trespass against us;
And lead us not into temptation,
But deliver us from evil:
For thine is the kingdom,
the power, and the glory,
For ever and ever.
Amen.

As I am saying the prayer, I see tears forming in my nurse's eyes behind her glasses, and they start running down her cheeks. I see others mouthing the words as I say them. I am crying as I say them.

I repeat the prayer over again…

Thank you, Father, I feel you in the room.
Bless these doctors and nurses,
*Father, to keep me alive, **your will be done.***

"Okay," I assure them. "I feel him here. You can start."

Dr. Night-Night says, "I'll keep you safe, Karen, like I promised… now count backwards…."

"Karen, you're in the recovery room and we need you to start waking up for us. We need to ask you some questions. Open your eyes for us," the voice comes from far away.

I was so scared to open my eyes. I thought I was going to be told that something went wrong. But more than that, was I alive? As I was trying to process that thought, the pain hit me. My throat hurt as I tried to speak and I didn't know why. I pointed to my throat and the nurse understood.

"Your throat hurts because the tube was in your throat for so long."

Okay, I get that now. My heels really hurt and I can't understand why my heels hurt. I ask the nurse. She tells me she doesn't understand why they would hurt so bad.

"How is your chest?" she asks me.

"It hurts and under my arm really hurts," I tell her.

"On a scale from 1 to 10, how is your pain."

"Past 10," I tell her and I start to cry.

"Okay. Now that you are awake, we can give you morphine for the pain."

I treat my body like a temple. During the surgery where they removed the tumors, I took extra-strength Tylenol for the pain. I have never had a hard narcotic before. But when I woke up, you could have offered me anything to make the pain stop and I would have taken it. It was unlike any pain I had felt before. It literally took my breath away.

As I waited for the medication, doubts started coming. What had I done to myself? "Oh, my God," is all that was running through my mind. My heels hurt so badly I could not believe it was right. Why would my heels hurt? What had they done to my heels? I had been in a car accident before where I felt pretty bruised up, but now, my entire body hurt. My mind was reeling, wondering how long was this pain going to last.

Dr. Night-Night appeared. "How are you doing?"

"Pain," was all I could croak out. My throat hurt like Hell and it was hard to talk.

"All of that will go away, don't worry. See, you are not throwing up like I promised, right?" He was so cheery, for a second I was thinking, *right, I'm not*, and then the pain came reeling back.

Dr. Watkins came in next. "The surgery went incredibly well, Karen. I am confident we got all the cancer removed and the plastic surgery went perfectly. You are ready to start your life again."

"We are going to start the pain medication now," she added, and they put morphine in my IV.

When I woke up again, I was in my room. I was no longer in pain but I could not think clearly at all. What were people saying to me? I needed to go to the bathroom. That was all I could think about. I tried to get up and my head was spinning. I remembered they told me not to get up without someone to assist me. Now I know why. They had put a catheter in during surgery but now I was on my own.

My husband pushed the button and a nurse came into the room. I told her I had to pee. She said, "You have to do it in bed."

"I never had to use a bedpan after other surgeries," I insisted. "I really want to go into the bathroom." She and my husband helped me up and started me towards the bathroom. I couldn't feel my legs or control them at all. The room was spinning and I could not control my mind.

"I need to get back in bed, NOW…"

As they led me back to bed, I knew I could not stay on this drug. I had no idea what other options I had, but morphine was insane. How was I supposed to know what people were doing to me? If I was going to be given other drugs, I would have no idea what they were or why they wanted me to take them.

I told the nurse that I needed to be taken off this drug for pain. She said, "Your doctor will be in tomorrow, you can ask him then." I didn't have the energy to fight. I needed to sleep. But I told myself I would when I woke up again.

That was sooner than I expected. I heard a nurse trying to wake me up, asking me how I am feeling. Who wakes up a person to ask them how they are feeling? "On a scale from 1 to 10, she insisted.

At this point, I can't think at all. There was pain, but I was not sure what the scale of it was. I just wanted to sleep. People were coming in and out of my room all night. I think I saw my husband but I could not be sure.

I know that Dr. Watson came in to check on me. I told her I needed to be taken off this drug because I could not move without feeling like I was going to throw up. I explained that I wanted to be able to understand everything that was going on with me, and I wasn't able to understand anything on this drug.

"People are doing things to me and I can't understand what and why they are doing them," I insisted.

"Karen," Dr. Watson said in a calm voice, "you do not understand the level of pain we are talking about if you get off the morphine. I am not sure other pain meds will be able to stop the pain enough for you. You need rest to heal. You can't sleep in that much pain."

She continued, "Your body sees this as a severe trauma. The surgery was the equivalent of a heart surgery where they open your chest."

I negotiated one more night of morphine, and then I said I had to be off the drug for good. She promised.

The next day, I told myself I was getting off this drug. I can handle the pain, can't I? I have never had severe pain before but I think I can handle the pain. How do you know the amount of pain you can handle until you're in pain? I guess I will find out! Was it worth the risk of pain to get back in control of what was being done to me? YES!

If morphine was out, what were they going to give me instead? Dr. Watson explained she was going to give me Darvocet; a strong narcotic but it wouldn't make me unable to think. She would give me a strong dosage to try to stay ahead of the pain.

I guess it is one kind of pain to remove your chest and one kind of pain to take out your lymph nodes… and then there is the pain of putting in new implants and expanding them. No one really knew the pain I would be in with all of these things being done to me at once.

"You will have to taper off the morphine and be given Darvocet instead. Darvocet is a closely timed drug and only so much is given at a time. You have to wait a given period before the next dosage. If that dose doesn't take care of the pain, there is not much more they can do. Do you understand? They cannot switch drugs back and forth, so this is now going to be the choice of your drug." Dr. Watson wasn't certain this was a good idea, but she agreed to let me switch.

That was only if I promised to let my body sleep for a day or two as they made the switch. As I was taken off morphine and put on Darvocet, I started to realize where I was and what was being said around me. There had been choices made for me that I was not making myself about my care. Once I knew what was happening, I could see that I made the right decision to switch medications. I was able to directly participate in my care as I tried to deal with the pain on my terms.

As my mind became clearer, I realized I had not looked at my chest at all or, should I say, looked at where my chest used to be.

This was a good idea, right? Am I going to have a chest like Frankenstein now? Am I going to see all kinds of stitches everywhere?

I opened up my gown to assess what had happened to me. All I see are bandages and two bags on my sides with lines leading to my chest which are filled with red fluid—a blood mixture of some kind—coming out of my body. Is that good? I don't remember if the doctor told me about this. I used to have a nice size C chest and it is gone. As I look to see what is there now, it hits me: my chest is gone. All the way gone. All I see is a small bump where my beautiful chest used to be.

This is going to be a huge project to get me to the size I used to be. I never really grasped what that meant. Dr. Crane made it sound so easy and simple but this was going to be more than I thought, for sure.

Okay, get a grip. Crying is not going to help you in any way, right? You can't get your chest back by crying. You have a two-year-old daughter at home that can't wait for you to get your act together. You have to fight to get your life back, so what if it is going to take you longer than you thought. This is step one. You are going to get to the other side of this and be done with it. I mean, that is why you did it this way, to get to the other side as quickly as you could. To get your life back. To take it back from cancer.

Once they switched me all the way over to the other drug, there was no turning back. I noticed some of the nurses asking me if I was okay more than they had before. I think they were shocked I asked to get off the morphine. Now it was up to me to see if I could stand the pain and manage the pain in my mind.

If I stay still, the pain is manageable. When I move, my body warns me to stay still. In other words, my body is pissed off at me for doing this to her and she's going to show me how mad she is at me.

I became a clock-watcher. As it gets closer to the time the drug is going to wear off and the next dosage will be given, I start to feel the pain more. *Is that because I am telling myself that or is that the real reason I am in more pain?* My mind is playing such strange tricks on me.

Sitting for hours by myself is so hard to do. Watching the clock, knowing I am going to be in pain and waiting for it to happen. *What the Hell? Was it even a good idea to get my mind clear?* When I was on morphine, I never realized all this stuff. That drug took all care and pain away, but at what cost? When I was on the morphine, I was not feeling the pain. I would move and nothing would stop me from doing so. But I did not know the damage I could have been causing with that movement. And wouldn't that be extending my healing time? So, pain it is. *I'll let the pain tell me what I should do and not do.*

With my mind clear, I start to ask about the other medications they are making me take. What is it all for? The nurses are sick of me asking them what they are doing. *I'll bet they wish I was on morphine and asleep for most of the time.*

My mind had plenty of time to wonder about what normal people do.

Do they just take the drugs and not ask what they are for? Why do I have to take them? I don't need a stool softer. I stopped that drug. How many days do I need to be on this hard-core antibiotic? I want to know how long it is going to take to get my clean body back.

Every time I said no to a drug, the nurses had to call Dr. Crane to ask if it was okay to stop the drug.

"Good evening, Karen," he greeted me.

"Hi, Dr. Crane," I try to smile, wondering why he's here.

"Why are you harassing my nurses about the drugs I've told them to give you?" Dr. Crane always gets right down to business.

"I told you I don't want anything my body does not need to heal," I explained.

"Okay, let's go through the list one time and make decisions about each medication. I do not need them to call me over and over for just you." I was used to his scolding by now, and simply smiled.

The anesthesiologist told me I was going to be tired from the surgery, which I found out took hours! *How long would the anesthesia stay in my body?* It can stay in the body for days, even weeks, and make you tired. That explained why I was sleeping so much. I knew I wanted to get the drug out of my system and since I had plenty of time by myself, this gave me a project to concentrate on. *If the drug stays in body tissue, what flushes out your tissues?*

Water. Great, I thought. *Now I am going to have to go to the bathroom more, which means I'll have pain from moving and thereby slow down the healing.* But

Dr. Night-Night also said movement helps to remove the anesthesia out of the tissues. How was I going to do that? *Walking. I needed to start walking as soon as I could.* Pain again.

My life was going to have to be about pain right now. Drinking water all day was plan one.

When the nurse came in again, I told her I wanted to start walking to get the anesthesia out of my body. Since I couldn't walk by myself, I scheduled times when my husband could help walk me along with times for a physical therapist to walk me. They were supposed to come in once a day to start working with me.

The finance person came in to talk to me next. They told me in order to be released and get home, I'd have to be able to walk on my own. I had been going to the bathroom, trying to time it right after they gave me the drug for pain. They were talking about when I was going to be sent home.

What? Go home in this pain? How was I going to manage it on my own?

Then I remembered I'm on an HMO insurance plan. I only had so many days allowed in the hospital and they needed me to get out. How long did people not on an HMO insurance usually get? I had only been in for three days and three nights. Before I went home, I needed to be sure I'd be able to take care of my two year old. I had to figure out a game plan.

I needed to get up and walk, and I had a plan timed around the medication doses and when my husband could visit, only about an hour or so a day. Otherwise, I was on my own. I wondered what it would be like to have someone taking care of me all the time. I understood my husband had to work and we have a young daughter to care for, but this was hard to do on my own. I was glad that my dad had agreed to pay for a nurse to be there when I got home. This was way too much to deal with alone.

I hadn't really thought about going home until they brought it up. I wondered how I was going to explain everything to Kasondra. I didn't want to scare her with all the bandages and the "pain face." She is very good at reading my face and I couldn't figure out how I was going to get through this.

Don't get ahead of yourself, one step at a time. Just keep getting up and walking down the hall. That is all you have to concentrate on right now.

When Dr. Crane stopped by again, he said he wanted to begin filling the implants as soon as possible to not let any scar tissue build up around the small implants. That meant as soon as I got back home, I would need to travel to his office for the fills. Another hurdle to jump.

Today I am going home. My husband is coming to get me. I have drains with fluid hanging from my chest that I am going to have to measure and change all day. I have stitches in my chest and under my arms from where they took out my lymph nodes. These throb all the time.

Dr. Watkins has informed me this is because that is where the body pumps the fluid out of my arms.

"We did a lot to your body all at once and there is a lot of healing to be done," she said.

"How am I going to wrap my body in this ace bandage and keep it tight?" I asked.

If you are going to start crying do it now because you can't do this in front of Kasondra. She will not understand why you are crying. It is one thing to have all these professionals helping you but now you're by yourself.

Let the tears flow, let your strength go and just cry. But will I be able to stop crying? Will I?

My husband picks me up. I'm so scared to go home but I have not told anyone this. *If I cannot handle this pain on my own, who will help me?* As I get in the car, I raise my arm to try to hold the rail and pain shoots down my body, almost dropping me to my knees. I shudder and keep trying to slide into the car. I let out an, "Oh, my GOD!" and everyone freezes.

"Are you okay?"

"No. No, the pain. That really hurt. It's like my body is trying to warn me not to move at all. I don't know how to do this; how do I move and not be in pain!" I shout out.

I realized how different my life is now. I sat in the front seat of the car and cried. I cried for what I had lost, I cried for the fear of what was ahead, and I cried because my life would never be the same. I cried because no one understood how scared I was. I was trying to be so strong for everyone but no one knew what was really going on. I have never cried so much. Finally, I let everyone know just how scared I was. I took a long breath and settled in the seat.

Breathe through it. Karen, remember you are moving ahead. You're out of the hospital now, keep moving ahead.

Once we arrived at the house, I knew I couldn't move my arms to get out of the car, so I figure I'm just going to use my legs. My husband tries to grab my arm and pull me out of the car.

"WAIT, please!" I yell. "Please do not try to pull me up from my arm," I tell my husband. "Just wait and let me do it." How do I explain extreme pain to someone who has never been in this kind of pain before what I need?

I walk inside with my husband next to me for support and see the hospital bed in the living room waiting for me. I wonder how long it is going to be there. I realize there is another side to everything that is difficult. He leads me to the hospital bed. I try to use my arms again to lower myself to the bed which engages my pecs. I let out a scream of pain. My husband's face says it all. *What do I do to help you?* He just stands there, frozen.

Okay, that's twice my body has warned me I need to help it heal. Karen, you have to get in rhythm with your body. Your only job now is to support and protect your body so it can heal.

I climb into the hospital bed and lay back.

Kasondra is at daycare right now and when she gets home, I am going to have to figure out how to direct a two year old. *Is that even possible?* She is smart. I can tell her I have a boo-boo and it's hurting me. *But will I be able to stop crying when I see her?* Until now, I was scared that I would never even come home to her. I did not realize I had so many feelings until the situation was in front of me. At least I would have a nurse tomorrow so I will have someone here with me for a little while when my husband goes back to work.

The hospital told me to take pain medication when I got home and to begin a routine for pain management. I wanted to feel good when Kasondra got home from daycare. My husband hands me the pills but I hesitate. I don't really like taking pain pills, even if they are not strong, because my body is so pure. I don't know if I will accept them.

Am I supposed to feel this way? Is my body feeling kind of numb? I never felt this way before when they gave me the pain pills in the hospital. I tell my husband, "I don't feel right."

"What do you mean?" he asks, trying to figure it out, too.

"My body is feeling weighed-down like a million pounds are on me right now. It is getting harder to breathe. I think you need to call the paramedics now, right now," I insist.

He places a call to Dr. Crane explaining how I am feeling: "…numb and like she is going into a tunnel."

I don't know what is happening right now but I hear him say, "Her body is having a reaction to something?" Dr. Crane tells my husband to call the paramedics.

When the paramedics arrive, I tell them I feel like I am going down a tunnel. My arms were so heavy I could not lift them up. I kept saying, "I feel like I'm going to die."

"You're not going to die. We will get you to the hospital."

"No, I am dying." *Please, Lord, do not let me die.*

They load me into the ambulance and try to get an IV started. They cannot find a vein.

Oh, my God, I am going to die right now. After all I have been through, a drug is going to kill me? Please, Lord, help me….

They pull into the emergency entrance, transfer me to a room and close the curtain. Someone finally gets an IV line into my arm. I can hear my husband beyond the curtain calling my parents.

"They do not know what is going to happen, they have an IV in trying to flush her body to see if it is a reaction to the drug," he explains. "Yes, I think you should come down. They are not sure what is going to happen," I hear the panic in his voice. "Kasondra is with the neighbors."

I started to cry. *I am going to die. Please, Lord, take care of Kasondra. I am so scared for her. This is not fair, Lord, you bring me this close to death and let me die from a drug? Please, Lord.*

I feel someone put their hand on my right shoulder from behind the bed. A voice comes into my head.

Karen, it is not your turn to die.

I crane my neck to see who is supporting me in such a way. I want to ask, "How do you know I am not going to die?" but no one is there. I cry so loudly my husband comes into the room.

"What's wrong? Are you hurting somewhere?"

A nurse arrives. "What's wrong? Is she okay? What is happening?"

My husband keeps asking, "What's wrong? Talk to us!"

I can't talk. I am crying so hard now I can barely breathe. Every fear I had been holding inside was rushing out. The fear of leaving my daughter behind came pouring out. My entire body was trembling from all the fear leaving my body.

People were going crazy trying to see what was happening to me. I finally say, "I am not going to die."

"I know. You're in the hospital and they are going to do everything to save you," my husband confirms.

"I don't have to be scared anymore. God is with me."

Everyone in the room was reassuring me. "You'll be okay. We are doing what we can to help you."

"No, you don't understand. God just spoke to me," I tell them. "I felt Him in the room. I felt Him touch my shoulder and say, 'It's not your turn to die.' I truly feel it is not my turn to die."

I can't explain the calm that came over me then. All of the decisions I made that I was afraid of came clear; I felt they were all right. I knew without any doubt that I was going to live. I had never felt closer to God in my life. I knew this feeling would never leave me for the rest of my life.

They pushed new drugs into the IV to counter the other drugs. I was resubmitted to the hospital to get the drugs flushed out of my body. They wanted to give me a better chance to heal some more before they sent me home again. They had sent me home on the protocol of a regular mastectomy, but this was not a regular mastectomy.

I begged Dr. Crane to let me stay a little while longer to heal more so I could be stronger on my feet. He agreed that I'd been through a bigger trauma to the body than normal and that the hospital should have kept me longer.

They discovered the reason for the attack: a combination of the stress from the surgery and the prescription they had sent me home with was a higher strength than before. I should have taken a smaller amount. My body couldn't take everything at once and started shutting down from the stress and the drugs.

I was going home again, this time feeling more secure than the first time. My husband had to go right back to work. Thank God, my mom and dad said they would pay for a nurse to stay with me for a while longer. With so much work done all at once, my body was still in shock. Since they had never done this long, combined surgery before, my medical team did not know what to expect and neither did I.

I was still scared to be alone at home and I was so glad for my nurse. I knew I would try to sleep a lot while Kasondra was in daycare, and knowing the nurse was there allowed me to sleep. In many ways, it was fortunate that Kasondra was so young that she was unable to comprehend the situation or ask too many questions. I wasn't sure how I was going to keep everything from her.

For one thing, I was hooked up like a monster. I had huge drains on both sides of my body draining the fluid out of my chest. From what I understand, the body sends fluid to the chest wound trying to heal it. *If the fluid is not drained off it properly, that can cause problems in healing. God's answer to healing is now causing problems for his creation?* I really don't think God thought people would ever put plastic in our bodies to make a chest!

I have to remember to keep my arms by my side and not use them so they can heal. I need to lay still and heal as much as possible and I know I have to walk every day to get my system back to normal.

Okay, Karen, do not get ahead of yourself. See what works.

On the way back home, my husband looked at me and said, "Now what do we do?"

"I have no idea at all and no one else does either. I guess it all depends on what my body tells me to do. I won't know what to do if I am all drugged up on pain pills. I could do things that will hurt my body and not even know I have hurt my body until it is too late and the damage is done."

I decided I would not take another strong pain pill of any kind. I found the strongest over-the-counter medication is the arthritis-strength Tylenol 8-hour pain relief. This was going to be my new pain-control routine.

Fortunately, the pain was not as intense as when I left the hospital the first time. I would not let them drug me to the point of no pain. There was still pain medication in my system from the hospital. They were always telling me to stay ahead of the pain. *But what does that mean now?* They told me I could take both medications because they were both timed. I decided to take the Tylenol right before the other pain med wore off.

I am still concerned about how I am going to keep this from Kasondra. The tubes leading down to the drains on both my sides have a blood-like substance emptying into them. I have decided that I am going to wear a big workout t-shirt to cover everything and that will have to be my shirt of choice for a long time, or at least until the drains come out. I can't remember how long that is going to be.

I take a deep breath and walk in the house for the second time after my surgery. My husband is holding me under my arm as I walked in. *Do I tell him how sacred I am and if I am going to be able to do this?* He doesn't ask me. I have to go through all this and there is no other choice now.

Kasondra is still at daycare. It is so weird to be here without a medical support system. I would be lying if I said I am not so glad the nurse is coming tomorrow. My husband sits me on the hospital bed in the living room and I realize how tired I truly am. I put my hands down to scoot myself back in the bed again and pain shoots into my chest. I let out a scream. My husband doesn't understand what is happening and I start to cry. "What's happening?" he asks me over and over.

"Pain in my chest," is all I can get out. I start telling myself *breathe, breathe, breathe through it,* and with every thought I let out a breath and calm myself down.

Okay, lesson learned not to use your arms, Karen. They are at your sides, right? They are broken and you cannot use them at all to help you in anyway.

I finally lie down and rest. I think my body has given up and cannot do anything anymore.

My husband wakes me up to let me know he is going to pick up Kasondra from daycare and bring her home to me. I don't think I am going to try to explain to her what is going on. I think she is too young to understand what I would be saying, so I am going to just let my actions speak to her. I am going to have to take it easy with her and not lift her or hold her too tight so she can't feel all that is under my shirt.

I asked my husband to get me one of my big t-shirts to cover up the drains attached to all the bandages wrapped around my chest. They were so tight. I have to empty my drains because they look full of the bloody-white liquid. I have to keep track of how much fluid is coming out per day. They will only take the drains out when the fluid stops. When the fluids stop, the body has healed and is no longer trying to send fluids to help heal the injury. My little drains are full of fluid. No one knows how long this is going to take to heal.

Father, I know we have talked before, but I beg you to give me strength to be able to give me the ability to heal through this pain and fear I have from being home.

I have prayed for years, but things were different now. I remember the chills running down my arms when the angel told me it was not my turn to die. I knew I was still here because of a plan God has for me. I felt so close to

God, and knew I could speak to Him about anything at all. I will talk and He will listen, and I know now He hears everything I say to Him.

Father, I am so tired all the time. I am in so much pain and I truly do not know if I can manage it. I know pain is your way of telling me what is going on with my body. It is your warning sign of what I should and shouldn't be doing to heal this body. Please let me lean on you, Father. Hold me up when I can't do it myself. Tell me what to say to Kasondra. Help me figure out how to heal your body quickly.

Lead me, Father, to a place that is so new for me. Let me know what I am doing is the right thing to do. Amen.

I hear them coming home now. My husband is talking to Kasondra, "Mommy is sore, you have to be gentle with her, okay?"

"Sore?" she asks?

"Yes, so it's like when we pet a puppy, be nice and gentle."

The door opens and I am happy and scared. *Please, please don't let me scream out from any pain.*

"Mommy!" I hear her sweet voice. And life is just the same? Yet it is not the same.

She comes into the living room to my bedside. "Hi, pumpkin. Come here and give me a hug," I say, trying to have a normal Mommy voice, all the while thinking, *don't pick her up, lean over to give her a hug, arms at your side.* As I put my arms to my sides, I feel a drain under my shirt. I had pinned them low and kind of under my arms so she would not feel them.

"Mommy, yay!"

"Yes, baby, I am home now. I missed you so much. Did you miss me?"

"Yes!" She looks so happy. I almost started to cry.

I whisper to myself. *Father, thank you so much for keeping me alive. Thank you for this hug. Thank you for allowing me to still be in my daughter's life.* I feel I'll start crying but I stop myself. She pushes back from the hug.

"You okay, Mommy?"

"Yes, baby. I am just talking to God."

"Pumpkin, it is time to take a bath," I announced.

"Mommy," she called out, waving for me to come with her.

My husband speaks up. "Not tonight, Pumpkin, but she will be waiting for you when you get done."

He takes her to the bathroom and puts her in the tub. I hear them laughing. What a joyful noise. *How could I have not felt blessed to hear that before? How could I be too busy to truly notice how much joy she has in just taking a bath?* I noticed now how it was so different. It was as if I was hearing her giggle and laugh for the first time.

She comes back in showing me, "All clean."

"Baby, come over here. Crawl up in bed with me," I smile. I had lowered the hospital bed so she could climb in without my help. My husband stood behind her—just in case—as he knew I could not catch her if she started to fall. I had already scooted over in the bed to make room for her while she was in the tub.

"Isn't this fun? A bed in the living room so we can be cozy and watch TV?" She nods yes.

As my husband leaves us to make dinner, I realize I also need to eat to heal. My life now needs to be based on healing so I can be the same old Mom to my daughter. I have to heal all the way and nutrition has a huge role in that.

I tell my husband I want to come to the dinner table. He doesn't think it is a good idea but I want to make it seem the same as it was before for my daughter. He distracts Kasondra with finding a book to read in her room while he helps me up. He holds me under my arms as gently as he can and seats me at the dinner table.

Breathe and pray, Karen, it's going to be okay.

I start to feel pain and I decide to take the extra-strength Tylenol with dinner. I pray this works. How nice it is to have a family dinner. *Thank you, Father.*

After we eat, my husband distracts Kasondra with playing hide-and-seek as he helps me get back in bed. I don't want her to see me in pain as I try to settle in. When all the gadgets are in their place, I yell, "Ready," and he lets her back in the room to join me on the TV bed. That's what I'm calling it to her. This time is so precious. She grabs the book and we start to read in bed together.

Too soon, the moment had passed. "Time for you to go to bed, baby." I tell her. "I would love to put you to bed but Daddy wants to do it by himself. I am too tired to get up this time." She kisses me and my husband takes her to bed.

"Night, Mommy. Love you," she calls back to me.

"I love you, too, baby." I hold back my tears once again.

I look at the clock. It is time to take another extra-strength Tylenol. *No, not yet. I have to hold off as long as possible, but I can't anymore.* I remember I need to stay ahead of the pain. As I count the hours ahead, I realize I will be awakened by pain in the middle of the night. *Maybe it won't be so bad because I am asleep and not moving at all.*

My husband decides to sleep nearby on the couch, just in case I need him. He has been helping me get in-and-out of bed to go to the bathroom. We decide to empty the drains before we turn in. There was still a lot of red fluid coming out. I was disappointed.

Naturally, I have to go to the bathroom in the worst way, but now it is the middle of the night. I think, *I can do this by myself.* I lower the bed and try to slide to the side of the bed without waking my husband. I put my arm down to scoot over and pain shoots through my body.

Nope, that was too much pressure on my pecs. I let out a little scream of pain and he wakes up.

"Why didn't you wake me? That is why I am sleeping out here!"

He tries to lift me by my arm. "No! I have stitches in both my armpits, remember?" I press my arms hard against my sides and ask him to help me up by my elbows. We manage to get me to the bathroom. He helps me lower my sweats and I use my thighs to get me to the toilet seat. As I finish, I try to get up by myself by pushing off the seat with my arms. Pain. My husband helps me get up. *Things are so different now.*

Climbing back into bed, I realize I am feeling pain now but it is too early to take another Tylenol. I went from an independent person to a clock-watcher. In a heartbeat, I went from a person who never took anything but supplements to someone dependent on an over-the-counter drug.

Finally, I wake my husband to tell him it is time to take the Tylenol again. He goes to get the pills and a glass of water. He helps me and we look at the time to calculate when the next time will be to take them again. As he goes right back to sleep, I wonder when I will be able to just go to sleep.

Father, I am not sure I can do this. I feel so alone. I feel like I am falling to pieces. I look at my chest and I don't feel so much like a woman anymore.

My husband and I have not talked about how my chest looks. *I wonder what he is thinking.* This has happened very early in our marriage. We got married, within months we were pregnant, then we bought a house, and now this.

Father, there is so much I don't know how to do right now. All I can do is lean on you. You have not let me down yet. Please, Father, bring people into my life to help me. The nurse comes tomorrow....

*I know there is another side to all of this, the side where I am healed and my life is moving forward, and **this right now** is my past. I will get to the other side, Father, with your help.*

Wow, it is time to get up. I made it through the rest of the night. Kasondra is waiting at my side.

"Good morning, baby," I try to make my voice sound clear. "You get to go to daycare today. I am so excited for you."

"Come on Mommy?" she asks, knowing I usually drop her off.

"No, Daddy is going to take you to daycare today and I am going to rest. I will be here when you get back and we can lay in our TV bed together and watch a movie, okay?"

I hear a knock on the door. I have asked my husband to keep it unlocked in case the nurse comes while he is gone. I ask her to come in and tell her my husband will be right back. I start to tell her what I need her to do for me: help me change and empty the drains, take a sponge bath, go to the bathroom, and get in and out of bed. She responds so sweetly to all I have asked for, "Yes, I can do that, no problem."

My husband comes back to meet her and then leaves to go to work for the day. She is a sweet person and I am so excited to have her in my life right now. I feel as though I have a woman who will allow me to cry if I feel like it. I can be whoever I want to be with her.

I tell her the first thing we have to do is go to my appointment with Dr. Crane, which is a 30-minute drive to La Jolla. I ask if she is okay with taking me. "Yes," she confirms. "I was told I may need to drive you places."

As I arrive at Dr. Crane's office, I realize this will begin the next steps to rebuilding my chest. I know he went over the procedure with me, but I am not entirely clear yet how it is all going to work.

I have been taking supplements that the acupuncturist at Dr. Tann's office had recommended and I have done my own research on surgery-healing supplements. But blood is still mixed in with the liquid being sucked from my chest.

Dr. Crane removes the dressing to see how the implants are looking. I see two little lumps where my beautiful size C breasts used to be. I let out a gasp. *There are no nipples on my chest. I don't remember him saying there would be no nipples left.* My chest looks flat with just two little lumps.

Then it hits me just how different my life is going to be, just how much this makes me not feel like a woman anymore. *How is my husband going to react? Maybe I should have seen a therapist to deal with this? You're already dealing with it, remember? The safest way not to get cancer again is not to have a place for it to grow, your breasts! This is how you are going to stay alive for Kasondra.*

What did he just say? I ask him to repeat it.

"Everything is looking good and healing nicely. I looked at your chart on the fluids and you need to remember this might take longer to subside than it would for most cases because of all the work that was done all at once. We do not know what the body is going to do or how long it is going to take to heal."

I processed his words.

"What I am going to do now is find the fill valve," he continued.

"The what?" I blurted out.

"The fill valve. It is a valve in the implants you have in your chest. The implants I put in your chest are called expander implants. Remember? We went over this."

We did? I don't remember this at all. I am in shock.

"They allow me to expand the muscles in your chest to make a pocket for your permanent implants. I'll stick a needle in the valve and fill the implants in your chest with water to expand them. We are going to do this slowly so you will not be in too much pain from it. You are already dealing with the lymph nodes removal, which is a huge shock to your system, and all the other surgeries for taking off your chest. So, we do not want to do too much too fast to your body as it heals," he explained.

"Now, you have been taking your antibiotics daily, right?" It felt as though he were scolding me.

"Yes, I promised I would," I assure him.

"Let me see the bottle. I want to count the pills," he says.

"What makes you think I won't just throw them away?" I argue.

"You would not lie to me, Karen."

"I am glad you're keeping your word and taking them. It is so important for your healing."

"I don't like taking them because of the damage they do to the stomach and intestines, they make such a mess of the body and now I will have more things to heal as I go, but I promised."

He gives me a numbing shot for the area he is going to stick the needle in. He proceeds to stick the needle in my chest. It looks so weird to see it go in and not feel anything. I feel the pressure of the fluid going into the implant.

"This is so weird," I tell him. "If you give me more, will I get through this part quicker?" I want to know.

72

"Yes," he responds. "But we are not going to do that to your body. I'll see you again in a couple of days."

He puts a very tight bra on me instead of the ace bandage. "You can now take a shower, as long as you do not get your chest wet, or under your arm wet."

I was so happy to hear I could take a shower. My hair was gross and I felt horrible and dirty. I don't know why, but my thoughts went to how strange it would be to have the nurse wash me. *Okay, let's come to that later.*

Dr. Crane attaches the bottles to my bra with safety pins. The nurse shows me out.

I am so tired when I get back home. *From what? Is the anesthesia still in my body, is that what's making me tired? If so, I need to start walking as soon as I can to force it out of my tissues as soon as possible. Or is my body in so much shock it is trying to repair itself?*

The nurse helps me get back in the TV bed. It is so nice to have her here with me. *I don't think I could defend myself if someone came in right now to attack me.* That thought seems so out of place, I turn my mind back to my new breasts. I know Dr. Crane is going to make them incredible. *Time is what I have to endure. Give it time.*

The nurse sits next to my bed, waiting for instructions from me. Since I don't have any, she offers the incredible: "I will clean up a little, if you want me to?"

"That would be so great," I tell her.

"I'll clean the kitchen and do you want me to make dinner for your family?" she asks.

"Oh, yes, please. Thank you so much, that will take such a load off my husband," I tell her.

"I will put in a load of laundry before I start dinner," she adds.

What? Thank you did not seem enough.

All I have to do now is lay here and rest. This was such an emotional day. Tomorrow, I am going to try to walk. I remember I can take a shower now and tell the nurse I would like to before my husband gets home with Kasondra.

As she helps me undress, we take my bra off and I start to cry. I don't want to look in the mirror yet. I climb into the shower and she helps wash my back while I hold the fluid-measuring balls attached to the drains.

I then ask her to hold the fluid balls and I wash where I can without getting the surgery area wet. She tells me to sit in the tub but I don't think I can get back up again without using my arms. I ask if I can sit on the edge of the tub and lean back to wash my hair using a pan of water to rise it. It works and I feel 100 percent better, more like myself then I have for days. It was such an emotional day I just want to lay down.

Back in bed, I am so tired I realize I'll have to lay down for the rest of the day, but at least I'm clean.

"We're home!" I hear the call coming from the door as my husband and Kasondra walk in. Kasondra is so excited to tell me everything that is going on at daycare. I listen, praying and thanking God for the time I have with her right now.

The nurse has made dinner and we all sit down to eat. What a way to end a very stressful day.

Before bedtime, I tell my husband I know he is not getting enough sleep on the couch and I am stressing with trying not to make any sounds that will wake him up. We decide he can go to bed in our room and he will have a baby monitor by his bedside if I need help. He sets up a small table with everything I will need for the night: the right amount of Tylenol for the next dose I was to take, a glass of water and a pitcher of water.

Now, I'm laying here by myself and trying not to cry too loud in case he hears it through the baby monitor. I'm watching the clock, waiting for my next pill.

Why is it I only feel comfortable really crying when no one is around? Does everyone expect me to be so strong and press on as though nothing has happened? Is it fair for me to hold everything in?

With Kasondra, it's one thing to put on a brave front. But with the other adults in my life, why can't I let go and show them how much I need support? At night, alone, I know people are thinking they are encouraging me, but they are really not allowing me to be simply hurt and afraid.

Oh, great. Now I have to go to the bathroom.

I raise the bed up and sit for a minute, trying to get my head wrapped around the challenge before me. *You can do this, right? Okay, swing your legs around. **Don't** use your arms, remember? Feet on the floor, perfect….*

And I am up. The bathroom is only a little distance away. *I got this.*

I sit down on the toilet only using my legs. No problem. Now, I am finished and I can't get up. I try to use my arms and pain shoots into my chest and arms. I'm not going anywhere.

You have to call out for help.

My husband comes to help. He is pissed I didn't call him to help me. "You could have fallen," he scolds me. "And then where would we be?"

Right then, I decided this is not going to happen again. As I settled back into bed, I made promises. *I am not going to feel like this ever again. I am strong and can push through anything. Pain arrives only for a short time and then it is over. I need to heal as fast as I can. I need to get this anesthesia out of my body as soon as I can. Tomorrow, I am going to walk.*

There were so many other details racing through my thoughts. *I need to really look at the drains and pray over them. They are what is telling me how my body is really doing; if I am healing or not. And as far as they look now, I am sucking at healing.*

I have to watch my water intake and not drink past a certain hour so I don't have to get up in the middle of the night. So, I need to drink a lot of water when the nurse is here because she can help me get up and down.

Eventually, I dozed off.

⚬⚓

The morning routine took hold.

"Off to daycare school again, how fun, baby. I'll be sitting here waiting for you to come back to sit with me in the TV bed."

The nurse arrives and my husband leaves for the day.

I tell the nurse I have to heal as fast as I can. I need to walk today around the block. She helps me get ready and we walk down the street and back. I was so proud of myself but I was so tired, I had to rest for an hour.

I also wanted to find a way to go to the bathroom and get off the toilet without using my arms to push me up. I wondered how I could use my legs to help me up. I put my hands on my knees and started to walk my hands up my legs. It worked. I could get myself up now without help. *YES!* I was also starting to shuffle around the house, simply going from room-to-room to experience moving again.

I asked the nurse if she would go grocery shopping.

"I don't want to leave you," she worried.

"I promise I will stay in bed until you get back," I said.

She did it all. I knew I did not have much more time with her. She would only come for one more day. I wasn't ready for her to leave. I was not where I needed to be in order to be safe. I was feeling better every day but the drains were telling me I was still far from healed.

In the afternoon, Kasondra asked me to play dolls with her. I got down on the floor without thinking. Then it was time for dinner and my husband called us into the kitchen. I tried to get up off the floor. I put my arms down and pain shot through my chest. I tried to rock to my feet but I could not catch my balance and I fell back to the floor. I started to cry, partly out of frustration because I believed I had progressed, partly from the pain, and partly from the fear that tomorrow will be the last day the nurse would be here to help me.

I called my sister and told her what had happened. I explained how I could not get up by myself, that I was just trying to let the healing process take place, but now I was going to be alone. She could not come and help me. She had three kids and her husband worked. I know she was upset that I would be left alone. She called Dad and asked him to extend my nursing care through to the end of the week. He decided to help me for three more days.

Relieved, I now had four days to master walking and moving around by myself. The nurse continued to help me move around the house and we took longer and longer walks outside. I took all the vitamins, herbs, and oils the acupuncturist told me to take.

By the time she left for good I was moving so much easier. The fluids were about half as much as before, and it wasn't as mixed with blood. My body was finally healing. I kept my arms as still as possible and the pain was getting better. My constant state of fear started to leave me.

I now know my limitations so well that I can stop myself before I am in pain. I had been emptying my own drains and recording the levels for days. I was sad to see her go but I knew I could manage on my own now. And that is what I was: *on my own now.*

I felt secure as I hugged her, thanking her for helping me not only with doing the physical things, but with helping me to deal with the emotional pain I was going through, too.

My husband took my daughter to daycare and I was completely alone for the first time. I kept up with my walks and my neighbors knew what I was doing. They all watched out for me. I knew they were there if I needed help. One neighbor walked with me to keep me safe and to make sure I could get back home.

My next appointment with Dr. Crane was coming up for the second water fill to expand my temporary implants. I didn't think I should drive to his office in La Jolla by myself. The drive took about 30 minutes. I asked my mom if she could pick me up and take me since she only lived about 20 minutes away.

Now that I was feeling better, I started to joke with Dr. Crane because he was always so serious when he came in. This would be the same procedure as the last time, and I knew what to expect. My mother watched as Dr. Crane and I started talking while he began to fill my implants again.

"When do you start the chemo?" he asked me. "I need to know because that is going to cause some problems with what we are doing here."

"I decided I am not going to do the chemo," I told him.

"The protocol is chemo for you to live," he exclaimed. "Did they tell you everything about all that this cancer can do? You do understand about the fast-growing cancer you had in your body, right?"

"Yes."

"If it comes back somewhere else, it could kill you."

"Yes, I have been told about all the risks. I am not crazy. I have studied about this cancer and the tumor did not break out. It was encapsulated when Dr. Watkins took it out," I told him.

He peered at me. "Did you tell Dr. Watkins that you weren't going to have chemo?"

"Yes, I told her what I was doing. She was behind me. She said, fine, if that is what I wanted to do. Did you know chemo only gives you a 10 percent better chance to live, *and* it kills your body while it does? I am going to give my body the same chance to live without killing it," I declared.

"How are you going to do that?" Dr. Crane scolded me. "If you were my wife, I would make you do the chemo. There is no other proven method. You are playing with your life. You have a child, Karen, think of her."

"I am. That is why I not taking chemo, I'm changing my life. It will work. I just have to figure it out."

"I think you are crazy," he insisted. "But I knew one other lady where the cancer had gone into her bones. They told her she was not going to live. She was going to try to cure it with herbs and vitamins. She has probably passed away by now. I'll have my staff look her up and call her for you to see if she found someone to help her before she died."

"That would be great, thank you. Please let me know ASAP. I need all the help I can get," I said.

He numbed the area again and stuck the needle in the fill hole in the implant. It looked so weird to see this large needle disappear and me not feel a thing.

"I think that is enough expansion for now," he said.

"If I have you fill more, it will go faster, and I won't be coming back here as long, right?" I asked him again.

"Yes, that is right, but I would not do that. It may stretch the skin too much at a time and it can be painful."

"Can we try it this once to see if I can take it?"

"Okay," he agreed. "I think you are going to be in pain."

When my mother and I were driving back home, she confronted me.

"Karen, we were not aware you were not going to do the chemo treatments. When I had cancer, I did the chemo treatments and you were there during the treatment. I survived and I am fine now. You can do the chemo. It is not going to kill you."

"I understand you live life differently than I do," she continued. "But I think it is a mistake not to do the chemo. Does your husband know you are not doing the chemo?"

"Yes, Mom. He is leaving it up to me to do what I think is best for me," I offered.

"Did you go to the chemo appointment at all? What did the doctor say?" she insisted.

"He said I was taking my life in my hands and I should do the chemo. I told Dr. Watkins, my cancer surgeon, I was not doing the chemo. She told me off the record she would not do it either."

"We need to talk to your dad about this decision. I don't think it is a good one," she said. "This thing you are trying to do is crazy. You are going against all the things that are normally done… and you have Kasondra to think about."

"I understand you don't understand, Mom. But I know this is the way I should go. My body saved me, God saved me, and kept the cancer encapsulated. I do not want to harm my body for a 10 percent chance!"

Later, when my father was brought into the conversation, I held firm but wanted to be reasonable. I knew they were worried about me.

"Dad, I know what Mom told you. I know all medicine has evolved in terms of cancer treatments. But I am not going to do it that way. I know I am not a doctor but I have studied up on this cancer, I asked a lot of questions, and I feel this is the right course of action for me."

He was not convinced until I agreed to go see an oncologist for a second opinion. I also explained that my insurance would not pay for a second opinion and I couldn't afford one on my own. I told him I would accept his help to pay for it if it would put his mind at ease. But I told him I didn't think I would change my mind. We agreed I would ask Dr. Watkins for a referral to the top oncologist she knew, and he would pay for it.

I called Dr. Watkins to get a referral and the office told me my test results were in and I could ask for the referral at the time of the visit to go over the results. I was not sure I was ready for the results, was I ever going to be ready to find out the results. I knew Dr. Watkins thought I was safe just hold on to that thought. As my husband and I walked in, we were ready for anything at this point. I knew in my soul that my body had saved me and I felt at ease that it would be fine. Dr. Watkins walked in with a smile on her face.

"Karen, I took out 15 lymph nodes and they were all clear," she exclaimed. "Your cancer did not spread to your lymph nodes; it stayed encapsulated like I thought when I removed it."

I started crying, I could not believe it. Crying because I knew my body had saved me; God saved me. At this point, I knew I did not need chemo, but I had made a promise to my dad to get a second opinion. I shared this with Dr. Watkins, and told her I needed the name of the best oncologist she knew, someone who could help my family understand that I knew what I was doing. She referred me to the top oncologist at Scripps. When I told my dad, I think he felt certain this doctor was going to make me change my mind and save my life by convincing me to follow all the people before me who had been saved by chemo.

The next day when I woke up, Dr. Crane had been right. The pain in my chest was severe. I felt as though someone had beaten me up with their fists.

What was I thinking? Trying to move too fast again.

I called Dr. Crane's office to see what I could do to stop the pain. They said I could return and he would take some of the water out. I wanted to know how long the pain would last until the skin had stretched enough. They were unsure.

"When can I come back?"

"Tomorrow," they said.

"Let's make an appointment for tomorrow." I knew he was going to tell me, "I told you so."

At the appointment waiting to see him, I made a type of punch card I could use to record the fills I was going to have in the future. Every time Dr. Crane filled my stretching implants, I wanted him to check a square off. And after ten fills, he had to buy me a bra.

He walked in the room and before he could lecture me, I handed him the card.

"What is this?" he asked.

I explained the card and it was the first time I heard him laugh. I mean, he really laughed hard. There was no lecture. Less water. Lesson learned.

I also kept the appointment with the top oncologist. I had my notes in hand, ready to ask the best oncologist in San Diego all the questions I could think of. She was head of the oncology department at Scripps Green Hospital.

"Okay, Karen. Please put this gown on. The doctor will be right with you."

How many times have I heard those words in the last couple of months? And each time, I felt anxious as to what I was going to hear next. But this time, I was ready to ask questions I wanted heard—not to be told what they think I should do. It was time to find out what my options were.

Keep telling yourself, they are not smarter than you… they just studied longer.

She walked in with a lot of people behind her. *What's all this about?*

"Hi, Karen," she started. "As you know, we are a teaching hospital and I have a group of med students following me today. You have an unusual case. Would it be okay if they observe?"

This is a teaching hospital? Now what am I supposed to say?

"Okay," automatically came out of my mouth.

She began by reviewing my case and explaining the course of treatment she had planned out for me. She showed her students my chest as if I was not even in the room. She pointed and prodded like I was a lifeless thing. Then she said it:

"It is rare that a tumor of this size did not break out and rapidly spread cancer through the body." She explained that considering the severity of the type of cancer I had, if the cancer had broken out, I would have been in a very serious, different situation.

You mean dead, right? You're just not saying it.

As she launched into the chemo treatment plan, I started to get sick to my stomach. The students asked questions about the plan and were starting to get into the weeds with details.

Okay, enough is enough. Come on, ask the question I have been waiting to hear.

Bingo. I heard the question. She turned her attention back to me. "Do you have any questions?"

I think she was expecting me to say no. Why would I be asking such an important doctor a question, right? She no doubt was ready to move on to the next patient when I said, "Yes, I have a lot of questions."

The look she gave me was one of contempt. I could read her thoughts. *Really? Do you know who I am? I just told you the plan!* But I didn't care what she thought. I blurted out my questions.

"Is it true chemo kills all the white blood healing cells?

"Yes, but the body will be able to heal regardless," she offered.

"How? I mean, I just had a very invasive surgery. How can it heal with the chemotherapy starting in my body?" I asked.

"They will give you antibiotics to help with the healing," she said matter-of-factly.

"But that is a drug. Isn't the best way to heal with white blood cells from your body?" I insisted.

"Yes, your white blood cells were designed to help your body," she said, I could sense she was starting to feel agitated.

"But now they will be compromised so how can my body possibly heal? Isn't it true that chemo can stay in your kidneys and liver, causing them problems now and in the future?" I continued.

"Yes," she answered. "The chemo will distribute there during the treatments."

"But then the damage has already been done, right?" I challenged.

"Yes, it could cause damage for the long term."

"The chemo goes wherever in the body it wants to, right?" I persisted with my line of inquiry.

"Yes, it goes throughout your body."

"And there is nothing to direct it, right?"

"Yes, that's right. It can go into your bone marrow and cause problems."

"Right," I agreed. "And bone marrow is where white blood cells come from to heal us, right?"

"Yes…" she agreed.

"And this can cause myopathy for years all over your body, making it hard to think, taste, and see and you can have tingling in your hands and feet?"

"Yes," she confirmed, "in most cases, but not in every case."

"And chemo treatments will only give you a 10 percent better chance to live, right?" I had made the point I wanted to drive home.

"Okay, Mrs. Campbell," she looked at me with seriousness. "With all that said, 90 percent of all my patients do the program to save their lives. Do you completely understand what I told you before?"

It was my turn to answer yes.

"If this cancer comes back, it will not be contained by a tumor and you will probably die. I am trying to save your life by killing off any small cancer cells sitting there, ready to come alive and kill you. Dr. Watkins is an incredible doctor, no doubt, but if she did not remove all the cancer it will come back and kill you."

"The tumor was encapsulated. She got it all!" I insisted.

"Are you sure? Are any of us sure she got it all? Do you not want to do the chemotherapy because you don't have the time?" That caught me off guard.

"What?"

"Do you think it is going to make you sick, too sick to live your life?" she continued.

"What?" I said again.

"I have hundreds of patients undergoing this right now and, yes, it is tough, but they make it through and so will you."

"But what kind of life do they have afterwards?"

"The key is: they are alive afterwards, right? We can help you make it through!"

"No, this does not make sense for my body, the body that just saved me. Thank you for your information but I am not going to do your program."

"Mrs. Campbell, you really need to think of your family right now."

"I am thinking of my family. Thank you for the advice." I was done. I knew I didn't want to change my mind.

"They will have forms at the front for you to sign indicating that I went over the procedure with you and you denied the procedure at your own risk to life."

"That will be fine," I said.

"Good luck, I hope it all works out for you, Mrs. Campbell." She left with her entourage and I started to get dressed.

Okay, Karen, that is the second no for the chemo. So, you know exactly what you're going to do now, right? No. What are you going to do? You have no idea?

God had my answers when I got home. Dr. Crane's office had called about the woman who had refused chemotherapy. She was still alive and ready to help me. Dr. Crane was baffled himself. She had cancer that spread to the bones and it was amazing to hear she was still alive. But he had talked to her and she was ready to talk to me. I was going to meet someone who had beaten the odds and done it her way.

The office gave me her number. I was a little worried that if I called her, she would tell me how hard it is to do and how crazy I am to try it. *You came this far, right?*

I reached for the phone.

"Hi, my name is Karen Campbell and I had breast cancer; I am the one Dr. Crane told you about."

Her voice on the other end was reassuring. "It is so good to talk to you. I was exactly where you are but I had nothing to lose. They told me I was going to die away; so, it was just a matter of how quickly did I want to die. I decided to try a different approach. I wanted to find a natural way to heal myself."

I was relieved. "I can't thank you enough for talking to me today," I said.

"No, I want to tell as many people as I can what happened to me," she insisted.

"Perfect, I am all ears. I don't know what to do, I just know I want to do it your way."

"Well, here's what happened," she explained. "I kept asking if anyone knew a holistic person who worked with cancer patients. I had been told by Western-medicine doctors there was no hope, so maybe the other side would give me hope. Finally, I heard of a man in Escondido who people were saying cured cancer. So, I went to him. I went on his program and stayed on it and my cancer has never come back. I since then, I have been telling everyone I can about what he did for me."

"Please," I asked, "I want to meet with him and see what he has to say. Is he really expensive?"

"No," she said. "In fact, it is so inexpensive, it made me question at first if this was a good program or not. The cost is $49 for the visit and then there is the cost of the supplements. He'll tell you upfront he makes a 20 percent profit on the supplements."

"What?" I was astonished. "That makes no sense at all. I manage holistic centers and I'm amazed to hear this!"

We went on to talk about her diet and all the extra stuff she needed to do. She assured me he would go over all of that on the first visit. She also warned me that he is a little different from most, and to say open-minded. "He is a healer," she said.

I have been around healers most of my adult life. The healer I have been blessed to work with truly had a gift beyond the normal doctor, they did amazing work. *Lord please let this be a true healer.*

"It is a starting place, right?" she offered. "Where else do you have to go at this point?"

She was right.

I made an appointment with Keith Stanton at the herb store in Escondido.

As I mentioned, I have managed holistic centers and there is little that can really freak me. What could he possibly do to me that I have not had done or heard of being done? What could I not understand about what other patients have tried? I was scared and excited about what he was going to say to me. I thought I was doing pretty well in terms of my diet. *I was in good shape*, I thought. There is not going to be too much to do to really change.

Okay, keep promising yourself that, Karen.

I walked into his clinic and I was surprised. The place was not fancy at all for a guy who had been healing cancer. The person behind the desk was not official-looking or anything like that.

"Hi, how are you?" came the greeting.

"Fine! Okay, who are you here to meet?"

"Keith Stanton," I answered.

"Okay, have a seat. He will be right with you."

Looking around, I see a cabinet with herbs, a cash register, four chairs, and lots of books on health. That's it? I immediately started thinking about how I could fix this place up. I have designed places like for years. *Maybe some fresh paint to start and new chairs... all the furniture should look as though it was meant to be here and not at a garage sale. There should be something to read while people wait, crazy they don't know how...*

Hey. Why haven't they given me any paperwork to fill out while I wait? Maybe they forgot?

I decided I better get this taken care of right now.

"Excuse me," I pipe up. "I didn't get any paperwork to fill out for my visit."

"Keith will fill out paperwork with you in the room. Okay?" the desk person responds.

This is going to take up my whole visit just explaining all the cancer stuff, I hope he can write quickly!

As I continue to design the proper office decor for this place in my head, someone pops out to say, "He will see you now."

I walked through the door and there was nothing I had expected to see. All the powerful healers I knew had very nice, organized offices. I made sure of that! There was plenty of natural light, *okay, that is a good start*, but papers were everywhere. I mean everywhere: on the desk, floor, book shelves, everywhere.

A short, kind of heavy-set man greets me. He is wearing a golf shirt but he's not tan at all. I'm thinking he must come from the East Coast. I don't know what I expected, but this was not it. I guess when someone tells me you'll be meeting a person who cures cancer, I expect to see a giant man arriving to kick cancer's ass. It was so funny, I almost let out a laugh at myself for my illusion. Keith was not a stereotypical hero. He was slightly balding and didn't fit my preconceived picture at all.

Then I looked at his eyes. I had never seen such blue eyes. They are like the sky-after-a-rain blue, like a fairy-tale blue. I was just taken aback by them. As he met my gaze, I swear he was looking into my soul. It was freaking me out.

"Have a seat," he said. I almost did not hear him.

He took out a piece of paper. He wrote down my name and phone number at the top of the page with today's date.

"Let me tell you why I am here," I begin.

"Let's just see what I find first. I'll ask you if I need any information from you, okay?"

Okay? If I am not going to tell him anything, how is he going to know what he is looking for?

He asks me to scoot my chair up towards him.

"I am going to talk to your body now," he declares. He takes my hands and looks me in the eyes, I mean, deep in my eyes. After a few moments like this, he takes out what looks like a magnifying glass and examines my eyes with it. He brings out a crystal that is hanging on the end of a chain. He asks me to uncross my legs. He places the crystal necklace over my thighs and it starts to move by itself. It is moving back and forth, now side-to-side.

Is he asking it questions? Is my body doing that? Why a crystal? Am I allowed to ask questions?

It's as though I'm in a weird movie. I am so interested to see what is going to come next. I was going to start asking questions but before I could, he started asking me questions. The first one knocks me back to reality.

"I know you feel like your mother did not really want you. You were the last of a lot of children. She was just overwhelmed and did not expect another child."

I'm thinking, *WHAT? How did he....*

"Are you going to keep getting sick to get her attention or are you done with that now?" he calmly asks.

What the Hell?

"Because the next time you get cancer, it will kill you," he says.

Okay, I am all the way freaked out now.

"She is not going to love you more or take care of you. That is all up to you now. Do you understand what I am talking about?"

"Yes, that is right," was all I could get out. I wanted to cry but I knew this was not the time or the place.

"Now," he continued. "Let's look at how your body is reacting to the stress you have been through."

This is the quietest I have ever been when being assessed by anyone. *Was I allowed to ask questions?* I just sat there, not knowing what to do or say.

Next, he asked me to put my hand on the top of my head with my palm facing up. Then, he took my other hand and put my middle finger and my thumb together. He asked me to press them together as tight as I could.

"Don't let me pull them apart," he instructed. I could press them tight enough so no matter what he tried; he could not pull them apart.

He asked me to flip over the hand on my head so that my palm was flat on my head. He asked me again to hold my finger and thumb together tightly so he couldn't pull them apart. I could not hold them together no matter how hard I tried. *This is crazy; what is this test for?* I wanted to ask, but I did not want to disturb him as he was testing me.

He was writing on the paper with my name. I could see some weird characters. There were single words and figures. *What does that all mean,* I wondered. *Now, I really am in a movie of some kind.* I am ready again to start asking questions, but he starts talking instead.

How does he know just when I am about to ask questions?

"I was testing your body to see if it was what I thought was going on," he tells me.

"What did you think was going on?"

"I found something a long time ago that people with cancer were switched."

"What does switched mean?" I ask.

"It is easy for me to explain it like this: it's when your body thinks where your feet are the sky and where your head is the earth."

I must have looked really confused.

"Your body was made to process gravity easily and not be affected by it, correct?" he explained. "So, when your body is switched, it has been extremely affected by gravity and starts to break down your body from the force. It shows up where you are weak physically and emotionally. With women it is their breasts."

Okay, this is making sense, I think?

"I found women don't nurture themselves at all, they are trying too hard to show everyone they can do it all. They keep comparing themselves to the women of the past saying, 'Look at how much more I can do.'"

He went on. "At what expense are you doing it? And why are you doing it? Are you being asked to do it or are you taking on the responsibility yourself as a badge of honor? Who is going to present you with the award? Is anyone going to care about the award when you have passed away while earning it?"

"Your chest is the nurturing part of your body, right? It is warning you, asking you to honor yourself. Society is treating your chest like it is holding you back from being a man. Men are treating your chest like it doesn't exist. You are forced to be in a man's world. When do you get to quit being a man and just be a woman? When do you get to let your guard down, be vulnerable, be a full woman?"

As he is speaking, I feel vulnerable. I can't think of the last time I felt protected as a woman or a time when I was not trying to be like a man. *Had I been forced to act like a man, taking charge, making all the decisions in my work and personal life? I like having an opinion on things but have I been too strong?*

Even now, no one expects me to be weak and scared. I know I have to be strong and force myself past the pain to get to the other side. *But at what cost? Why don't I feel supported enough to just be?* I guess because it is my decision not to be.

Keith tells me he has a program that has worked on getting people un-switched.

"You have to follow the program all the way, every day, without fail. If you change back or stop the program, it will not work at all," he warns.

"Okay," I tell him, willing. "What do I have to do?"

"I am going to give you four herbs to take—without fail—every day. Let me explain them to you." I listened to him explain the list of herbs:

» Immune 2 to support your immune system and help you heal.

» TJM for your thymus gland and to help your body produce white blood cells to fight against the cancer.

» Spirulina which gives your blood oxygen because cancer cannot live in a high-oxygen environment.

» Valerian root to help with the healing of the tissue and to bring overall rest to your body.

He made some more notes before asking, "You do not have a breathing problem, do you?"

"No, not that I know of," I answered.

"You cannot take Valerian root if you have a breathing problem. It is also a muscle relaxer, and it can affect your breathing," he explained. "It can also give you different kinds of dreams. If this happens, please stop taking it right away."

"How often am I going to take all of these?" I asked.

"Each herb will be taken three times a day, with food."

"Okay, thank you," I replied.

"I am not done," he warned. "Next is what you eat."

I nodded, knowing there would be more to all this than just taking a mix of herbs.

"You cannot have any caffeine or stimulants of any kind? Do you drink alcohol?"

"No."

"Okay, no smoking and no sugar either. You must bring your body back to basics, the way God intended it to be managed. I would suggest you eat organic foods as much as you can afford, since it is very hard on the liver and kidneys to process chemicals of any kind."

I told him I understood.

"When do you start your chemotherapy and other therapies?" he asked next.

"I have decided against chemotherapy and I am just going to let my body heal itself."

"I cannot tell you either way what to do about that, but I can help you on your decision to help your body heal itself. They will help you with the supplements at the front counter."

I was surprised that was all there was going to be to this visit. "Can I ask questions?"

"Yes, you can," he said.

"Okay, how did you know everything you just said to me?"

"Your body told me."

"How exactly did it tell you? I do not understand."

"I do what is called ideology," he explained. "It is an accent method of looking in the eyes and letting the body tell you what is going on in the organs of the body. It would take a very long time to explain exactly what it is, but I have been doing it for many years with many patients."

"What is the crystal swinging over my lap used for?" I wanted to know.

"It helps me test the energy of your body with which way it sways."

"I think I understand," I was trying to process everything. "Why don't you ask questions when I come in?"

"I don't need to know. Your body tells me all I need to know," he responded.

"Why didn't I fill out any paperwork? Are you only basing your advice on what my body says and not my medical history?"

"No," he told me. "I have been shut down before because so many people were saying I cured their cancer. Someone turned me into the FDA."

"What, are you kidding me?" I couldn't believe something like that would happen.

"No, I wish I weren't. But now, I don't write anything down that anyone else can understand to protect myself."

"But you are curing people," I argued.

"No, I cannot say that. I have no clinical studies to back up what I do," he said.

"But isn't the proof in the living people who were supposed to die?"

"No, they do not see it that way."

I could see the pain in his eyes and it made me so upset. *Who does this to a healer?*

"How often do I need to come back?" I asked.

"It is entirely up to you," Keith explained. "If you do the program exactly as I tell you, then come back in two weeks and we'll see how the program is working. They will sell you enough supplements for that amount of time. When you come back, I will know how well you followed the program."

As I walked out of his office, I wondered how he was going to know what to do next. Of course, I was going to follow the program. I only knew what to do for myself from my holistic clinic experience. But this was way beyond that now.

I went out front to schedule my next appointment. All the supplements he prescribed were already on the counter waiting for me. I was so glad I had a credit card because there were so many bottles.

This is going to be a fortune. Fine. This is my life we are talking about here.

The visit cost $49 plus another $150 for the supplements. *What? This is all it is going to cost to keep me alive? Are you kidding me right now?*

"Why are the supplements so cheap?" I asked.

"He only charges 20 percent over what they cost him," came the answer.

"Why?" I just had to ask them.

"He believes what he does is a gift for others."

"Wait, what?" I clarified. "He does not do it for the money? The money will come from the service to others?"

I stood there for a minute, soaking in what they just said. I paid gladly, knowing I had just been seen by a person put here to truly help others.

I started the supplement program and it was harder than I thought. Not taking the supplements, mind you, being without caffeine. I did not think I could stay awake at all. Headaches seemed to last all day long. I knew from experience that water was going to be my saving grace. Water would help cleanse my body of the toxins. But the withdrawal from caffeine addiction was going to be tough.

I wanted to do exactly what Keith had told me to do to see how it would affect my body. Somehow, I felt sure he could save me. I knew not only one program or course of action could save me. But if I put everything together, I could save my life.

So many things have changed since the surgery date. The TV bed was sent back and I was sleeping next to my husband for the first time in weeks. Every time I let out the slightest noise, he would wake up to see if I was okay. I had to be quiet when I felt pain so I wouldn't wake him. I learned pretty quickly to roll on my side and push down on the mattress with one hand to get myself up without using my pecs. I was determined to not use my chest muscles during the healing time. I knew they had to be still and heal without interruption. This meant no cleaning the house or laundry of any kind. This meant my husband had to do so much more until I was healed. I tried to help where I could; cooking dinner and taking Kasondra to daycare.

We also had a new puppy and I used my walks to train her when Kasondra was at daycare. This forced me to get out of the house and move. Some days, I only walked a few blocks but that was better than nothing. My neighbors were still keeping a watch on me.

Before I knew it, it was time to go to Dr. Crane's office again. I was worried about getting there because I had not driven so far from my house before by myself since surgery. Dr. Crane's office was only 30 minutes away so I'd been calling people to help me get there. I determined I could do this by myself.

At the appointment with Dr. Crane, I sat in the waiting room. For the first time, I noticed all the people who were there to see him. *Why hadn't I really noticed them before?* They were in all different stages of healing. I wondered how many of them were healing from breast surgery. *Was anyone dealing with cancer like I was right now?* Cancer is so silent you can't always tell from the outside what is happening on the inside.

When I got into the exam room, I was excited to show him the drains. The liquid was clear and finally, no red mixed in. The volume was way down; there was only a little at the bottom of the bottle. *These were all good signs, right?*

I knew it was Keith's program that was healing me so quickly.

I was so ready to have the drains out. I was still trying to hide them from Kasondra. I couldn't take a real shower to get all the way wet, either. Yet, the most important thing was that I was healing and moving forward. I was reaching the other side. I knew cancer would always be a concern in the back of my mind, but not in the same way.

Dr. Crane came into the room, looked at the drains and my chart. "These look great. Let's take them out!" he exclaimed. "The nurse is going to take them out and then I will come back to take a look before you leave."

I was so happy.

You have no idea all I am doing to heal; I am so glad it is all working. All you have to do is just get to the other side of all of this, Karen. Just concentrate on the end of all of this and getting your life back, this is step one, no more drains... YES!

The nurse came in to take the drains out. I was so excited when she cut the stitches on the sides that were holding them in place. I hadn't remembered seeing or feeling any stitches there. Then she held what looked like pliers on the end of the drain's tube, explaining, "I am going to pull this side out first, are you ready?"

"Okay, I'm ready," I tell her. *Wait, ready for what?*

As she pulled, I started to scream from the pain. She was going so slow and I could not stop screaming until she had pulled it all the way out. I started to cry. Dr. Crane burst into the room.

"What is going on here?" he demanded. "I could hear you screaming all the way down the hall. There are other patients besides you here, you do realize that, right?"

All I could get out was a weak, "Yes."

"The tissues have grown around the drains and it is going to hurt," he said. "It's like ripping off a band-aide so you have to do it fast. Are you going to scream again?"

"I don't know?"

"I will pull it out quick. It will be all over fast," he assured me. He looked around the room and then took a ball of gauze out of the jar. He placed it in my mouth and told me to bite down.

"Ready?" he warned me.

I nodded yes.

He put the pliers on the tube and pulled with a strong tug. As it was coming out, he put his hand on the tube and pulled again. I was screaming into the ball of gauze.

He said in a stern voice, "It's out. Spit out the gauze."

I started to cry.

"It will burn for a while but it will calm down. It usually does not hurt this much when they come out, we will have to watch them for a reaction of some kind."

Then he turned to the nurse. "NEVER, and I mean NEVER, pull these out slowly. Do you understand?"

As I calmed down and the nurse straightened things up, I realized I was now through the first phase. The drains were out. Dr. Crane returned to go over the remaining phases of filling the implants. I could also have a full shower now without the worry of getting the drains wet.

"We are going to continue to fill the implants to expand the muscles under your chest," he explained. "I think I want to expand them to a size D chest. Once we are done filling them, we will have two more surgeries. First, we'll put in your permanent implants, the ones you will have for a long time, usually around 15 years. Then we will put on your nipples and we will be done. Do you understand all we have to do?"

"Yes, I understand. Two more surgeries," I confirmed. But, of course, I had more questions.

"What did you say about this is the first of other surgeries, something about 15 years?"

"Your implants have to be replaced about every 15 years," he repeated.

"Wait, what? I don't remember that part when you explained this to me before." I insisted.

"Yes," he answered. "They will wear out being in the body and they will need to be replaced several times throughout your life."

This was something new. *I will need to ask more questions about this.*

"We are not going to do any filling today. Your body has been through enough for one day," he added.

I stuck to Keith's herb program faithfully. My energy levels were much better and I knew I was doing the right things to protect myself from getting any new cancer.

As I returned to Dr. Crane's for fills, I began to feel more like my old self. My chest was starting to look like a chest again. I felt hopeful for my life. I teased Dr. Crane every time I came in for the fills. I don't think he knew what to do with me. He checked off the boxes on my punch card and I told him I was waiting for my free bra. Each time I handed it to him, he smiled. It felt good to get a smile out of Dr. Crane.

I was also sticking with the diet recommendations from Keith and felt I was doing great, but I wanted to go even further—I wanted to be all the way clean. I would only put food in my body that would easily digest to make it easier for my body to concentrate on healing. Food was there to feed my body, period. I considered food as though it were a medicine I needed to heal.

I saw Keith again. I was getting used to my new routine. He retested me and said I could go on a lower dose maintenance plan while I went through the other surgeries to help me heal as I went along.

Instead of taking three of each type of pill three times a day (a total of 27 pills), I could now reduce that to two of each twice a day (16 pills). I was used to swallowing a lot of pills all at once, so this would be a breeze. Honestly, I would have taken just about anything he wanted me to as many times as he said to in order to get through this. I was to come back after the next surgery to see how my body was handling the lower amounts.

Dr. Crane had filled my chest and I looked great. It was hard to tell I had a double mastectomy. My chest looked so real and it was larger than before, too. At my next appointment, he started to talk about the upcoming surgery to take out the muscle-stretching implants and put in my forever implants.

"Do I have to take these out?" I asked him. "They look incredible and so real."

"Karen, they have a port on the top of them," he pointed out.

"I don't mind if you don't," I said.

"They are not meant to be in your body for a long time."

"Okay, why not? I mean, they like me… I like them… it is perfect," I argued.

"The fill-top will be pushing on your skin and that may become painful," he insisted.

"Let me see, you think this is pain? Are you kidding me? This is nothing compared to the pain I have had!"

In the end, he wanted to change them out and I reluctantly agreed. I knew I'd have to keep moving ahead, but I was finally feeling good.

"I'll have my nurse call you to start setting it up," he confirmed.

Okay, I told myself. *Just think, this is a lot less surgery already, right? All we're doing is replacing the implants. At least I have them in already. But I am not happy to start this surgery route again. My life was getting just getting normal!*

I can finally walk Sidney around the neighborhood and it is easy. It is such an incredible distraction training our new puppy. I honestly do not know what I would have done without her. She was so smart and only wanted to please me all day, every day. She came to us before I found out about the cancer. Sidney and I had become so bonded I know she could feel my fear. She would stay especially close to me in those moments.

At first, just around the block was fine. After that, she made me push myself. She needed more walking time and since she was going to be a big dog, I had to make sure she was trained. Kasondra was young and I did not want a big, untrained dog knocking her down. I wanted to train her to protect Kasondra and know that she could protect us both if I was unable to.

She was the reason to keep moving forward during the day. I could not sit and feel sorry for myself all day. She demanded our morning and afternoon walks every day. The best part was I felt guilty if I did not take her. That pushed me even more.

"Sit" "stay" and "wait" were commands she learned quickly. She would let me catch up to her on the leash before she crossed the street. "Leave it" was the most important command so she did not pull me when she saw other dogs. My arms still needed to stay by my side to heal. If she pulled hard, I would need to engage my pecs to hold her back. I just made sure to stay away from other dogs when we were on our training walks. "Girl" meant Kasondra and she knew to find her and sit by her until I came. "Find your girl," I would say.

It was amazing that she knew to look around the house for Kasondra and then stay by her side. I felt so much better knowing she would protect her. We started a game in a ravine down the street from our house. Kasondra would run down the dirt path, I would hold Sidney back, and then command, "Stop your girl!" I would let her go and she would catch up to Kasondra to herd her, keeping her in one place by making her body into a u-shape, gently pressing up against Kasondra until I could reach them. It was also a good way to wear them both out for the night.

Father, I want to thank you for all you have done to spare my life.

These trainings also became my prayer time to thank God for my life. I noticed as I walked around the neighborhood how beautiful my neighborhood was. I noticed the nice neighbors who waved as I walked by. I knew they were checking in with me with a glance and a nod, encouraging me with a look and a smile. You could tell they were worried as Kasondra walked by with me and the dog.

"She is so young," one neighbor said when they found out what I was going through.

"It's going to be fine. God has saved me so many times," I assured them.

"You are so brave. I would never do what you are doing, going with alternative treatments. Aren't you concerned for Kasondra?"

"Yes, that is why I am doing what I am doing." *Could anyone really understand? It's okay, I can.* But I could see it in their eyes as I walked by and I could imagine their thoughts, *"Will she be alive later...."*

Dr. Crane's nurse called to schedule the surgery to switch the implants. As we talked, I remembered Dr. Night-Night and how he did exactly what he promised. He had kept me alive during the very long surgery.

"I do not want to do this without Dr. Night-Night?" I insisted.

"Who?" she asked.

"The doctor who put me to sleep. I want him again."

"Karen, it is not going to be a long surgery. You will be fine. To schedule around an anesthesiologist is going to be hard to do and Dr. Crane is very busy. I am sorry," came the answer.

"But that is the only part that scares me," I said. "I'll wait to schedule for him."

"Can you please hold," she responded.

After a wait on hold, Dr. Crane came on the line.

"Dr. Crane, I am sure they can all put me to sleep but I want him," I told him.

"Karen, are we going to have to do this every time?" he said, exasperated with me.

"Yes, this makes me secure. I really need this," I explained.

"Okay, fine, but it is going to make it harder on my staff." There was a long pause and I was not going to fill it with "I give in" because I was not going to give in.

"I will tell them to find Dr. Ross," he finally agreed, "but this is not necessary. Any one of doctors can read his notes and put you to sleep the same way."

"Thank you, Dr. Crane. I knew you would understand."

When the nurse called me back, she had found a day where they both had openings and there was an available surgery unit. *Wow, I guess that was a little hard to coordinate.*

"It will take two weeks longer so you will have no more fill dates, just wait time for the surgery," she explained. "Dr. Crane will see you one more time before surgery to pre-op you for the next surgery."

How does life go on when you know you are going into surgery again? I had to put it out of my mind and put the facts into perspective. *It is one day longer to no more surgeries and life will be back as I know it.* I was reminded again that I fought to get to the other side. But what will life be like when I was done with this chapter? Would I ever really be done? *I guess I am really only done with this stage.*

I called Keith to tell him about the surgery delay and he said to stay on the lower dose maintenance program.

When the day for the pre-op appointment came, I was still bummed to see this chest was going to go away. It really looked beautiful. It was so real-looking, Kasondra could not tell it was not my own chest.

"Your chest looks great," Dr. Crane confirmed. "It has healed really nicely and the swelling has gone away. I am going to put a slightly smaller implant in when I replace these. Your muscles should shrink to fit around it."

"Wait," I protested in my usual manner. "Why smaller? These look so amazing."

"I want the muscles to close around them and not be so stretched," he explained. "And the implant amount is way too high for your lifestyle; they may pop from the pressure."

"Wait, what? They can pop?" I asked, hearing this bit of news for the first time.

"If they are filled too high, they can pop and these are already filled too much for an everyday lifestyle."

"I understand," I responded, a bit defeated. "I guess it was like an incredible win for a lot of pain."

"I know you are on some kind of supplement program," he ventured, changing the subject.

"Yes, from the patient you told me about, I've been going to the man she went to. He has helped a lot of people stay cancer-free."

"Okay, fine," he said, adding, "Anyway, you cannot take the pills right now since I do not know what they are doing to your body and I do not know how they will affect your healing. They may also affect the anesthesia so I do not want to risk anything and I know you don't want to either. You need to stop taking them to be totally safe."

"Are you sure I have to stop the program?" I was not convinced.

"Yes. I will not do the surgery if you have not stopped taking the pills." He was not budging. "Karen, this is not something you can say yes to and then continue taking supplements I haven't authorized or recommended. I know you stopped taking the antibiotics before they were done. But this is serious and can cause intense problems."

I yielded. "I guarantee you; I will not take the supplements from now until the surgery. I do have one more question, though."

"Yes, Karen?"

"I need to know there are not going to be drains again. It was hard keeping Kasondra from seeing them and they were hard to manage. And I will not soon forget the pain when you took them out."

"There should be no need for drains since we are changing them so quickly. Your body has not had enough time to build up scar tissue, so it should be a quick 'swap them out' surgery and we are done," he said.

"I can't tell you how afraid I am of that pain," I reminded him.

"I will always take them out for you from now on, how about that? If I have to put them in, I will personally take them out. We need to move on from this, really."

"Okay," I said quickly. "Thank you." I had bothered him enough for the day.

Dr. Night-Night arrived.

"Hi Karen, thank you for requesting me," he smiled.

"I would not go to sleep without you," I told him.

"Okay, you know the drill. I put you to sleep and you wake up. Easy, right? I'll see you inside."

Once I was in the operating room, things went very quickly. Dr. Crane asked me if I was ready and he said, "We will be in and out in no time."

"Thank you," I said. "Time to move on."

"Exactly. This is only going to take an hour or so, a lot easier than the first time, right?"

"Thank you, Dr. Crane," I said again.

Dr. Night-Night came waltzing in. "Okay, so let's get the IV in and start putting you to sleep." He fiddled with me for several minutes.

"Okay, Karen. Say good night. We will see you when you wake up." I'm not sure who said it.

"Karen, you are in recovery now. The surgery is all done and the new implants are in. We need you to start waking up now, try to move around a little. How are you feeling? Are you in any pain? Let me know if you need any pain drugs, but we want you to wake up more before we give them to you."

"Karen, it's Dr. Crane. We need you to start waking up. Good, that is better. Let me see your eyes. Good, can you understand me now?"

"Yes," My throat was scratchy. "What is going on?"

"When I went in for what I thought would be an easy surgery," he started, "it was not as easy as I thought so we had to put you under deeper so I could work."

"What was wrong?" I finally got the words out.

"There was so much scar tissue around the implant I had to scrape it all out to get the implant out and then clean the area where the new implant was going to go. So, the surgery was twice as long as I thought it would be," he explained.

"There should not have been that much scar tissue in this short amount of time," he went on. "The amount of scar tissue had built up as though you had been healing for months or even a year. I have never seen that much healing in such a short amount of time. What I thought would take an hour took a couple of hours… and that was working fast."

I was trying to fully comprehend what he was telling me.

"It is all done now and they are in and ready to go. I have one final thing to tell you. I had to put the drains back in. I had no choice, Karen. Your body is going to see this as another injury and it is going to start sending fluids to heal you again. After I saw what I did today, I am going to go with caution and give your body all the help it needs to heal you quickly again."

The news was too much to bear. I started to cry. All I could hear in his entire explanation was drains. Healing fast and DRAINS. *He told me no drains and I was counting on no drains.*

Get ahold of yourself, you're alive, this is your last implant surgery, he said you had healed the fastest he has ever seen. Oh, how are you going to hide the drains from Kasondra again?

I knew that none of this was an accident. This was a result of Keith's herbs, walking, drinking water, eating organic food, and not moving my chest. It had all paid off. *But did it, really? He said he had to carve all the scar tissue away.*

Ask questions. Wake up and ask questions.

"But it worked to carve it out right? This is the last time you will have to work with the implants for a long time, right?" I wanted to hear the right answers.

"Yes, the permanent implants are in and you are ready to heal again," he said. "Since I did so much work, we are going to admit you to the hospital. We do not want to go through what happened to you last time I worked on you. Your body goes into shock so easily I want to make sure you are okay before I send you home. I'll come and check on you once you are admitted. Just know this is going to be a lot easier, no more filling them up, no weekly doctors' appointments, just healing and then you're done with the implant part."

"Okay." I was coming around to clarity and acceptance.

You are so blessed. This is the last time you have to have the implants worked on for years. You healed them once and you can do it again. You know what you have been doing is working so it should not be a problem. You can get to the other side now, you're almost there. I only have to stay overnight for observation to make sure my body is okay with everything he did and will not go into shock.

You now have time to go over a game plan. This changes everything. You thought you were going to wake up and move on with your life, but this is an unexpected change in plans. This time, you do not have a hospital bed. How are you going to get up without your arms? Always remember to roll to your side first, push just with your forearm to get up. You still cannot carry anything or pull things, and no lifting. Keep telling yourself that.

I now had a goal: to surprise everyone with my ability to heal faster than they had ever seen before.

Dr. Crane was such a skeptic. He did not really believe in healing the body naturally and now he wanted to know everything I was doing. Could it have been all the things I was taking that truly saved my life? I think he believed that now. My body had encapsulated the tumor, how did it do that? This had saved me for so long and kept me from dying. Now he was witnessing speed-healing. He was amazed and nothing amazes him.

I am glad he let me stay in the hospital. But the medication routine would rear its ugly head again.

"We are going to give you this medication to help you," the nurse announced.

"Before I take anything, I like to know what it is and why I am taking it," I objected.

"Be assured we only give you what is written in your chart by your doctor," came the familiar reasoning.

"I understand all of that, I just don't like to take unnecessary medication. If you do not mind, can you tell me what the pills are for that you are trying to give me?"

"These are antibiotics and they are to help you heal from the surgery."

"I agree. I will take those as I told the doctor I would."

"This is your pain medication to help you with the pain from the surgery."

"I don't really want to take those. Can you give me extra-strength Tylenol instead?"

"I don't think you understand. This is going to be painful and you should stay ahead of the pain right now. I am not allowed to change your medication without consulting your doctor."

"I totally understand. He is used to having you call him about me, please call him."

"Oh, wait. This is Dr. Crane. We only call him when we absolutely need to call him." *Was she treating me like a child, too?*

"Look, I totally understand but he is probably expecting a call about me."

"I will try to reach him," she finally agreed.

"For now, I will take the antibiotic because I told him I would," I promised, wondering if she was really going to call Dr. Crane.

Before too long, Dr. Crane and the nurse were back hovering over me.

"Hi, Dr. Crane," I said, trying to put on a cheery voice.

"You're lucky. I was in the hospital doing rounds when they tell me you are causing problems."

"I'm not. I just want to start out being aware of the pain."

He turned to the nurse. "Okay, let's give her want she wants. Just do what she says. She is the doctor, right?" I didn't think he was finished.

"Really? No Karen. You will take everything I prescribe, but to compromise I will change the pain medication to extra-strength Tylenol," he barked.

"Can I just take those two drugs, please?" I pleaded. "Let's review: I healed so fast, remember?"

"Fine. Those two drugs. You are going home tomorrow so I will not be there to see what you do or do not take. I do not want to receive any more calls, correct?"

"Yes," I obeyed.

As he examined his work, I took a good look, too. They seemed so much smaller. Maybe it was because the bandages were so tight? My beautiful chest I was really starting to love and accept was gone and now there is something new to get used to?

"Oh, crap the drains are full of fluid and blood. I cannot believe we are back to square one?" I asked, my voice on the verge of total despair. *Okay, don't start crying. They are done. No more implant surgery. You are getting to the other side.*

We went about emptying the drains and Dr. Crane left.

It feels so good to be back home, but it's different to be home from surgery and not have what I am used to having in order to heal.

I would have to compromise and adjust as I went along. Keith said to start taking the full herb regiment as soon as I could, so today is the day to start healing again.

I had my trusty list to start the healing:

» Positive thinking.

» Lots of water to clean out the anesthesia.

» Walk the dog to get the drugs out of my system.

» Eat easily digestible food to give all my energy to healing.

» Don't move my arms away from my sides so I do not engage my pecs.

» Rest. Lots of rest.

» Become friends with extra-strength Tylenol again.

I also knew this would be the last time I would take antibiotics for Dr. Crane. I hate taking this medication as it messes with my digestion and my stomach. There is no conductor in my stomach telling the drug, "Hey, this way. Only go to the injury! Pass over the rest of the body, go directly to the injury!" No, it's going to mess up the rest of my body along the way to where it's needed.

I was ready to rest until Kasondra came home from daycare. *I wonder if she wonders where I am when she does not see me? Does she ask where I am? No one tells me what happens when I am not here.*

Oh, my God, the pain just shot up my chest, I can't breathe. I forgot where I was. All I had to do was go to the bathroom. What the Hell just happened? Wait, wait, wait, I can't just put my hand down and push myself up out of bed. My God, how do I get out of bed again? Clear your mind. How do I get out of this bed without hurting myself?

Oh, right. Roll on my side and push with just my forearm and keep my arm to my side.

I was there, healed. I was not thinking about any of this for months and here I am again. Is this ever going to stop?

God, I am so angry right now. Angry is not the right word. Frustrated is the right word. I know I should not be crying but I don't have the strength to just push through. I feel so alone sometimes.

I remembered the hospital giving me information about a cancer support group. I promised myself I would check it out when I was healed from this surgery.

I was finally able to drive myself, and I headed out for the post-op appointment so Dr. Crane can look at the stitches site and check the drains. I haven't seen the new implants yet, and I hope I'll like them. The temporaries looked so real and it was hard to tell they were man-made. The permanent implants were a different size and shape.

When I walked into the office, I felt self-conscious that the staff was looking at me differently. They walked me into the exam room. The nurse arrived and immediately asked, "How did you heal so quickly? Dr. Crane said it looked like you had the implants for years."

"I have been taking herbs and supplements, eating clean, and not using my pecs so they can heal," I told her.

"That is amazing," she claimed.

Dr. Crane walked in, all business-like. "Let's take these bandages off now and see how everything looks." As he examined me, he mentioned how nice the implants were healing. I was looking at the size. From the top, they looked so much smaller. They were definitely not as full as the first pair. *Why did I have to take the first ones out? I loved them.*

He picked up a mirror and held it so he could explain the healing around the implants. He remarked how especially quickly I healed. I wasn't sure if I should tell him I didn't think I liked the way they looked. I felt he could tell I wasn't happy with the way I acted when I saw them. I felt I had to say something.

"They look so different, why?" I started.

"Because the temporaries were more expanded in order to make room for these," he explained. "Now the body has to heal around these and it will be fine."

"But the shape is so much different than the other implants," I insisted. "These are kind of long and the other implants were round and full." He didn't offer a response. I wanted to question him more, but I didn't. He had been right about so many other things, maybe he would be on this, too.

"The drains will hopefully come out on your next visit," he said instead.

"Okay," I said half-heartedly.

It is so strange how people think things are going to be the same as usual. *Cut the cancer out and go back to normal.* I'm not doing chemo or any other treatments, so I'm done. *Let's not think about it anymore; we are ready to move on.*

Life is not the same, I wanted to scream. It will never be the same again.

God, how do I move on? Please help me, no one looks at me the same. I don't look at me the same. I am so tired of being strong, but who am I going to cry to?

I have to trust that it will all be fine and that they will look okay once the swelling has gone down.

At the next visit, I declared myself an expert on drains. I can measure and empty them by myself. The fluid color is clear and there is not much fluid coming out anymore. I knew they were coming out on this visit. *He promised he would take them out this time and I am going to hold him to his promise.*

"Okay, they look great. Let's get these out," Dr. Crane confirms after a quick exam. "Here, put this in your mouth." He hands me a tongue depressor. "I can't have you scaring my patients away."

"Are you kidding me?" I ask.

"Yes, and no. Yes, it is going to hurt again because you heal so fast. No, I'm not kidding. Put it in your mouth and let's get this over with. I'm going to cut the stitches and then I am going to do one side, move around, and do the other side right afterwards. It is going to be quick, so don't get in my way, just let me do it. Are you ready?"

"Yes," I hope.

"Okay, put that thing in your mouth."

I wanted to let out a scream. All I heard from him was, "Don't move. I'm doing the other side now." Another silent scream and my body started to shake. It was over.

"I told you, piece of cake," he gloated. "Spit out that thing."

Tears were rolling down my face.

"I'll be right back," he said. The nurse gave me a hug as I whimpered.

"The burning will stop in a minute," she said. "You just heal so fast there is nothing we can do to help it not be painful."

"That is the last time you will have to have drains for a long time," Dr. Crane said when he walked back in. "Now, we need to plan for the last part of the reconstruction: your nipples. You said you wanted them to look as natural as I can make them. We have options to go over to make sure that happens and we are going to let you heal for a month before we start that part."

I agreed it had been a lot to go through already and I needed a break.

Will life be the same? Kasondra loves daycare and I can take her and pick her up each day. I am still being careful about lifting her and remember to only use my forearms.

I can't believe how long it has been and how used to the changes I've become. *How did I get used to not having breasts?* Is it because I am a woman and we tend to move on through difficult circumstances? For me, I try to get through by focusing on the other side and not looking back.

Today is a day of reflection and finally, a day where I can relax. I don't have a project to do or anything to fix on my body. Just breathing is beautiful, but I know taking a breath will never be the same. I will forevermore feel the pressure of the implants on my chest. But I will be thankful to feel that pressure.

Sidney is so well-trained she can walk with me off her leash now. She is my rock. She is who I cry to and hold onto when I am scared. She does not push me to be strong, instead, she waits patiently, allowing me to melt into her; to let go, to be weak. Our walks have gone from barely making it around the block to clocking two miles around the greenbelt.

I've gone from pain with every step—emotionally and physically—to being grateful for every step. I know I have to get ready for the last step, but to be here right now, I am relishing in how much I have been able to endure. Every second and minute, I am blessed by so many people. Finally, taking a breather, gives me time to relish the support and love I have. I truly do not think I could have done this without it.

I also live in an amazing and beautiful place. Not only San Diego, but my neighborhood in particular. Neighbors Ken and Tracie, Ralph and Elkie, and Pat and Mary Kay are incredible. I know if I asked them for help, they would be there in a second. And they have been. *Have I told them enough how much I appreciate them?* I cherish the kind words they gave me every time we met. "You look great," they'd say, when I knew I looked scary and in pain. I could not recognize my true self, but they could.

My good friend, Alisa, comes to mind as I reflect on how many times she helped me try to stretch my scar tissue and move my arms. "Why didn't the doctors tell me what you are telling me? That I should be stretching," I wondered. Thinking on how we met and the friendship we have developed, I couldn't ask for any better support from this amazing physical therapist and true, loving friend.

Did I tell her that enough? Did I tell her that my life had been a blur for so long?

But there were other people who stepped out of my life and left me when cancer hit. Some checked out because they could not handle the situation or deal with what I had to face each day. I suck at saying what I want and need. Perhaps when people see me being so strong, they think I don't need any help. Maybe they think I don't want their help. Ultimately, it is my fault for not asking for help, so I should have no resentments because they *should* be asking, I'm not telling them, I guess we are both at fault? All that truly matters is I am alive and moving forward in my life.

Kasondra is so amazing and funny, I could watch her for hours. She loves life and I can't imagine her life without me. I think about all I would have missed. *Would she have remembered me? She is only two, how could she? She is why I will work every day to be healthy and stay healthy. I know no one will love her as I do. How could they?*

I found the keys to staying healthy and Keith was a critical part of the chain. I'm still on his supplement program and I feel stronger every day. I am ready to have all of the trauma over and behind me. I haven't forgotten my promise to look into the cancer support group. That is next on my list for healing.

The appointment is here to go over the final step with Dr. Crane. Should I tell him I am still not sure I like this new implant size and the way they look?

I have also become aware of numbness on the back of my left arm. I am not sure if this is a symptom that will eventually go away. No one mentioned anything like this would happen. The sensation isn't especially painful, but if someone touches my arm, it feels like when your foot falls asleep. I started to trace the pain to see if I could tell where it starts and ends, but I couldn't find either point. I can see my left hand is a little swollen and also feels a little numb. I wonder if this effect will disappear or get worse. I decided I will ask Dr. Crane if he knows what is happening.

"Okay, Karen," he gets down to business as usual. "We are at the final phase of the reconstruction the nipples. I know we went over this, what seems like a long time ago. Do you remember what I told you at that time?"

"No, I'm sorry, I don't," I admit. "But before we go over that, can I tell you something? I have noticed lately the back of my arm is numb. It feels like my foot is asleep but it's in my arm. It is a little painful but in a weird way. And my hand feels swollen. Should I be concerned and will this go away or get worse?"

"What you have is called lymphedema," he said, surprising me that he knew so quickly. "It is a condition when you take out the lymph nodes to check for cancer and your body can have a reaction. The lymph node function is to help the fluid circulate throughout your arms down to your hands. When you remove them, there are not enough nodes to help circulate the fluid so the fluid backs up and your arm starts to swell with fluid."

"Will it keep getting bigger? Will the pain get worse?" I wanted to know what to expect.

"We can start to try to get the fluid down by putting on an arm sleeve, that will stop the swelling from increasing, acting like an ace bandage but it will be on tight," he explained, then added, "You'll need to see Dr. Watson about this, as this is not my expertise."

"It is not life threatening in any way," he continued, "but this is something that will be with you for life."

"What?" I exclaimed. "What caused it? Did I do something?"

"No," he assured me. "It just happens to some patients."

"Could I have prevented it in some way?"

"No, when you take the lymph nodes out, you disrupt the flow for fluid removal by the body, so fluid gathers in your arms, chest, and sometimes in the legs."

"Why did it happen to me?"

"They took a lot of your lymph nodes out, so there was a lot of disruption. Once this was set in motion, all you can do is try to control it," he said. "We will make an appointment with Dr. Watson to manage it for you."

I couldn't believe what I'd heard. *This is going to be with me for life? Will I feel this numbness forever? Is my hand going to get so swollen I am going to look funny for the rest of my life?*

A part of me wanted to brush it off; *I was alive after all, right?* But I wanted to get my body back to as normal as I could get it.

Wait until you get the information from, Dr. Watson. Focus on what he is saying right now.

"Let's proceed with the consultation about the nipples to complete the breast reconstruction surgery," he insisted.

"I want my chest to look as real as you can make it look. My daughter is very young and I am worried about scaring her if she sees me when I am naked," I told him. I felt I had to explain further to drive home my concern. "I remember when I first saw my mom's chest after her cancer surgery. To this day it frightens me and that was years ago. Plus, I was an adult at the time, not a two year old."

"Karen, you will feel like a full woman again. I have seen patients come out of depression when I put their nipples on. I know you are thinking of your daughter, but at some point, you will think of yourself as a woman again. I want to make you as close to whole as I can," he promised.

"Okay," I said. I believed him. "I am ready to be whole again."

"We have two options, as I went over with you before. You can tattoo your chest to look like nipples. It is a flat appearance if you can imagine that, but from a distance, they do look like nipples. I don't think your daughter could tell the difference." He went on, "Or, I can do a specialized grafting procedure as we went over before."

"We did?" I asked. "I don't remember."

"This procedure is a lot more extensive but you'll really look like you have nipples, even in a tight shirt. What I will do is take about a 2-inch-wide by 6-inch piece of skin out of your groin area by your inner thigh. The piece will start from where your leg comes in all the way down to where your butt starts."

What the Hell? I do not remember talking about this. Stay focused.

"The reason I take it from your inner thigh is because skin is darker by nature," he explains.

It is? What the Hell? I never knew that but who looks down there?

"Then, I graft that skin onto the top of your new chest. I take the middle of the graft and fold it in, like the tip of an airplane, to make the tip of the nipple. I will then sew the skin all the way around causing it to lift up, which causes the appearance of the milk ducts you have naturally around the outside of the nipple. So, when you wear a tight shirt it will look like you're a little cold, if you understand what I mean. You will not be able to tell these are not your nipples."

"I understand what you mean," I confirmed. But I had plenty of other questions. "Is this surgery painful? What is the recovery time? What are the chances of something going wrong? Do I have to have drains again? I will not do drains again, no matter what. You promised it wouldn't be for years, if at all, to do drains again."

"There will be no drains," he assured me. "As fast as you heal, it will not take long for you to heal from this," he added.

"Okay, for each option, please tell me the pros and cons," I asked. "The tattoo option will be done quickly, but it does not look as real, right?"

"Yes, I would go with the skin-grafting surgery. You have come this far, why not do it all the way correctly?" he suggested.

"Since this is a skin graft, could something go wrong?"

"Yes, your body could reject it and then we would have to take it off. It could get infected and cause problems with the new implants. I have not had these complications before so I am not worried about them now. You are very young and you want to look as natural as you can in the future. These nipples will not need to be touched up. They will be with you for life. So, this part will be done forever," he explained.

"How about my leg? What is the healing time for that? How painful will it be since it is so close to my groin area? Will it take a long time to heal? How will it restrict my movement?" I was trying to think of anything else I should be asking.

"The incision will be sewn on the inside with dissolving sutures that do not have to be removed. You will have to be careful, but it will not affect the way you walk. For a time, you'll need to be careful taking large steps, slow going up stairs, nothing that will stretch the area. You will have to be conscious not to spread your legs too far apart until the area heals all the way. You need to treat your leg the same way you treated your chest: think about how you move in order to give yourself the best ability to heal you can."

He went on. "You will be sore, but not in constant pain. And you heal so quickly, I am confident this will heal in a short period of time, too."

Everything made sense so far, but I was still hesitant about the skin-grafting procedure. "The biggest question I have is, this is a skin graft and that could not take, right? What are the chances this will not work and you will have to take them off?"

"If the skin graft doesn't take and we remove the nipples, we would tattoo nipples for you," he said.

"Would the scars left behind make the tattoos look bad or different?"

"There would be a thin line where we cut them off and bring the tissue together again. Karen, I think this will make you feel the most like a woman again and you would not have the fear of your daughter being frightened to see your chest."

"Yes, I want to look as natural as possible. When I saw my mother's chest after her surgery and she didn't have nipples, it looked so strange to me. Plus, I want to do this one time and never turn back. I want to do the skin-grafted nipples," I decided.

"We will schedule the procedure," he said. With that discussion done, I felt I had to bring up what was bothering me now, or never.

"Dr. Crane," I started, "I wanted to go over one thing with you. I am not sure I like the way the implants are now. The shape does not look the same as the temporaries. I really liked the fullness of the old pair and these look different."

"Those where expanders and we could not leave them in. The body will form around these permanent implants over time and they will look better and better. You need to trust me," he insisted. "I'll send in my scheduling nurse to go over dates for the skin grafting with you."

I'm not sure I will like these implants, they just weren't the same as the others I had grown to love. But I was trying to accept it. When the nurse arrived, I had to focus on what was ahead again.

"Okay now. Let's go over when we can do this procedure," she said, consulting some notes.

"I really want to have the same anesthesiologist I have had with all my other procedures," I told her. "His name is Dr. Ross."

"I am not sure that is possible in the period Dr. Crane wants to do the surgery," she responded.

"I will wait for him. The only thing that scares me about the surgery is going to sleep and not waking up."

"Let me go over this with Dr. Crane. I will be right back." She didn't take too long to return with Dr. Crane.

"Karen?" he said sternly.

"Yes, Dr. Crane?"

"You cannot make us wait every time we want to do a procedure for Dr. Ross, there are plenty of anesthesiologists out there I work with all the time."

"But he has kept me from getting sick each time… he's kept me alive each time," I protested.

"This is a short procedure so that will not be a problem. I can't keep waiting for this doctor, Karen. I think it is time to use my doctors so we can schedule this whole thing through my office. Can you trust me on this one short procedure so we can get this done?"

"I want to get this done, yes, so I will use your doctors," I said. And that was the end of that.

∝

I am finally facing my last surgery. I can't imagine not having to heal from something. I am so grateful and blessed to be alive.

Thank you, God, for all the amazing doctors and the treatment I have received. I know tomorrow is going to be a shorter surgery as far as surgeries go but I still place myself in your hands, Lord. I am only brave because I know you are with me. This is the last time I am going to have to go to sleep, it still scares me every time.

"Hi, Karen, I am the anesthesiologist who will be working with Dr. Crane today for your surgery."

Do I tell him how scared I am that he is not Dr. Ross? I am not even listening to him as he continues talking. *Wait, wait, back up. What did he just say?*

"What did you just ask? I say, finding my voice again.

"Do you have any questions at all?"

Oh, well, here it goes.

"Yes. I have a lot of questions. I had a great relationship with Dr. Ross and I trusted him. I'm so scared to go to sleep. I have *never* gotten sick with Dr. Ross after surgery or felt sick from the anesthesia. How are you going to do the same thing for me?"

"Karen, I have gone over all his notes and I know the formula he used with you each time so I can copy it for you. I have a few tricks in my hat I can use with you as well. You are going to be fine," he assured me.

"I have a daughter. I need to stay here for her, you have to do everything you can to keep me here for her," I insisted.

I saw compassion in his eyes as I passionately explained my fear of leaving Kasondra.

"I have children, you will be fine."

Dr. Crane stepped in. "Are you ready now, Karen? Because we have to begin getting you ready."

"Yes, I am ready."

"Let's go over this together again. I am going to take the skin from your inner thigh and graft that skin to make nipples for your chest. Do you have any questions before we start?"

"No, I completely understand everything that is going to happen," I tell him.

"Okay, I will meet you in the operating room."

When we were all situated and they were ready to begin, the anesthesiologist started us off.

"Karen, we are going to say good night now."

"Wait," I speak up. "Let me pray before we start."

Our Father, who art in Heaven,

Hallowed be thy Name;

Thy kingdom come;

Thy will be done

on earth, as it is in Heaven.

"Okay," I tell them. "Good night."

"Hi, Karen. Karen, we need you to wake up now. Karen, let's see you open your eyes for us. The surgery went well. The doctors will come in now that you are awake."

I hear another voice.

"How are you feeling? Do you feel sick from the anesthesia?"

I take a minute to get my bearings. "No, Doctor, I feel fine."

"Okay, that makes me so happy. I knew I could do it for you. Dr. Crane will be here in a minute. It went really well and I think you are going to be pleased with the results."

"Karen?" I hear a familiar voice.

"Yes, Dr. Crane?" He is smiling down at me.

"The surgery went really well. I do not see any problem with the graft. I think it is going to take and be fine. I am very pleased with the results so far. Your chest looks real with the nipples. I think you are going to be pleased with it, as it is exactly what you asked for. Your daughter will not know this is not your real chest," he promised.

"I did take a big piece of skin from the inside of your leg to make this," he went on. "The skin is tighter than I thought. You are going to have to be very careful how wide of a step you take; you are going to have to baby your leg. We will constantly watch your new nipples until we are sure they are out of danger. I need to know if you feel pain, if any redness occurs, or if any strange color appears anywhere on your chest or your leg, as this could be signs of infection."

I tried to take in everything in detail.

"Go home and try not to move around too much for a couple of days. No bending that leg, no pressure on the stitches. You must keep your chest dry and still. No lifting until the body accepts the new nipples completely," he ordered.

"When will I be able to see them? Can I take the bandages off when I get home?" I was so curious to see what they looked like.

"No, when you come to your follow-up visit, we will unwrap you and check them to make sure they still look healthy at that time. The office will call you and make a follow-up visit with you. If you see any redness above the wrap, or feel hot, like a fever, in either area, come in right away or go to the emergency room," he warned me.

When I was awake enough to go home, it started to sink in that this was my last surgery. I had one last time to listen to my body and let it lead me as to what I should and should not do.

Please, Lord, let the nipples be okay, let my body accept them so this truly can be my last surgery.

The nurse came in and helped me get dressed. As she was helping me, tears filled my eyes. It was over.

"Are you in that much pain?" she asked. "Do I need to call a doctor?"

"No," I promised. "It's over and I made it...."

"You made it, you surely did, you made it," she agreed and gave me a hug. I let the tears flow.

"Let's get you out of here. We need to get you dressed." As I sat up, pain brought me back to reality. Not everything was over just yet.

Okay, we have to heal without complications for this to truly be over. I really want this, nothing is going to stop this from being the last thing I have to do, and everything is going to go smoothly.

She handed me my pants. As I lifted my leg, pain erupted and I let out a gasp of emotion.

"Don't move your leg," she warned. "We need to slip these on without moving your leg. You need to step into the pants and pull them up."

I made a mental note of what that meant. I had no idea putting on pants would be such a challenge. It was the first I noticed what was going on. The stitches were covered but, I could see the incision had gone from my pelvic bone to the end of my leg. The nurse showed me.

"They are deep, here, feel gently along the bandage."

I had no idea the cut was going to be this long and deep. She explained that Dr. Crane had to take a large section to make two nipples.

"Try not to put pressure on that leg," she added.

"For how long?" I wanted to know.

"The skin is pulled really tightly to bring it back together and then it has been sewn at a very movable joint. Your whole leg attaches at the crotch right where the stitches are now," she explained.

"How long before I get the stitches out?" I couldn't remember.

"These are dissolving stitches, they are not taken out," she answered. "They are sewn inside your body and as time passes, they just get absorbed by the body."

Exhausted, I wanted to go home and go to sleep. Once again, I couldn't pick up my daughter and now, I couldn't walk very well either.

You always have a plan and this is nothing different. Make up a plan to heal yourself.

They put me in a wheelchair, took me outside and helped me get into the passenger side of the car. There was pain in my chest and pain in my leg. I did not expect this. I stepped into the car with my left leg, my right leg still outside, and the pain from the stretch about put me through the roof. I let out a little scream. "How can I do this?" They lifted my right leg and put it in the car for me. *No, this is not what I expected at all.*

Keep telling yourself that this is the last surgery.

Once again, I had to consider what I had been through so far. *How far could the other side be?* If this was the last healing I'd have to put my body through, I would just pray my way through it.

And my prayer this time was for the healing to only take a month or so.

Dear Lord, please help me to realize all you have done for me and to listen to the body that has saved me time and time again. Please help me to know my limitations and to move slowly to let my body heal.

"Are you okay?" The hospital staff must have thought I had lost consciousness because I wasn't talking. They did not know I was talking to God.

"Yes," I assured them. "I am just praying."

As the next few days went by, I continued taking Keith's supplements and worked to heal myself again as quickly as I could. I did all I could to boost my immune system to help it heal with this new situation.

The day arrived when I would get to see my nipples and find out what my finished chest would look like. At the doctor's office, the nurse confirmed Dr. Crane would be checking the stitches and to see where I was in the healing process.

"Okay, Karen," he started in when he got to me. "It is not going to look now exactly as it is going to look when it is all healed, but you can finally get an idea of what everything will look like in a couple of months. As you know, skin grafting is all about how the body accepts the new skin."

I watched his face as he cut away the bandage. I know I'm holding my breath.

"They look great," he announces, "and they are healing exactly as we planned. And, of course, your healing is faster than we expected." I was happy to hear that part once more. He asked the nurse to hand him a mirror.

Before he held it for me to see, he warned, "Remember, they are going to look more and more real as they heal."

I finally take a breath. "They look so real! They look like I have real nipples. How did you do that?" I ask, excited with the results.

"The redness and the healing scabs will fall off," he said, ignoring my praise for the moment. "The area will be soft where it still looks rough right now. Your body is showing no signs of rejection so I think we are clear to say this is going to be perfect."

"Dr. Crane, you were right. I feel whole again. I feel like a woman again. I know Kasondra will not be able to tell they are not real." I took in the moment of joy.

"Does this mean I am done?" I asked to be 100 percent sure. "It is done now, right? No more surgery? You don't have to take the stitches out?"

"Yes, that is right, you are done," he said, and then asked, "How do you feel now that it is all done?"

"Do you know that feeling when you hold your breath because you know something is going to happen and brace to get ready for it? I feel like I have been doing that for a year," I said.

I couldn't keep my emotions inside anymore. The tears fell again. *I have no more reasons to be brave, to push through, to be strong… it is an amazing feeling.…*

"Let me look at your leg now," Dr. Crane brought me back to reality. I had forgotten about my leg for a moment. He took the bandage off.

"This is healing well and looks great. The stitches have pulled away a little so you have to be more careful with your leg movements. It will take a long time to heal because the incision is at a stress point already."

As I positioned the mirror to have a better look, I could see how long the cut was and how much skin he had taken.

"Yes, I needed a lot of skin," he confirmed. "The stitches will dissolve, like I said. Just be more careful, okay? We will see you once more to make sure everything is all healed, but you are done with the surgeries."

As I walked out, I was overcome with emotions. I didn't know if things felt real or not. *Can my life really go on normally now? Am I really all done? Had I won this battle with cancer? Am I now Karen, the survivor, and not Karen, the cancer patient?*

All I have to do now is keep healing.

∝

Life began to go back to normal, whatever that meant.

Not too long after my last appointment, wildfires broke out in Encinitas. We were told we might need to evacuate. And just when I thought I was done with stress. *Keep calm; let's just go see how close the fire is to the house.*

My adrenaline is pumping as we drive up to the ridge. We can see the fire is very close and just beyond the ridge line. We need to get our belongs ready if we are required to leave. As I take a step into the truck, a shooting pain goes up my leg and I let out a scream.

I put my hand down my pants, expecting to find blood. There was no blood; only a gap where the tight stitches used to be. I didn't know what to do. I held my leg still and the pain started to lessen, I was at pain level 6 instead of 10 now, but it throbbed.

"We need to call Dr. Crane right now," I told my husband.

"Do you need to go to the emergency room, Karen?" the person answering the call asked me.

"No, I'm not bleeding, but my skin pulled apart where the stitches were and there is a big gap there now, but it's still together." The office asked me some more questions.

"No, it's not red, it is black and blue," I responded. "No, I don't feel hot or have a fever at all." They told me to keep an eye on it and to come in the following morning. They told me to go to the ER if the area got red or if I developed a fever. I could take Tylenol if I needed to.

That night, I felt blessed as we watched the evening news and found out that we did not have to evacuate. *How could I have possibly moved anything out of our house and into the car?*

The next morning as I drove to Dr. Crane's office, it struck me that I'd need to get used to the fact that I will always have things that are going to happen to my body now that it had been changed forever.

In the exam room, the nurse told me to undress from the waist down. "Dr. Crane will be right here. Try not to move until he can look at the damage," she said.

He walked in with a concerned look. "Sit back and let me see what the damage is and what I need to do to fix it," he said. He poked around a bit.

"You ripped some of the internal stitches and the skin is still holding together but the gap is much wider now," he concluded.

"I am not sure what to do." I said.

"How important is it for you to have a small scar?" he asked.

"Why? What do you mean?" I asked.

"Give me your hand," he said.

"What?"

"Give me your hand so you can feel what I mean," he repeated.

The good and bad aspects about Dr. Crane are that he is a "no messing around" doctor. He comes straight to the point. I'm still not sure what he is getting at. I'm scared, but he is not, which is a good combination overall.

"Lay back and look at what I am talking about," he says, handing me a mirror.

I had not looked straight into the wound before, so this was new territory for me. *Who wants to see a huge scar running through their crotch area?*

"Okay, Karen, can you see how the skin has pulled way apart right here? If you want this to heal as a thin scar, I will have to cut this apart again and re-stitch the inside of the scar." He is pointing from one end of my inner thigh all the way out to my butt.

Holly crap, this is a huge scar. Did I know it was going to be this big?

"Or," he continues, "We can leave it alone. You are half-way healed and you won't be seeing this unless you're looking with a mirror."

It looked like a monster scar now—ripped apart and dark purple— instead of the skin being closed neatly together with a little channel down the middle.

"Will it rip all the way apart again later on, if I work out or take a wrong step?" I ask.

"I don't think so. There are enough inside stitches left," he offered.

"I have to talk to my husband…." Once again, I was facing the knife.

As I left, I wondered if this news would put my husband over the edge. I was already feeling like a scar freak with my chest, and now this. There was no intimate place without a scar to remind us of the cancer now. *Our short marriage can only take so much pressure.*

When I told my husband what was going on and asked him what he wanted me to do, he said to do whatever was best for my body.

He must think I look like a monster. What isn't he saying because he doesn't want me to worry about us? We never talk about what is happening with my body. We just focus on staying alive and getting past all of this, but what will there be at the end?

The answer was there already. I was done with surgery. We needed the entire life-full-of-medical-drama syndrome to end so our life together could heal and return to normal.

I made an appointment with Dr. Crane, determined to tell him I wanted to let the wound heal all the way by itself. I couldn't face another procedure.

When the time came, I wanted to make sure I had considered all the ramifications of my decision.

"What do I need to do to assure it will be fine?" I asked him.

"Exactly what I told you before. No lifting, step easy, no lunging baby about and it will heal fine just as it is doing right now."

"Then what happens?" There was always something next to worry about.

"The skin-grafted nipples healed perfectly. You truly are the fastest healing patient I have ever had. There is nothing left to do."

This is the end?

"I do not need to see you unless something goes wrong?" I checked to make sure.

"Yes, you need to follow up with your other doctors, but Karen, as far as I'm concerned, you are done."

"Thank you, Dr. Crane, for all you have done," I could feel the tears forming, "and for all you did for me when I was so scared. I will never forget you."

We exchanged a knowing look of respect.

"I hope all goes well, Karen," he added. For the first time, I could feel the true emotions of Dr. Crane.

He had become my medical strength, my advocate for what I wanted to do with my life as a believer that the body can heal itself. He changed me but I know in my heart I changed him to look at the body differently.

"I'll come back to show you," I promised. And then I remembered one more thing as he started walking out of the room.

"Hey, Dr. Crane. You owe me a BRA!"

"Okay, next time I see you," he said as he glanced back at me. I think I detected a smile.

Father, I am healed.

Not too long after, Dr. Crane started a holistic center attached to his plastic surgery center to help people heal from surgery; we did have a deep connection after all....

WHAT YOU SHOULD KNOW MOVING FORWARD

What They Are Not Telling You

As you move forward, please study the articles and websites that are referenced in each chapter to keep yourself informed and to make better decisions. We can only make changes if we bond together and make them complete the studies on what is causing our cancer. Never forget that together we are one strong voice demanding change for ourselves but even more so for our daughters and granddaughters.

If only 25% of breast cancer is genetic
then what in the environment is giving 75% of us cancer?[®]

Sign the petition now, stand with me, fight for knowledge and never stop until we know so we can protect ourselves and the women we love.

TELLUSWHYWEREDYING.COM

Medical Knowledge

The information and reference materials contained in this book are intended solely for the general information of the reader. It is not to be used for treatment purposes, but rather for discussion with the reader's own medical professionals. The information presented here is not intended to diagnose health problems or to take the place of professional medical care. The information is neither intended to dictate what constitutes reasonable, appropriate, or best care for any given health issue, nor is it intended to be used as a substitute for the independent judgment of a physician. All content and opinions of the author are for general information purposes, only. If you have persistent health problems or if you have further questions, please consult your healthcare provider.

The recommendations put forth in this book do not establish a doctor-patient relationship. Individuals should consult a qualified healthcare provider for medical advice and answers to personal health questions.

The information presented is not to be considered medical advice and is not intended to replace consultation with a qualified medical professional. The primary responsibility of your disease management plan is with your treating physicians and you should only follow your treating physician's advice. DO NOT change or modify your disease management plan on your own without consulting your treating physicians.

Some research needs to be completed and it is our voice that will make them complete it. How can we make decisions without complete testing? It is our job together to make them finish it. Then, and only then, can we choose what to do with our bodies!

"Tell us why we're dying!"®

CHAPTER 1

Genetics

IT IS AMAZING HOW MUCH MY PARENTS did not tell me as a child or as an adult. I assumed things based on what I heard. Maybe I just didn't know what questions to ask.

Thirty years ago, my family did not openly talk about illness or disease. I think it was because they considered poor health to be a private topic. In those days, many people ignored warning signs until it was too late. Who knows how many cancer patients went undetected? But with so many friends and family members dying from cancer today, we have to talk about what's happening. Are we normalizing cancer? Even expecting it?

Before my mother was diagnosed with cancer, no one in my family talked about it. And it was still much later before I found out how much cancer was in my family. I had believed for years my mother's breast cancer was a one-time occurrence in our family history. When I was diagnosed, I learned my mother's mother died of cancerous brain tumors, my mother's sister died of ovarian cancer and her daughter had breast cancer twice.

All of this information was waiting to be considered, but no one wanted to bring it together until I became concerned about cancer in my genes. I realize that fear plays a large part in wanting to sweep any mention of cancer under the proverbial rug. Was it the fear of scaring our children and perhaps guilty feelings of having children in the first place, only to pass the potential of cancer on to them?

In my parents' generation, starting in the early 1920s, medical knowledge was limited to the experts. People believed whatever their doctors told them. There was no Internet to look things up, just your family's stories of what happened in the past. Most people assumed that cancer was the equivalent of a death sentence, with little in their power to do anything about such a devastating diagnosis. If the worst case fell on their doorstep, they would deal with it then.

Unfortunately, our parents direct us to accept the word of our doctors as gospel and to not question what they say on the subject. If I had a dollar for every time my dad said do what the doctors say. If I did would I be alive right now? Cancer treatments change and how we deal with a cancer diagnosis needs to change. Today's awareness of the benefits of preventative health practices was rare in those times. Thankfully, we now know so much more about how we can help our own bodies heal themselves. But first, we need to know exactly what our bodies are up against.

To find out, ask questions, do the necessary research, then find doctors who look at **all of the information** and create a plan for you. What you do right in this moment, can greatly impact your future. Had I known all I know now about cancer—and especially if I knew I was at risk genetically—I would have done so much more from the beginning of my life.

In many ways, I was already intuitively doing the right things without realizing it at the time. Because of my background in the holistic healing industry for more than 20 years, I knew good health had a lot to do with my lifestyle, stress levels, and eating habits. When I was diagnosed, I was already eating organic food, exercising on a regular basis, working part-time to reduce stress while raising my daughter, and generally living a healthy life.

I know these things saved me. My body saved me against my genetics.

And perhaps I was saved further by *not knowing* about the history of cancer in my family. As a critical-thinking person, I may have tended to anticipate the cancer to the point of actually manifesting it. My knowledge one way or the other about my family history didn't influence me then.

The one thing I am sure of is that you cannot compare your life to that of your past family. This is a sure way of dying from cancer. There is no cancer in my family so I will not get it? **Cancer is not a genetic-only disease.** Your family background matters but it is not the way to program your mind to believe you will not get cancer because there is no cancer history in yours.

I've heard people try to justify their unwillingness to change their way of living claiming, "My dad lived until he was 90, so I will live that long for sure. He never went to the doctor, ate what he wanted to, drank like a fish, and smoked two packs of cigarettes a day."

Well, they bring up a good question. Why did this person live longer than those of us who would have died for sure if we lived like that? Why isn't anyone studying that? The only way to arrive at the exact outcome of something is if you start with the exact same conditions. Even then, you may still get different outcomes because nothing is ever exactly the same when it comes to our bodies and the ever-changing world.

Your grandparents did not eat the same foods when they were developing as your children and families do today. Vegetables were grown in dirt of different qualities. Livestock was raised and butchered differently. The air and water about them could have been vastly different, from one extreme to the other. Today, we can find hormones in our food that weren't present before. Most food was grown locally or regionally, not trucked into markets from foreign countries. Preservatives were not as prevalent, and so on.

The things we stress about today can also be different from past generations. Throughout history, people have endured tremendous amounts of stress we can't comprehend today. But our ability to cope with what life throws at us is subjective, no matter the severity. In one family, you can observe varying degrees of stress over the same thing. Our attitudes and support systems are critical parts of understanding our overall well-being.

Many of our modern medical advancements would have been considered miracles in our grandparent's time. The drugs we use for colds, flu, and infections were not available when they were children. They also didn't have the vaccinations we have now, and horrible conditions, such as polio, could crush a family's dreams. Yet, the vaccinations we give children today can come with properties that may do more harm than good.

One positive aspect in our ancestor's lives is that they tended to move a lot more. They did not sit for hours on end looking at a screen. I am sitting for the majority of eight hours a day at a job. Yes, I get up to stretch, but not nearly enough. We condense our organs against each other for hours and hours a day, and our children are also falling into sedentary practices. What is that doing to their organs?

Your family tree has many clues about you. It's a great starting point to knowing who you are genetically and to prepare you for how to live. Both sides of your family have merged to create your individual body make-up. If you know who one or both of your biological parents are, start your research. Make a family book detailing as much as you can find out about their health. Look at their lifestyles to see if that helped them to live longer or die sooner. Both are equally important to study for clues.

What environment did they grow up in? What types of food did they eat? Ask what they remember about sickness and health from their childhood. What did their parents complain about? List any diseases or serious illnesses they had. Did they drink alcohol excessively or smoke? What was your mother's diet when she was pregnant with you? What did she feed you as a baby? Were you breastfed? Were your children breastfed? What are you feeding your children now? As our understanding of these connections progress, these types of questions will be medical questions you are asked. With advances in DNA testing, your genetics will play an important role in how your body will be genetically able to handle certain things.

My belief is that your genes will tell you how to eat and live to keep yourself disease free.

You can start by having a genetic test so you can see what your genes are trying to tell you right now! I used 23andMe, a DNA Genetic Testing and Analysis tool.[1] I learned that I am 24 percent Swedish. My mom had told me I was 50 percent Swedish and that she was 100 percent. I found out that wasn't true once I saw the test results. Since my mother and father have died, I do not have their DNA to test. I do not know exactly what genes come from my mother or my father.

I have such a strong component of cancer in my genes it would have been amazing to break apart my parent's genes to see if I could see where the genes where coming from to maybe shed some light on what was going on. These tests are in the beginning stages and not as accurate as they need to be to see where cancers originated from in your family genes.

But I believe it is where money needs to be spent to help us see and give us a fighting chance in knowing cancer from the genetic standpoint.

Why don't we know if eating certain foods with our particular genes could put our bodies under stress? And what if we ate certain foods compatible with our genes to help us stay strong? We are all a melting pot of genes in the United States. Is this why we have so much cancer? If we lived in an environment similar to our ancestors and ate similar food, could that be analyzed to see if those conditions were more or less likely to give us the chance of disease? I'm not a doctor but isn't this making good sense?

I believe we need to press for studies on this topic to see if it can help us live longer lives in the culture we are living in. With knowledge comes power; without knowledge we leave it to chance.

---

1 23andMe is a privately held personal genomics and biotechnology company based in Mountain View, California. Visit their website at https://www.23andme.com.

Please find out medically all you can about your family. Put it together, not as a curse to endure, but as a blessing for discovering the ways you can change your life to avoid the same. Having this information at hand is important before it's lost to you forever. It may be key in helping you and your offspring avoid cancer. You will also be helping your greater community by working to stop the cancer epidemic.

Remember, we work to get to retirement one day. Think about the kind of body you are going to have to retire with. Find out the damage your genes may spring on you one day and work to repair it now, as fast as you can!

CHAPTER 2

_____

Statistics

THIS IS ONE OF THE MOST IMPORTANT chapters of the book because statistics play a big part in what you're going to do now and what decisions you are going to make next. Without true statistics, how can you possibly make great decisions?

Well, here's the ugly truth: the statistics that you're given by medical professionals may not always be based on facts.

For a statistic to be true, it has to have all of its principles put together by category correctly. I found this out when I was given the statistics about the percentage the chemotherapy would help me. Let's say, for discussion purposes, that was incorrect.

The reason for this is because they don't break their statistics down by category, such as considering a patient's basic lifestyle.

Category 1 includes people who eat well, exercise and generally respect their bodies. Category 2 includes those who eat terribly, don't exercise, drink alcohol, and generally don't care about their body.

Unfortunately, most studies don't break down their findings by these basic lifestyle conditions. That means, when a doctor tells you they have a statistic that recommends chemotherapy for your case, they are giving you statistics that have lumped healthy and unhealthy people together.

I was told that in order for me to survive with the type of breast cancer I developed, I had to undergo chemotherapy. And that by doing chemo, I would be giving myself a 10 percent better chance of surviving the Stage 3 estrogen-based breast cancer that I had. This was a long time ago so the chemotherapy may be different now, I don't know. I'm not a doctor. If you have a different type of cancer there may be totally different stats for your type and chemotherapy. But it is your right to see the reports they are quoting to you. What they may not give you are the statistics about how your organs will handle the chemotherapy or any indication of how to protect yourself. Find out all you can! Read the chapter on chemotherapy for some insight.

What They Didn't Tell Me

What was the most important thing to tell me in order for me to make the best decision? That their statistics had not been broken down to consider patients like myself. They hadn't calculated the percentage based on my history before I had cancer. I was not only eating healthy foods; I was eating organic foods. My husband used to tease me that I walked into an organic grocery store like other people walked into a jewelry store. I live in San Diego and in the early 1990s, organic grocery stores were sprouting up everywhere. A family opened one a short distance from my house called Cream of the Crop. I became fast friends with the owners. Their store was the only one of its kind and they were far ahead of the trend. They helped save my life. Harry was incredible and let me ask him mounds of questions. I had the supplement knowledge but his food knowledge was so incredible. Years later, I moved three towns away but still drove back to Cream of the Crop to get my vegetables. Finally, another store, Jimbo's, opened in my town and I was in Heaven.

I know I was fortunate to have organic food available to me, long before the rest of the world got on board with it. As I mentioned, I was fit and kept my working and mothering-life balanced. My lifestyle had protected me.

So, when I was given this statistic, at first, I didn't think that the chances were high enough compared to having chemo drugs destroy the rest of my body. This was confirmed when I started asking questions about their statistics, which is something I don't think enough people do when an expert person is giving them serious-sounding statistics.

In my quiz, I wanted to know if the study been broken down by females in my age range (35 to 40) who:

» Don't drink;

» Don't smoke;

» Don't do drugs;

» Exercise four days a week; and

» Eat healthy, organic foods.

The answer shocked me. "No," I was told. "We don't have statistics like that."

I wondered if they had done any type of separation by lifestyle, even if it was broader in terms of, say, those who are overweight compared to those who are in relatively good shape.

There were no statistics like that either. This told me the case they were making—that I needed chemotherapy in order to survive—was based on putting me in a group with potential drug addicts, alcoholics, overweight people, and people who don't care about their body.

In reality, then, I argued, you really don't know the true percentage of help I am going to gain by that taking chemo. Because with my lifestyle, it's only a "guess." How can I make a really good decision if you aren't giving me statistics that correspond to *my* body type and lifestyle?

Because they couldn't give me these answers, I was left in a really scary place. It's difficult to make good decisions when you have incomplete information. Think about what you are being told when it comes to statistics. Do your own research and ask questions.

Now you're wondering, as I did, what if I can't use what they are saying as truth? I make my decisions based on facts. When the facts aren't there, I have to go beyond what's been presented and search for the secondary facts.

You know what you have done to your body for years leading up to this moment; how you have treated it day after day. You know what you are capable of doing and how much you are willing to change. Making a lifetime change right now might save your life.

The chapters following will show you what I did to change "the statistics" ruling my life. Whatever your choice is right now, remember there is not only one way to do this thing. Do not let anyone scare you into a choice with numbers. Don't let my experience influence you in any way to make the choices that are right for you.

Knowledge is power, and until we work together to uncover the truth, I can only explain what I have personally discovered. The way I look at it, my body saved me, and not having chemotherapy was the right decision based on the facts I had at the time. I used "statistics" of my own to prove that doing more harm to my body was not the way to help my body.

No matter what you choose to do, choose to help your body help you as much as you can.

If you are deciding on a particular treatment, ask about statistics that show what it will do to your organs so you can choose. Then if you decide to have the treatment, find out what you should do to help your organs heal or be able to withstand the side effects. Look for more stats as to what has happened to others in the past who took these extra measures.

The stats may show you a treatment stops cancer from spreading but you still need to know how to save your body from other aspects of the remedy. If they do not have such statistics, as cancer survivors we need to press experts to find them and to help us figure out what has worked and not worked in the past with numbers that tell us how to fix all aspects of the body.

CHAPTER 3

Biopsies

WHEN APPROACHED BY OTHER CANCER PATIENTS, I am often asked my opinion about biopsies and if I think they are a good idea. In my situation, I wanted to find studies that would help me weigh the pros and cons.

The only information I had to go on initially was what Dr. Pearl had told me on the phone in 1994. "It is hard to see underneath the tumor if you do not take it out." It made sense to me: even if the tumor is not cancerous, we still don't know if there is a cancer growing underneath the fatty tumor if we can't see that area.

Breast cancer spreads to other organs when traveling in the body's fluid; not just through the blood system but also through the lymph fluids. I wanted to know what would happen if the tumor was ripped by inserting a biopsy needle. Would this spread cancer into my fluids?

If the sac did not mean anything to the outcome of my cancer, why was Dr. Watkins so surprised when she discovered the tumor had been contained in its sac when she removed it? Why was I so blessed by this remarkable situation?

In my research for this book, I searched for any studies that might help me understand why this made a difference, and just how much of a difference it had made.

I was hoping to find any information on breast cancer cases where a patient had a PET scan to see if cancer was found anywhere else in the body, followed by a needle biopsy, and then had another PET scan to see if the sac being punctured by the biopsy resulted in the cancer spreading.

Since I could not find this particular study, I was concerned that research hadn't truly seen the effects of biopsies. One study, "Risk of tumor cell seeding through biopsy and aspiration cytology," didn't make a conclusion one way or another.[1] However, it made sense to me that if the sac is torn, cancer cells can be dragged out as the needle withdraws the sample. This confirmed to me that during the biopsy process, there may be harm and risks to weigh.

Another thing that bothered me about biopsies is after they take the sample, it takes weeks to receive the results. If the sac is opened during the procedure this could allow cancer to start circulating before you are able to remove it surgically! Cancer cells can break off and start traveling immediately while you are waiting, perhaps up to a month, before you have results and can schedule surgery.

I now wonder about so many things being on this side of cancer. I now know cancer can't live without blood. As I was writing this book, I wondered if breast cancer is like other cancers. If you cut the blood supply to the tumor would cancer cells die in the tumor sac and save the breast? I could not find any research on this procedure.

I searched for clear studies indicating the percentage of cases where cancer seeded while waiting for biopsy results or surgery. I couldn't find any. Seeding is the spreading of cancer, or starting a new cancer site deposited by the cells of the original site. Is there a study where breast cancer is more likely to seed next if it spreads to the lungs, brain, and ovaries? Once it has spread to those areas, where does it go from there?

The lungs, brain, and ovaries are the places your doctor will watch the closest. I was told if cancer was spreading, these are the places to look for signs from the body. But there is no talk of how the cancer can spread to

---

1 "Risk of tumor cell seeding through biopsy and aspiration cytology," by K. Shyamala, H. C. Girish, and Sanjay Murgod, as published in the Journal of International Society of Preventive and Community Dentistry (2014). https://www.ncbi.nlm.nih.gov/pmc/articles/PMC4015162.

other places in the body. I think this leads you to only be concerned with those places the doctor has told you about. Please tell your doctor if you have a history of problems in any of these regions. Is this the only places cancer can spread, **absolutely not**. Cancer has no agenda and can spread anywhere. You need to become of aware of your body and what it is telling you. If something does not feel right have it checked out by your doctor until you feel at ease. There is a difference of aware and worried, worried takes over your life and cancer wins. Aware means be in tune with your body and maintain the control. Do not let the doctor tell you oh breast cancer would not spread there. There is absolutely no clinical studies that say it ONLY spreads to the above regions.

And since I have yet to see a clinical study proving that cancer cannot seed from biopsies, I feel tumors should be removed whenever possible.

Dr. Pearl saved my life from the one thing she said: you can't see underneath the tumor. Her comment will always stay with me.

The other doctor told me, "This does not feel like cancer; the tumor has a weird shape." Does it hurt? Cancer hurts to the touch. General practice doctors are just that—general knowledge doctors. They are not experts in cancer. Making a broad spectrum statement makes you feel safe but you are far from safe. Dr. Watkins knew it was cancer in a second when she saw the ultrasound because she is a trained cancer doctor, not a general practitioner using their limited expertise. Why leave it to chance if your doctor is right in what they were trained to look for? Also consider how long ago was their training. Studies change things all the time. How much time does your doctor have to study the latest research across the world?

My personal belief is that you can only be safe if the tumor is taken out. Cancer can't spread if it is removed from the body. Cancer can't grow underneath a tumor if the tumor is gone. Until I am proven wrong by several clinical studies and unquestionable methods to make sure a tumor is cancerous, I will always favor taking it out. I would never allow someone to simply watch your tumor in question because they're not sure if it is cancerous. Please remember, doctors are wrong all the time—they are human. You have the right to say exactly what you want to do. Don't side with the doctor simply because they are a doctor. So many of my loved ones have passed away believing their doctors knew everything and they did not question them. They did not want to make the doctors angry. You can change to a new doctor if they get angry.

But you only have one life! Push for what you want by looking for knowledge about your particular case. Cancer is different for each person and so is how your body adapts to its presence and treatment. Please do not allow the doctor to take your life in their hands until they know for sure what you are dealing with so you can make clear choices.

CHAPTER 4

Blood Work

HERE IS A LIST OF QUESTIONS I want you to consider while reading this chapter:

> » Why isn't there a breast cancer blood test to save us?

> » Why are we accepting this?

> » We have a voice, isn't it time to start using it?

> » If there is a race for the cure, why isn't money being used to tell us the reasons we are dying?

> » What in our lifestyles are we all doing the same across the country that might be clues to cancer rates?

> » If 75 percent of cancer is not genetic, what is the cause?

Get mad, don't accept this. Sign the petition on my website, telluswhyweredying.com. We have such a strong voice together for our children and for our daughters. Let's make them listen.

Blood work is a very emotional topic for me. My sister passed away from a false sense of security. She had been given wrong information about her blood testing results. She was coughing but told me, "I was just tested; my blood work did not show anything, it's nothing," until she coughed up blood in front of me. Cancer can spread anywhere and should never be qualified from blood work. If you have cancer anywhere, there is no blood test to confirm this yet.

So, we have to take the logic of doctors out of this word "blood work" and just use common sense. If there was a blood test that could tell us if we had cancer in our body then we could take blood from every person in America and we would know right away if they had cancer or not.

If we do not have a test to do this yet, then how can they tell you that you do not have cancer based on your blood work? There is no blood work test for cancer, right?!

We do have the BRCA gene test, but we can only use these to see if we are at risk.[1] Only 25 percent of cancer patients have cancer in their genes. So, this test only tells us about genetic cancer. Is this a distraction tactic to say, "Look what we are doing to help," but does it really help all of us?

No, it does not. I was given the BRCA test and so were my nieces. I tested positive. My sister's children did not test positive, so they now have a *false* sense of security they will not get cancer. They are so wrong. According to the American Cancer institute, they now have the same chance—like so many who are not genetically disposed—of getting cancer, a 1-in-8 chance.

How did the BRCA test help me? What did it tell me that I didn't already know being a cancer survivor? Not a thing and I feared the insurance company now had a record they could use to raise my premiums as a pre-existing condition. Perfect.

If it were that simple to just take blood work from every woman aged 35 to 80 to be able to tell them whether or not they had breast cancer, then why would we need mammograms? Because, as of writing this chapter, there is no such blood work that will tell you if you have cancer growing in your body.

When I first had cancer diagnosed as large centimeters in Stage 3, doctors wanted me to have blood drawn every 3 to 6 months to make sure I didn't have cancer anywhere.

---

1 BRCA stands for BReast CAncer gene. The BRCA gene test is a blood test that uses DNA analysis to identify harmful changes (mutations) in either one of the two breast cancer susceptibility genes—BRCA1 and BRCA2. In 1996, clinical testing began for BRCA1 and BRCA2 mutations.

What are they really testing for at this time? I finally asked that question and found they were testing for a rise in my white blood cell count. Does an elevated count mean I have cancer? No. I could have an infection somewhere. As of this writing, there is no global cancer blood work test. Always remember that.

So, when strange and obscure things start happening to your body, you don't consider it to be cancer because of your negative BRCA test results? This is so far from the truth that it's scary. When hearing your results, ask the question, "Is this a cancer test?" They will tell you, "No." This test does not tell you if you have cancer or not!

I think this is why many people die from cancer. Based on their assumptions and a false sense of security from blood work results, no one is helping them determine if they have cancer in the first place.

To find the truth about blood work, these two articles, "Cancer blood tests: Lab tests used in cancer diagnosis," and "Follow up Care After Breast Cancer Treatment," will blow your mind.[2, 3]

> "If symptoms, exams, or tests suggest a possible recurrence of your cancer, imaging tests such as an x-ray, CT scan, PET scan, MRI scan, bone scan, and/or a biopsy may be done. Your doctor may also look for circulating tumor cells in the blood or measure levels of blood tumor markers such as CA-15-3, CA 27-29, or CEA. The blood levels of tumor markers go up in some women if their cancer has spread to bones or other organs such as the liver. They are not elevated in all women with recurrence, so they aren't always helpful. If they are elevated, your doctor might use them to monitor the results of therapy."

---

2 "Cancer blood tests: Lab tests used in cancer diagnosis," by Mayo Clinic Staff, as posted on the Mayo Clinic website (2019). https://www.mayoclinic.org/diseases-conditions/cancer/in-depth/cancer-diagnosis/art-20046459;

3 "Follow up Care After Breast Cancer Treatment," as posted on the American Cancer Society website (last revised 2019). https://www.cancer.org/cancer/breast-cancer/living-as-a-breast-cancer-survivor/follow-up-care-after-breast-cancer-treatment.html.

About six years after my cancer diagnosis, my doctor ordered blood work to look for a higher white blood cell count as a precaution. I remember him telling me the results showed that my white count was way up. I cried all night thinking I was going to die. Later, we discovered I had an infection in my toe.

Blood work used to look for tumor markers or elevated white blood cell counts is not conclusive, as I found out by reading many articles. This is crazy. If your cancer is in an obscure place that has nothing to do with these two indicators, then there's absolutely no way doctors can tell if you have cancer from blood work results. For example, if cancer lands in your shoulder, or you develop cancer in some obscure place of the body, if white blood cell counts and tumor markers are normal, there is no way your doctors can know about it unless you tell them that something's going on. If you feel strange or you have a problem that does not make sense, you have to PUSH to see what is going on. This does not mean letting cancer own your life. It means to become in-tune with your body—to know it and listen to it. When in doubt always check things out. You are in a battle so be aware of your opponents inside and out.

My mother lost her sight because she had a brain tumor. Doctors had no idea she had cancer in her brain until she lost her sight. If you are having trouble breathing and you are coughing, as my sister was, remember that lung cancer does not always show up in blood work as an elevated white blood cell count for a very long time. If something starts happening to your body that isn't normal, speak up now.

Another testing method that may provide much better results is an MRI with contrast.[4] The test uses gadolinium-based contrast agents (GBCAs), a type of dye, to assist in adding clarity and decipherability to the MRI image.

---

4 "What Is an MRI With Contrast?" as posted on the Envision Radiology website. https://www.envrad.com/what-is-an-mri-with-contrast.

The contrast enhances the visibility of tumors, inflammation, certain organs' blood supply, and blood vessels.

As you will read in the chapter on <u>sugar</u>, cancer feeds on sugar and the cells leave a traceable trail behind them that can be picked up with a dye and then the dye can be seen on an MRI. Until we convince the medical industry to come up with an easier method, this is our best way of finding out if the cancer has returned.

We need to band together and demand that the government support efforts to devise a simple self-test—similar to how diabetics check their sugar levels—to see if your individual cancer cell markers are present. If they test your tumor and find its tumor component, they should be able to load that information into an analytical application as a marker, and then, using a finger-prick blood drop test, see if the marker is present in your blood. You would know instantly if a re-occurrence is happening for early-detection remedies.

Or, if you and your mother tested positive for the BRCA gene, why not set your mother's marker as the measure, and then test your blood for matches?

Wouldn't it make sense to spend some of the billions of dollars used in cancer research on this type of testing? I have yet to see any massive progress being made on anything like instant blood testing. Why not? Why are we passively settling for only what we can get when cancer is killing us? We need to keep asking, "What is it they are not giving us?" We need to tell them, "We've had enough; it's time we were able to detect our own instances of cancer recurrence."

It's time to find cancer early before it takes our life.

CHAPTER 5

Dying

I HAVE WATCHED TOO MANY PEOPLE I love die from cancer. I'm guessing it's the same with you. There are so many ways to help those you are going to leave behind cope with your leaving. When faced with certain death, the main concern is really no longer about you. You'll need to make a shift to think about those you are leaving behind and how they will be able to live with your passing.

This shift needs to start as long as possible before you are actually close to dying. The one good thing about cancer I always say is that it gives you time. Time to help the ones you love cope with you leaving. Time in the sense this is not as with a sudden heart attack or fatal accident where they don't have time to heal from the heartache of losing you so the loss is more bearable.

If there is a gift from cancer, perhaps it is not leaving anything unsaid; there is a chance to heal wounds from the past and to not leave any new wounds that may never heal once you are gone. As I watched my sister die, I became clear about the unanswered questions there would be if she hadn't addressed them before she died. She had enough time to talk with the people she loved; she talked them through her death.

Don't be shy about asking an expert how to do this. It is so important to the life you are leaving behind. I cannot tell you the number of children living with guilt because they were not able to say goodbye because no one told them what was going on. When you have a good day and see an opening, talk to them about what is going on. Tell them about the choices you have made about how much you can be with them and when.

If you don't, consider the loss they will feel. You are not saving them from anything; you are trapping them in an emotional place that is difficult to get out of. Don't leave behind a life sentence of things not said, with no one left behind to tell them because you will be gone.

I am truly sorry if this causes you any pain reading these words. But it is so important and I'm going to break it down to show you areas where you can help them cope.

To start, let others help you. One thing people feel guilty about is not being able to help or not knowing what to do to help. I get it: you want to be left alone. You're tired and scared about what is coming. But what you do now is how your loved ones will be able to cope with you leaving.

To leave emotionally-healthy people behind, there needs to be no question in their minds that they did all they could do to help you. Don't leave them with "what ifs" to think about for the rest of their lives. This is so important for children. I've heard many people express to me their feeling that there was nothing they could have done to help. I usually point out several things I'm certain they did do to help their loved one, if only to try to give them some kind of relief.

To avoid this, give everyone—and I mean everyone—a job to help you. Don't start excusing them by deciding they are too young, too old, or too busy. If your parents are alive, there is nothing more painful than being on the outside looking in.

Keep in mind there is a big difference between helping and taking over. Whoever is your primary caregiver, you can work with them in delegating tasks, but in the end, the choice for everything going on around you is yours.

Children can be asked to paint your nails, read to you, be the official pillow fluffer, mail opener, card opener, flower changer, bathtub-get-ready person, fresh water changer… you get the idea.

Teens can be asked to be the playlist-music-maker, dog walker, board game partner, thank-you-note-writer for anything done for the family, or movie selector.

Adults can be asked to coordinate meals, babysit the younger children and plan activities for them out of the house, pay bills, run errands, and help you coordinate appointments.

You can also ask an appropriate person to be the one who creates and updates a private Facebook group or CaringBridge account so that everyone concerned about you can stay in the loop.[1] These are great platforms for sharing what is going on with a loved one. Here, people can ask questions and offer support. As you reconnect with friends and family, you can direct them to these pages.

For the youngest children, or for those who aren't able to access these sites, please ask them to ask a parent to help them, to direct them away from you and your children for answers. If you designate one person to have the answers that will be a huge help to you. Direct them to call the parents of younger people to explain how all the questions can hurt your children emotionally. This important role will need to be given to someone with great patience. Your family might be tempted to respond, "How do you think she is doing? She's dying!" Instead, this person can explain the websites and why they are so important to the family's emotional well-being.

Another idea is to have a business-size card made with information that is commonly asked. An example of what to include might be something such as:

> Thank you for asking about me. Please pray for me (optional). Please request access to my private Facebook group or CaringBridge page which has regular updates and a place for you to write to me. I love to receive your well wishes. I may not respond, but please know that reading your words warms my heart.

---

1 CaringBridge is a free, nonprofit website or mobile app with tools to keep family and friends updated during a difficult time. https://www.caringbridge.org.

Other ideas for the card include tangible ways that people can help. For example:

> I am so blessed you asked if you could help my family. If you would like to cook a meal, please ask for access to my Meal Train page.[2]

Ask your family and caregiving team to help by handing out these cards. Please, I beg of you to do this. One of the most difficult things can be explaining over and over what is going on and what to say when people ask if they can help. We are fortunate there are many online programs designed to help those who are sick or dying. This is one of the best ways to communicate your needs to those who otherwise might feel helpless in the situation.

I mentioned the incredible program called Meal Train. This site lets the people who love you and your community sign up to bring meals for your family, without the family having to coordinate everything.

Find out what you and your family members like to eat and post simple, clear meal instructions. If a restaurant or the prepared food section at a grocery store has items you like, mention those for people who don't want to cook themselves. There is also GrubHub and so many restaurants and delivery options. You can list what you like from them making it easy for people who do not cook but want to help. You can always update your lists if you get too much of the same food.

For those who are cooking, ask people to label their dishes or even better, ask them to buy disposable containers that can be left behind. When my sister was in her final weeks, it was stressful to try to return dishes. When they started to stack up, even this small task became a burden on the family. When they come over to pick up bowls, they need to know this is not a reason to question the family or try to talk to the ill person. I suggest you leave a basket out front for the bowls to be picked up.

---

2 Meal Train is a site where people can organize meals for people recovering from surgeries or illness. https://www.mealtrain.com.

Also, politely remind people that when they do drop off meals, this is not the time to chat or visit. It is so much easier if you put a cooler away from the house and ask the meals be put in there by a certain time. Tell them not to bring any frozen meals that could take hours to thaw adding more strain on the family.

Ask them to leave notes or video messages on your other personal pages that you can see later. For those who believe the rules don't apply to them (there will always be a few!) set a timer for a short visit and blame the policy on your caregivers, otherwise your precious energy will be zapped, leaving you less time for making your transition in peace. Don't be shy about cutting them off from bringing meals if they can't honor your wishes. While you and your family are dealing with illness, you should not feel obligated to entertain anyone.

If you need help financially, consider using a crowd-funding source such as GoFundMe.[3] This will allow people to donate funds to help pay for a range of expenses, including child care, medical bills, treatments outside insurance networks, housekeeping, and other caregiver charges. In many cases, the person working to stay ahead of the bills is also your primary caregiver at home. They may not want to accept money from others but remind them they would be one of the first to give to others in need. Being able to hire additional help is an amazing burden-lifter for people coping with your illness and allows them to have more quality time with you.

So, I say to those of you going to meet our God: be mindful now about how you can help those who are going to be left behind. Ultimately, cancer is a gift of healing. If you are not dying suddenly, there are many ways to help them heal emotionally by not leaving things unsaid or undone.

When it was close to the end, my sister asked me what she should do for her children. She wanted to know what she could do to help them cope with

---

3 GoFundMe is a for-profit crowdfunding platform that allows people to raise money. https://www.gofundme.com.

their loss. We decided to create audio messages for all the occasions ahead in their lives. She shared the feelings she had for them already stored in her heart as she envisioned their future milestones. I knew how bittersweet it would be for them to hear these, but this effort would pay off in so many ways as the years ahead unfolded.

We also knew how important it was to allow each child and loved one to spend time with her alone. This gave her the opportunity to ask them what they were feeling and if there was anything they wanted to say to her. She made it clear that even if they had felt angry or upset, it was okay to express that and that this was the time to bring it up. She was not afraid to broach a subject if she knew it might be sensitive or if she knew they didn't want to bring it up because it might upset her.

I have helped many people deal with the passing of a loved one and often suggest they ask a professional to lead them through ways to ask the many questions they have and to help them say goodbye in a balanced and positive way. When looking for such a person, make sure they are licensed or qualified in grief counseling and have solid experience. This help can be an amazing gift of love and closure.

Being thankful for all of the good times together is a given, one would think. But taking the time to continue the good times now that the end is near is not a gift to be wasted. The good times don't have to be over. Help them find ways to remember you in a fun, positive light even as you are facing your final weeks. As a cancer patient, you need to understand the importance of the time you are being given right now. You, and you alone, can leave those behind a better ability to move on without you.

No, you can never demand them to move on, or even ask them to move on. That is up to them. But when they feel they are doing everything they can to help you, then you remove the guilt they might suffer, wondering what else they could have done to help you. If you have told them how to help you, you've gone a long way in helping them. This is not a selfish act. Let everyone help you, even in the smallest way of some kind. There is nothing more damaging than when you insist on doing everything by yourself, believing you won't be a burden on others. You do not want them wondering for the rest of their lives if they should have done more.

Even when you just want to be left alone, there is no shame in saying that, but talk it through. Please don't leave them out of your process. I realize your environment may feel engulfed by anger and fear when you are dying. But the gift that is yours to give is the gift of serenity for those you are leaving behind.

Based on my own experience, I would like to caution you on asking your loved one to "do something" specific after you have passed. My sister asked me to watch over her children to show them the love she had for them. She asked me to be there for whatever they needed from a mother. She made me promise and I did. This burden affected me for years. She lived in another state and I didn't know how I was to hold up this promise. Should I meddle in her husband's world as he made his own adjustments? How should I approach her children to make sure they were okay? I could not afford to travel to Oregon to check on them, so I did my best to call often and send gifts and letters. But it didn't seem that I was doing enough. I understand why she asked and why I said yes, but the heartache it has caused me still hurts to this day. Please be careful about making any dying requests.

As my sister was dying, I called her nearly every day. Finally, I was able to visit for a week. Since I had been diagnosed with cancer before her, I had gone through what she was going through. Unfortunately, cancer spread and she was unable to overcome. I wanted to stay with her longer, but I had a family and a daughter to get to school. Her doctors had no idea how fast the cancer would move so I went home, planning to return as soon as I could. She died before I could. I cannot tell you the guilt I held onto for leaving her and not being with her to the end.

I had so much guilt I went into depression. Through therapy, I realized that only God knows when someone will die. I could have returned many times and still not have been there when she died. I was finally able to cope with my decision to come back to my family. Please be aware of the situations of those you are leaving behind. How great would it be to go to therapy while you're alive to help those you are leaving behind cope with you leaving?

Asking for promises on your deathbed will be taken seriously. Am I telling you not to ask for them? No, but please make reasonable, attainable requests that are shared and agreed on by everyone involved in the promise. If you don't, you may be setting the person up for pain that lasts years after you are gone.

Your loved ones simply do not want to burden you. They believe their needs could not possibly be important at a time like this. But their needs are important. For the rest of their lives, knowing you have given them their best ability to cope and live on in a positive way is a great gift. You do not want to leave them with a life of ongoing pain that may never go away. Remember you will be gone and now is the time to help them.

As your last days approach, please be aware of the image of yourself you are leaving behind for your loved ones. If you choose to be at home while passing, please talk about how you are fine with them making changes to the room after you are gone. Talk with them about how they plan on erasing the image of you dying with an image of continuous love. If your loved ones are going to keep living in the house, please pick a room for your final place that can immediately change after you are gone. If you are in the living room, it will thereafter be the dying room, and no one will want to come home. Select positive things you want changed in the room when you are gone so they do not feel guilty. They will want things to stay the same as a way of holding on to you, but tell them how important it is to you that they change things.

I would suggest maybe moving to a positive place to pass, leaving the house as a positive place, not a place to remind them of the last place they were with you. I have seen so many families not move on, older kids not want to leave, and younger kids getting depressed as they pass the room. This would be a good time to talk to the family about moving and starting fresh. They can take pieces of you with them, one or two things, but not the entire house. What would be the point of moving then? If you like to garden, select a favorite plant from the garden, or ask them to plant a rose garden in memory of you. I suggest you release them from staying in the house for you.

If you are younger and your husband will get married again, talk about that openly with him. It needs to be a subject that is talked about while you are here. Not just for your husband but for your children to release him without guilt to move on. Tell them these are your wishes. Please do not leave behind angry kids who think they are protecting you.

When my therapist was helping me process the deaths of my sister, mother, and best friend, he said it's important to take down the pictures and reminders of ourselves during our process of dying and remove them so they don't become triggers. Perhaps keep one, but don't have them all over the house. Set aside some time with the children and put them in an album for safe keeping so they will be there when your loved ones are ready to see them again. Maybe make this a project with special thoughts written by you by each picture. This is something you can do now and it will help to not feel bad about moving them later. You can replace them with special, positive images or verses that reflect joy.

This is also the time to say how you want the celebration of your life to go so there is no question about your desires. Please keep in mind if you have relatives or friends that live far from you, be sensitive to them not being able to come. If you moved away, plan a second dinner celebration where the other people live to leave them a positive gift. You could set up a charity where they are or have a plant-a-tree ceremony, or a bench ceremony so they can celebrate you without feeling guilty for the rest of their lives or getting into debt to attend your celebration.

My sister planned everything, which made it so easy for us to fulfill her wishes. The more positive and simpler you can make things, the better you will feel knowing you did it all to help them as you are dying. This is such an AMAZING GIFT. I pray you give it.

CHAPTER 6

Working Out / Exercise / Just Move

(Don't skip this chapter.)

WHAT IS A GOOD WORK OUT? Getting your heart rate higher than when you are sitting still. You want to get your heart pumping to circulate your blood throughout the body. At least 20 minutes of steady activity is needed to accomplish anything truly beneficial. You also need to move all of your extremities to push out the toxins stored in the tissue of your muscles. Moving is the object right now.

It's widely known that compressing your internal organs for hours on end and for days at a time can create problems in organ function. If you are sitting and not stretching out, or if you are constantly laying on your back, you are putting pressure on the organs and they need relief. Add chemotherapy and radiation treatments to this and your organs are going to need help.

Help your body help you. You would think this would have been the first chapter I wrote since I exercise throughout the week. If you think this is what I live for or that I'm the "gym rat" type that would be a resounding NO! I exercise to be able to do what I want, when I want, without thinking about it much. To be able to do that, I had to move. That's it, period.

I started to work out to stay alive longer, as you read in my story. I walked to get the anesthesia out of my system so I could heal.

You: "I know doing some form of exercise will prolong my life in the cancer world but I don't want to read this chapter."

I understand; believe me.

You: "Come on, Karen." And our list of excuses goes something like this:

» I am so tired.

» I am trying to heal.

» I don't want to go to a gym.

» My mental mood is not into working out.

» I am sad about my body.

» I am getting used to my new body.

» I don't want to go to a gym.

» I don't have the money to go to a gym.

» I don't want to change at the gym.

» Will people stare at me when I can't do things?

» What things should I not do with my new chest?

» The workout clothes don't fit me.

» Sports bras don't work now.

» I have scars that show.

I have been there with every one of these reasons and more. While writing this chapter, I kept stopping to get up because this was such a sore subject during my journey in beating cancer.

Here is why you have to get back in shape the right way through working out and eating right. One study the insurance companies have done on cancer is the connection between weight and breast cancer. The more overweight you are, the higher the chances are of getting breast cancer again. So, I'll repeat myself. Don't skip this chapter and read the next chapter on <u>weight and cancer</u> as well.

Had I known this, I would have exercised much more, but in 1994, this was not common advice and there were no studies pointing out the relationship between belly fat and estrogen. So, what did it matter? I was raised in a family that put a lot of your worth on your body and your ability as an athlete. I was not an athlete so I ran from working out. My husband wanted our life back to a point where I could do anything, anytime without getting tired.

"You should work out, Karen, it will help you."

"The way to stay alive is to get in shape again."

I heard these warnings so many times, they made me want to completely avoid working out at all. Couldn't they realize trying to accomplish what I had to do during my day was hard enough without the added pressure of working out? As a result of my stubbornness, I gained a lot of weight. The weight gain was not because I was eating the wrong foods, I was simply not moving enough to counter the calories. I had so many surgeries, a two-year-old daughter, housework, clients, and about as much as I could manage. *Please see all I am doing and how tired I am!*

Add the emotions I was trying to hide from me not liking my body. Put all those together and I passed on working out; I had earned the right to sit.

Then, I realized this is my journey. How did I want to live it? A new dog had come into our lives before I got sick. This was not going to be a small dog. As a Golden Retriever–Australian Shepherd mix, she would become a large dog. Since I need to walk, I decided to train her every day, and most days I was able to walk with her two or three times.

She became my constant partner through my recovery journey. She was always there for me without judgment. If I could walk one block or five blocks, she did not care. She took my focus off the pain and directed it into something positive. Our training went so well, before too long, she could walk with me and respond correctly to my commands. We started with one block, then two blocks, then one block running, two blocks walking, training all the way along. She is how I got my life back on track.

I want you to know I am with you all the way. I have been through it all and I made it. I want to inspire you to know it can be done, exercise can save your life, and that is what we are working for right.

You: "Hey, Karen. I am not going to get a dog."

Unless you have a horrible dislike of dogs, ask the neighbor if you can walk their dog. I know this sounds weird, but my motivation for working out was as simple as knowing my dog counted on me doing it. Too many dogs sit home all day and never get walked enough. There are shelter dogs that need walking, senior centers with dogs that need to get walked, which means there are no excuses that you can't find a dog.

If you are a gym person, or you want to become one, let's look at some issues you might face.

Many people I met wanted to go to a trainer and asked me how they could find one. I started to ask questions of the trainers at my gym, a 24-hour-type place. When it came to working with women recovering from breast cancer, they were clueless. I was afraid to refer anyone to them.

Trainers, and gym personnel in general, think you are like other women they know when you say you are recovering from breast surgery. They assume you are talking about breast augmentation (commonly referred to as a "boob job"). So, they will blow you off as though this is no big deal. I asked the trainers in my gym about precautions when dealing with a mastectomy and they still thought it was no big deal. Well, it is a big deal and here is why.

Breast augmentation, if done correctly, places saline or silicone-type implants under the muscle, using your own breast tissue and muscle to hold the foreign object in place. The surgery takes around an hour. The implants have nothing to do with the lymph nodes so they are not affected.

We, on the other hand, have all kinds of complications to deal with, and they should know how to handle them, which, I found out, they do not. If you have had a double or single mastectomy and lymph node removal, you have scar tissue everywhere. You do not have breast tissue; only a thin layer of muscle holding in the implant. Unless your trainer also happens to be a physical therapist, please be careful about following their instructions.

When I started at the gym, I kept my arms at my sides. Physical therapists will tell you to move the scar tissue to keep the implants from becoming encapsulated in scar tissue, which gives you the hard feeling around your implants. This scar tissue can cause the implants to move as a whole when you engage your pec muscles. It can cause the implants to move up your chest and not look normal.

But this is a different kind of workout and more like stretching. I did this at home. My friend who was a physical therapist helped me with this. I agree, moving in everyday life is already making you use your pec muscles which engage your implants. My body tells me when I am doing too much by giving me pain, and in my case, by having my arms swell from lymphedema. Laundry, sweeping, vacuuming, picking up my child, carrying groceries, and, not to mention, all the stretches against a wall the physical therapist wanted me to do. So, I was using the gym to help only my legs at this point. As I felt stronger many months later, I added very light weights to build my arms and biceps. I added pull downs, but limited the weights to about 20 pounds.

In most cases after surgery, you should not do everything they are used to telling other people to do. If you are going to take group classes at the gym, I suggest arriving early to your first class to tell the teacher you've had breast surgery and explain this was not breast augmentation but breast cancer surgery. They will probably give you a deer-in-the-headlights look and whisper, "Okay, do what you think is right for you." *What? You're the professional. Can't you help me?*

Their answers will likely be unhelpful. They will not help you specifically because they do not want to be liable for telling you something wrong that might be cause for a lawsuit. Your only option is to listen to your body and what it is telling you.

Muscle pain is not the same as scar tissue pain. Scar tissue pain is when your implants are directing the pain. Muscle pain is gradual and most likely hurts after the exercise, usually showing up the next day.

Warning pain is sharp or throbbing pain that happens during the exercise. Your body is telling you, "Hey, stop doing that right away! So, STOP doing it right away. To me, doing push-ups in class is a "stay away" movement for me. Avoid anything that engages your pec muscles, presses them too hard, or requires them to hold your body weight.

When using the gym after breast surgery, you are a beginner. Explain this even if you are somewhat in shape. The word beginner in their world is the signal to take things slowly and to build strength and muscles over time.

If you are attending yoga classes, there are very special things to watch out for. During certain poses, such as Downward-Facing Dog and the follow-through push-ups, you'll be engaging your arms and this motion will affect your chest and back muscles. Go easy on yoga poses that put your full body weight on your arms and chest. This can cause your chest to put too much pressure on your stitches and scar tissue, in my opinion.

So, remember to keep your arms pinned to your sides and don't overly use them. You will need to build strength in different muscles while protecting your chest area, just as people with back pain conditions need to adjust and allow for strains on their spine.

Also, not all scar tissue is bad. You do need to have it form correctly to hold the implants in place. You will never stop the body from forming scar tissue around the implants. The implants do need movement to help them from adhering to the scar tissue incorrectly, but from my experience, gym personnel and ordinary trainers are not the people to ask for help. Seek out a physical therapist who has worked with breast cancer survivors to help you, and, as always, quiz them before you work together.

Above all else, don't use the inadequacy of your gym's offerings as an excuse for not going in the first place. Instead, use everything you encounter as an opportunity to teach and learn. Even other gym members may know more (use caution!) but should anyone ask you, simply say you have an injury and need to watch what you are doing.

I have taught many teachers about what I can and can't do. I have protected my chest from so many things. My breasts look beautiful and I am fortunate that I've had no complications at all.

Another positive thing you can do with me is to tell your gym's owners or managers that one-in-eight women will be coming to them with breast cancer and their trainers need to be aware of what that means and how their exercise routines need to accommodate them. They might even do well to have a couple of trainers who specialize in teaching exercises to aid breast surgery recovery.

Many gyms already have specialized trainers for heart attack, stroke, and back surgery survivors. They need to help us, too. We are growing in number, unfortunately, and we need to be heard.

What a great class it would be to have a "survivor class" where we can receive positive, practical support in helping our efforts to heal ourselves.

Until that happens, walking is a boring but easy exercise. There are also loads of videos and programming with exercising. Find a video targeted to seniors and work your way up. Am I kidding? No! After surgery, this is where your body is. You will move up from here.

If your body does not signal you to stop, then you are moving up. Start with the treadmill to see what your body says. Remember, you and your body are a team now. You can no longer think without asking what it thinks. You will take so much longer to heal if you do not move. Ask your family to take you for a walk; just move. When a friend comes by to check on you, take a walk. Walk during your lunch break at work.

There is a great resource called Meetup where you can find or start a survivor-walking group.[1] Make sure this doesn't turn into a **depression group**. The goal is to move on and not to talk about anything that takes you back. Exercise is a way of taking your life back, getting healthy, and moving forward. This is not the place to hold people captive to the past. See this as a life group. If you don't have support, then there is someone else in the same situation. Why not get support for exercising from each other?

Bring people together and see what happens. If you are not the outgoing type, ask a friend to start a walking group with you. It's vital to keep moving!

This, along with the right diet, gives you the best chance of not getting cancer again. Please get into a group that is a fighting group that can kick cancer's butt!

---

1 Meetup is an online platform for meeting people in your local community who share your interests. Visit their website at https://www.meetup.com.

CHAPTER 7

Weight and Cancer

(Please read, so important, don't skip!)

I CHANGED SO MANY THINGS IN MY LIFE to avoid any return of cancer; I did not want my weight to come into the mix at all. I ate right; I exercised frequently, so enough is enough, right?

So far, you have read about all the things I've done to stay alive. The last thing I needed was to think about my weight. By the time I reached 60, I figured I could let *some* things go, and today, I could probably lose 15 pounds to be at an ideal weight for my body type.

I wear a size 12 to 14 in pants, which I do not think is big. What would I have to do to lose that weight? Stop eating as much or workout like a fiend? That's crazy. I don't need to change what I'm eating, which means I would have to focus only on more exercise and I'm already tired. I am working full time, writing this book, working out three times a week, and walking my dog twice a day for 20 minutes each. When am I supposed to clean, shop, and sleep? To add more to my routine, there better be an incredible reason, then I found out there was an incredible reason.

Here was the banter about weight with my doctor. Maybe you had the same with yours?

"You need to lose weight," says the doctor.

"What? I run, workout, eat organic foods, don't drink alcohol, don't eat red meat, mostly eat fish, don't eat sweets, and..." I explain on and on.

"You still need to lose weight. You had cancer," she insists.

That was the *entire* conversation. Didn't she know how to explain what she just told me? Did she read this astonishing fact somewhere and forget why it was important? Or did she assume I would accept that since she is the doctor, I would do whatever she told me to do?

So, how much weight did I need to lose? I will never be a rail-thin person. I have never been thin. I have a muscular build, not a thin one. She was the first doctor to ever bring this up after 20 plus years of being cancer-free. This was my first experience just being told something flat out like I was supposed to know what it meant.

Okay, challenge accepted. I started thinking about what this meant. What had she read or discovered in order to bring it up?

I looked into the connection between weight and cancer. That was me yelling, "What the Hell?" during my discovery in the library. What I discovered is that, once again, professionals are not explaining facts to us so we can make good, informed decisions.

Okay. Let me break it down for you.

Breast cancer: Many studies have shown that, in post-menopausal women, a higher Body Mass Index (BMI) is associated with a modest increase in risk of breast cancer.[1] For example,

> A 5-unit increase in BMI is associated with a 12 percent increase in risk. Among post-menopausal women (older women), those who are obese have a 20-to-40 percent increase in risk of developing breast cancer compared with normal-weight women. The higher risks are seen mainly in women who have never used menopausal hormone therapy and for tumors that express hormone receptors. Obesity is also a risk factor for breast cancer in men.

---

1 BMI is the measure of relative weight based on an individual's mass and height ranging from underweight to obese. You can calculate your own BMI using an online tool such as this one: https://www.cdc.gov/healthyweight/assessing/bmi/adult_bmi/english_bmi_calculator/bmi_calculator.html.

In pre-menopausal women (younger women), by contrast, overweight and obesity have been found to be associated with a 20 percent decreased risk of breast tumors that express hormone receptors.

Fat tissue (also called adipose tissue) produces excess amounts of estrogen, high levels of which have been associated with increased risks of breast, endometrial, ovarian, and some other cancers.

Basically, what this article, and others I found supporting it, are saying is: if you are pre-menopausal (a younger woman) and carrying a little extra weight, that extra weight may help you avoid cancer.

In designing your divine body, God knew women would need extra weight to help with carrying his new creations as they are being developed during pregnancy. He gave us a healthy place with hormones; powerful chemicals that affect mind and body, to grow and feed them. Estrogen (often thought of as the "female sex hormone") is derived from cholesterol and strongly influences the deposit of body fat—both in amount and location. During pregnancy, estrogen helps to stimulate hormone production in the fetus' adrenal gland and enhances the uterus. After the birthing period, the body innately knows you should not have this extra weight anymore.

Instead of releasing the estrogen to feed the uterus, the body now stores it under the fat. If you don't remove the estrogen, it can be used to "feed" cancer cells.

If you have excess fat around your midsection it can be used to store estrogen in your body. Most breast cancers—like the type I had—are estrogen-based. So, any extra estrogen being produced could increase my risk of getting cancer again.

This could mean that despite everything else I am doing to remain cancer-free, an increase in my midsection fat could decrease all of my other efforts.

I know what you are thinking. I searched the Internet to see if having liposuction could change the percentage of cancer recurrence. Doesn't it seem logical to study this? No studies found.

What's more, exercising can cause new estrogen to be produced. So, if I'm trying to lose weight through exercising, but my body is making new estrogen at the same time, am I at a higher risk than if I kept the extra weight? No studies found.

Hormones play a big part in fat storage as we get older. Personally, I will not take hormone replacement drugs. The only way I will be able to get the right amounts of hormones is through food and exercise. Metabolism and the body's ability to burn fat also plays a big role in fat storage. The balance between what you feed your body and how efficiently it uses the food for energy is the fine line we straddle as we age.

As I eat, I know how much exercise I'll need in order to burn off the equivalent number of calories and fat to keep myself from gaining weight.

On the next page is a chart that's helpful in figuring that out.

Let me explain it to you like this: I looked at the food I ate, which is organic and mostly vegetables, some protein, and not a lot of carbohydrates. I considered how much moving around I do every day by working out, walking the dogs, and so on. I should be skinny, right? Wrong. My hormones and the way my body burns calories all come into play now. And this is a bummer, but I gain my weight around the midsection.

With all the research I did on sugar, carbohydrates, meat, and so on, I decided I would only eat food that God gave me the enzymes to digest.

I did an experiment on myself in 2020. I decided to not eat sugar, or carbohydrates (which change into sugar), or fruit. I was only going to eat vegetables and protein, (mostly vegetables) to see what would happen. I also ate all day long instead of starving my body all day. When you read the chapter on sugar you'll see why I took that out of my diet and how hard it was to do.

I did not increase my workouts at all, but I exercised every day.

Calorie-Burning Chart for Various Activities			
Approximate calories burned, per hour, by a 150-pound woman			
Exercise	Calories per hour	Exercise	Calories per hour
Sleeping	55	Water aerobics	400+
Eating	85	Skating, blading	420+
Sewing	85	Dancing, aerobic	420+
Knitting	85	Aerobics	450+
Sitting	85	Bicycling, moderate	450+
Standing	100	Jogging, 5mph	500+
Driving	110	Gardening, digging	500+
Office work	140	Swimming active	500+
Housework, moderate	60+	Cross country ski machine	500+
Golf, with cart	180	Hiking	500+
Golf, without cart	240	Step aerobics	550+
Gardening, planting	250	Rowing	550+
Dancing, ballroom	260	Power walking	600+
Walking, 3mph	280+	Cycling, studio	650
Table tennis	290+	Squash	650+
Gardening, hoeing	350+	Skipping with rope	700+
Tennis	350+	Running	700+

I lost two pant sizes in 60 days and I have kept the weight off. That is how I got to a size 10.

After all, this is His creation, so why not follow the instruction manual? If your body can't digest something, it won't know how to get rid of it. The body knows how to get rid of vegetables and protein and we are working out to help it process the food into energy to move. This is exactly what the manual tells us to do: use His food to fuel His body.

If the body was created to perform physical work, how can we sit all day and think it will work properly?

I truly hope you get this. Excess weight means higher chances of cancer returning. Exercise has to be part of your daily routine. Do it responsibly, healthfully, and do not hurt the body in the process. Your body has been through enough, right?

Be sure to read the chapters on working out and sugar. Get a plan together to lose weight that fits into your lifestyle in a healthy way. The key is to ask people to take on specific roles to help you with different things. When my husband nagged me about losing weight, I only felt worse about myself. For me, learning on my own works best. Whatever it takes, when you have loving and supportive help that is best. If your spouse can't provide that, start a child-mother walking and talking or best friend support group.

Knowledge is power, so I want you to have knowledge so you can make the right decisions on how to help your body help itself.

I have been talking to gym owners about offering "Cancer Aerobic" classes for survivors to exercise and support each other as they return to good health. Hopefully, gyms will study what it is to be a cancer survivor and train their staff how to work with us. I know they have special classes for people recovering from back injuries and surgeries. I explained that I do not envision this as a "poor me" class, but as an uplifting class with a focus on speeding our recovery based on our special needs.

Please let me know if you start one in your town by contacting me at twentyfiveyearsandcountingcancerfree.com, telluswhyweredying.com or facebook.com/25yearsandcountingcancerfree. We all need support as we heal and move on in thankfulness for the life we have been spared to live.

CHAPTER 8

BRCA1 and BRCA2

I SEARCHED ONLINE FOR HOURS looking to find out what the hype about BRCA1 AND BRCA2 was all about. I could not find any major news flashes. What? I was told this is the newest thing to help stop breast cancer in its tracks.

What I did find were endless offers to test myself (for $250) to see if I had the gene. But once I had the results, then what would I do? Would I be saddled with fear forever? As I read further, there was nothing saying this test would let me know for sure I would get cancer if I had the gene.

I had to know what it meant, so I decided to take the test. I wanted to help my family in the event they developed breast cancer so my genetic results would be on file. I have a daughter, my sister has two girls, and my brother also has two girls. These women might one day have their own daughters. With my family's history of cancer, I felt like a walking cancer book.

I met with a gene specialist through Kaiser in 2019 to go over my results. I documented all the cases of cancer in my family and handed it to her. She looked at me like I was a ghost.

"Is this right?" she asked me?

"Yes," I assured her.

"All this cancer?" she checked.

"YES."

"OKAY." She stopped staring at me and looked down at the report.

"Let's look at your results," she started. "You tested positive for BRCA1."

"I kind of figured I would," I agreed.

She looked back at me. "How did you decide to do what you did?"

"What do you mean?" I asked.

"How did you decide not to do the chemotherapy at that time with all this cancer in your family?"

"I studied it and decided it would not give me a better chance to live," I answered.

I went on to express my anger about how cancer always seems like a back-burner thing. I started telling her about my book and all I had found out, of which she did not know.

"I want to read your book," she told me. "You seem to know so much about cancer."

"No," I explained, "I don't think any of us know enough about cancer. I hope my book gets the dialogue started and leads to helping us."

I continued. "I have a question. This test, what does it really do for the public as far as cancer is concerned? I personally think it gives people who test negative a false hope they will not get cancer, which is *so wrong*. A negative test only means they do not have the gene, correct."

She looked me dead in the face. "You're right. That is why we do not press people to get tested unless they have a history of breast cancer in their family." She went on. "We are worried the public will do exactly what you suggested. They will stop getting mammograms and let lumps go unchecked."

"So," I asked her to clarify, "the big advancement made with this test only helps a small group of cancer patients; to be exact, only the 25 percent who have cancer already present in their genes, the genetic group."

"Exactly," she confirmed.

It's blow-your-mind time.

Here is the crazy thing. Are you ready? Even with all the death from cancer in my family, my sister's two daughters do not have the gene. I figured the next generation would be heading straight into double mastectomy territory to stay alive. But they did not have the gene.

And I wondered, *why not?* What changed between our generations? My mom passed it to me, but adding my brother-in-law into my niece's gene pool stopped it. *Why?*

My daughter is now old enough to test and I will have her tested next. If cancer does not spread to her, then what good is the test for the next generation? Why does it skip a generation? Have they studied this skip? No. So, do we have worried mothers who are scared they may have passed a deadly disease to their children, only to find out that may not be true?

Where is the study for my sister's children who do not have the gene? There is no study.

The BRCA tests are only one area that we need to study and educate women about. I am adding the best explanations of the tests I could find, which were from the cancer.gov website.[1]

What are BRCA1 and BRCA2?

BRCA1 and BRCA2 are human genes that produce tumor suppressor proteins. These proteins help repair damaged DNA and, therefore, play a role in ensuring the stability of each cell's genetic material. When either of these genes is mutated, or altered, such that its protein product is not made or does not function correctly, DNA damage may not be repaired properly. As a result, cells are more likely to develop additional genetic alterations that can lead to cancer.

Specific inherited mutations in BRCA1 and BRCA2 most notably increase the risk of female breast and ovarian cancers, but they have

---

1 Excerpted from the article, "BRCA Mutations: Cancer Risk and Genetic Testing" on the cancer.gov website. https://www.cancer.gov/about-cancer/causes-prevention/genetics/brca-fact-sheet#what-are-brca1-and-brca2.

also been associated with increased risks of several additional types of cancer. People who have inherited mutations in BRCA1 and BRCA2 tend to develop breast and ovarian cancers at younger ages than people who do not have these mutations.

A harmful BRCA1 or BRCA2 mutation can be inherited from a person's mother or father. Each child of a parent who carries a mutation in one of these genes has a 50 percent chance (or 1 chance in 2) of inheriting the mutation. The effects of mutations in BRCA1 and BRCA2 are seen even when a person's second copy of the gene is normal.

What do BRCA1 or BRCA2 genetic test results mean?

BRCA1 and BRCA2 gene mutation testing can give several possible results: a positive result, a negative result, or an ambiguous or uncertain result.

Positive result. A positive test result indicates that a person has inherited a known harmful mutation in BRCA1 or BRCA2 and, therefore, has an increased risk of developing certain cancers. However, a positive test result cannot tell whether or when an individual will actually develop cancer. Some women who inherit a harmful BRCA1 or BRCA2 mutation never develop breast or ovarian cancer.

A positive test result may also have important implications for family members, including future generations.

Both men and women, who inherit a harmful BRCA1 or BRCA2 mutation, whether or not they develop cancer themselves, may pass the mutation on to their sons and daughters. Each child has a 50 percent chance of inheriting a parent's mutation.

If a person learns that he or she has inherited a harmful BRCA1 or BRCA2 mutation, this will mean that each of his or her full siblings has a 50 percent chance of having inherited the mutation as well.

Negative result. A negative test result can be more difficult to understand than a positive result because what the result means depends in part on an individual's family history of cancer and whether a BRCA1 or BRCA2 mutation has been identified in a blood relative.

Please note, that even if you test negative for the BRCA gene, you still have a one-in-eight chance of getting cancer.

So, don't think for a minute a negative BRCA test result means you will not get cancer. This statement alone should make you ask my question:

Why are we getting cancer?

CHAPTER 9

Chiropractic

I KNOW CHIROPRACTIC is a practice many of you think is crazy. I have heard all the arguments: "I would never let anyone push on me; they are going to break my neck!" The first time I was adjusted, that cracking sound scared me so much that I couldn't go back. I flashed on a movie where a tough guy broke a person's neck. That could be me next!

Fortunately, I got over my fear and have been seeing chiropractors for decades. I am certain their adjustments and special knowledge of the body helped save my life. If this is way too far out for you, I understand, and please pass on this chapter. However, I hope you will read what I have to say and think about it before you pass on chiropractic healing. I'd like to tell you why chiropractic help can be important to your body's healing process.

A common story told about how chiropractic was invented is when, in 1896, Daniel David Palmer (D.D. Palmer) encountered his building's janitor, Harvey Lillard, who Palmer discovered had a pronounced lump in his neck. Lillard's hearing was severely impaired and Palmer theorized that the lump and his hearing deficits were related. When Palmer examined the janitor's spine, he noticed one of his neck's vertebrae was sticking up above the others. Palmer pushed hard on the vertebrae and Lillard's hearing was restored.

Palmer is credited as being the inventor of chiropractic and its underlying philosophy. These observations led to the study of the spine and the nervous system that runs from the base of your head to the end of your tailbone.

We have thirty-one pairs of spinal nerves branching off the spinal cord that carry messages back-and-forth between your body and spinal cord to control sensation and movement. Basically, your nervous system tells your organs what to do. I think of the spinal nerves as telegraph lines that send out signals explaining to the organs what the body wants them to do.

The spine is made of 33 individual bones (vertebrae) interlocked and stacked one on top of the other to form the spinal column. Only the top 24 bones are movable. Those vertebrae move forward and back, and side-to-side. The bottom 7 only move forward and back, they are at the base of your spine from your tailbone up. When you bend over this is the little lumps you see going down your back. They sole purpose is to protect the nerves going down your back from harm, I call them the nerve shield. The vertebra have holes to allow the nerves to leave the shield and attached to the organs.

I think of the spinal nerves as telegraph lines that send out signals explaining to the organs they are attach to what the brain wants them to do. Have you ever tried to water a garden and everything is going great, the water is coming out strong and you're just cruising along when suddenly the water starts coming out really slowly? When you trace the hose back to the faucet looking for the cause, you see a kink in the line.

That little kink can make the water stop to a point where only a trickle is coming out. Once I get the kink out, water is spraying all over the place on the other end.

This is the same goal of a chiropractor. They trace the impulse from the nervous system to the organ it is trying to talk to. The chiropractor lifts the vertebrae off the nerve where it's kinking to stop the nerve from being pinched. Once fixed, the nerve can once again allow the impulse from the brain to reach the organ full-strength. All it takes is the weight of a quarter to cut the impulse of that nerve to the organ by 50 percent. The brain cannot tell the organ how to work effectively, since the full impulse has been interrupted. It appears that the organ is damaged. But often, this is only temporary due to the brain's lack of ability to communicate fully so it can function at 100 percent.

I personally think x-rays are necessary to show what has happened to the spine and where problems are coming from. Very routine things we do every day can affect the spine. During birth, for example, when a baby is pulled from the mother, their shoulders are taken out one at a time. While the rest of the body is still in the birth canal, the baby's body is twisted in order to generate enough force to complete the delivery. This can cause a problem in the spinal column for the rest of that baby's life. The nerve in the middle of their back sends signals to the stomach, causing problems with digesting food, developing colic, and feeling pain from gas in the intestines.

To find out which way the vertebra needs to move to put them back in place, I believe a chiropractor should look at x-rays. This way, the chiropractor knows exactly which way to push the bones back in place. With full spine x-rays, they can examine the overall health of the spine and inspect every subluxation of the spine bones and how they are affecting other parts of the body. The spine works as one giant unit. What happens to the neck affects the back and *vice versa*.

As with all doctors, it's important to research the chiropractors as they are going to be dealing with a very vital part of the body. How do I use chiropractic to stay healthy? I want all my organs working at full-strength all the time. The way I personally select a chiropractor is by the school they attended and the techniques they learned on how to adjust the body. I also consider the seminars they went to after finishing their degree. They all have to take continuing education to maintain their chiropractic license. Some specialize in a specific part of the body and focus on studies related to that field of choice.

As with all institutions, instructors have "A" students and "C" students that graduate. Which students do you have working on you? My personal opinion is the top-rated schools for chiropractic are the Palmer College of Chiropractic and Life University's College of Chiropractic.[1]

Is this to say other schools are not worth considering? No. One of my favorite doctors, Dr. Howard Cohn in Orange County, worked on me for years.

What made him incredible was that he had also spent hundreds of thousands of dollars on continuing education to be best chiropractor he could be. I managed his clinic for years and personally saw amazing healing take place.

Do your research. Many people pick doctors because a friend or co-worker suggests them. If they only know what they are told by the chiropractor they are going to right now, do they know what's right for you? Even if they are feeling wonderful and have nothing but praise for their doctor, it's important to find a chiropractor that has experience with breast cancer patients.

Do I go for adjustments as often as they want me to come? No, I am a bad patient in their eyes and I would be lying to you if I said I did. What I do is maintenance care. I get adjusted twice a month to keep my nervous system open and working. When I start to feel sick with a cold, aches, or pain, or when I'm under a lot of stress, I'll up my visits to once a week.

Always remember you are a cancer survivor and that makes you totally different. If you have breast implants, this means there is a different way to adjust you. As with working out, adjustments for people with implants following a mastectomy are not the same as adjustments for women who have had voluntary breast augmentation. A "boob job," as one chiropractor so politely called it, has breast tissue in front of the implant, less scar tissue, and has been filled more or less, depending on the size of implants you have.

---

1 Palmer College of Chiropractic main campus is located in Davenport, Iowa. https://www.palmer.edu. Life University's Doctor of Chiropractic (D.C.) degree is a rigorous, 14-quarter program that typically takes students four years to complete. https://www.life.edu/academic-pages/chiropractic-curriculum.

Yes, if you have very full implants, he *can* pop them. I had a chiropractor pop my implant even though I warned him over and over to be careful.

The skin surrounding the implants that holds fluid is much harder now, but as you age, the implants themselves can become weaker. The implants are to be replaced every 10 years, so they do eventually break down.

When he popped my implant, the insurance company did not want to pay to fix them both at the same time. I wanted them to age together and look the same. I had to fight to get a full new set, both implants replaced, and I won but it took time. I went months without an implant on one side.

During the adjustment, ask the doctor to use a chest pillow to put your implants into when they push down. Make sure they use it every time. They also cannot push very hard on your sides when adjusting your lower back. This can cause the implants and the scar tissue to move. Don't allow them to push hard on your chest when adjusting the middle of your back, either. This can cause problems with your implants. I had one chiropractor (he thought he knew everything because he had adjusted patients with implants before) who pushed on me so hard that the scar tissue was so rattled I could not breathe. I was in pain for two weeks. As with any doctor you go to for help, only go to the ones who will listen; if they won't listen walk out and find one who will. Do not change what you want from the fear of the doctor.

Keep reminding them your number one concern is protecting your chest. But the first time they don't, it's time to move on to a new chiropractor.

They might suggest using an activator in order to treat you especially carefully. However, I think the hands-on adjustment is the best. An activator is a little tool that pushes the vertebra instead of the doctor using his hands. If they are worried about using their hands, it's time for a new doctor. If they become frustrated with you because you constantly remind them you are different, it's time for a new doctor.

Is it worth finding the perfect doctor to treat you? Absolutely. Your body needs to work at its optimum to keep you alive. All organs need God's infinite wisdom in body design to be working at 100 percent to keep you alive. Just think: if the nerves to your stomach are sending its strongest signal, you will be digesting food at 100 percent and that's what is needed for healing; the nerves to your heart need uninterrupted blood flow to help with healing; the nerves to your intestines need to signal absorption of food for healing. We need all the organs to working at 100 percent!

Again, I am not a doctor or a chiropractor but I have worked with them for more than 20 years and I know what an incredible chiropractor can do to help you. Do your research and help your body help itself.

CHAPTER 10

Chemotherapy

THIS IS SUCH A HARD CHAPTER for me to write. I do not want people to do what I did just because I did it. I am not a doctor, nor do I confess to be one.

Everything I did was because I studied my options. I made the right choice for my situation, and me only. That does not mean it is right for you and what you are going through.

My story is just that: my story, my body. Your story maybe similar or completely different than my story. Only you know. Because it is your story and you have your beliefs on what you should do, period. I have always believed you cannot make a good decision if you have not been presented with all the facts. My doctors were only telling me about one outcome. They did not tell me anything about my lifelong outcome—what would happen in the aftermath of my choice?

In my research, I found out that breast cancer can only grow in breast tissue. That's it. So, I knew that if I wanted to take the breeding ground away from cancer, I had to have a double mastectomy. My doctors wanted me to do chemotherapy to safeguard against any random cancer cells that were roaming around in my body. They thought with such a large tumor—and the fast-growing rate of this type of cancer—they were sure cancer would turn up somewhere else.

My body had encapsulated the cancer three times. My doctor said it was like an egg when it came out. They could not find any cancer in my lymph nodes. God had saved me. When they cut into the cancer during the biopsy, it did not appear to be cancer. They had to send it out for further study to see what those cells were doing inside that tumor. It was amazing, and it saved my life. I had to take my situation into consideration to look at all the possibilities and the damage I would be doing to my body—the body that just saved me—by adding chemo.

I studied the effects of chemotherapy to find out what it does to the body. None of their answers made any sense to me. They had absolutely no studies what would happen if I waited to start the chemotherapy until my body healed. This was the protocol period. We need to force them to do a formal study to help the body heal before they put this much strain on it right after surgery.

Please study this on your own before making the kind of decision I made. I found out all kinds of things my doctors did not tell me. There are great articles out there to teach you so you can come in prepared to ask questions. This is definitely NOT something you just do without knowledge; this can and probably will affect you for the rest of your life. I have put an article below to give you a head start.[1]

1. Chemo drugs can't differentiate between cancer cells and healthy cells. That's why chemotherapy harms or kills both types of cells. Included in your healthy cells are the rapidly dividing white blood cells that help the body to function normally. They just took my chest off in a 8 hour surgery, and now they want to kill all the white blood cells I need to heal? And they did not want to postpone chemo treatments at all— for any length of time. I asked if I could let my body heal from the surgery first and then start chemo. I was told I couldn't wait. How was I supposed to heal? What about the stress on my body? After all it had been through, why did they want to stress it out again? Why give it no healing time in-between? None of their answers made any sense to me.

1 Please see https://www.mayoclinic.org/tests-procedures/chemotherapy-for-breast-cancer/about/pac-20384931.

2. Chemo stays in the cells of the body for up to two months. I found out that the body has a dumping mechanism. When it gets too full of anything, it dumps it, and that includes chemo. So, how effective can it be if the body is continually dumping it, trying to get it out of its system? Read to the end of the article below, this is not the only article, but a start for you. The body's cleaning filters, the liver and kidneys, work overtime trying to clean chemo out of the system. The strain from this can cause major problems later in life.[2]

3. Chemo kills your appetite. You will not feel like eating at all. Doctors will prescribe nausea medications to help, but you will not feel like eating. In helping so many people I love, I truly believe this side effect alone is what killed them faster. They could not eat; they did not want to eat. I went into protein-shake-mode to give them something so their bodies wouldn't starve on top of everything else it was trying to manage. Putting the body into starvation mode will cause serious problems.[3] Please read the chapter on protein bars and shakes for the shakes I use and be very clear what to make. Ensure is a drug and should be seen as one.

4. Smoothies tend to go down easy and stay down, but take care not to have drinks that are too sugary. Add protein powders or other amino-acids with essential nutrients. Chemo patients have to feed their body nutritious food to return to health. Here is the thing: you cannot force yourself to eat. It is so hard to eat; you need to understand that you have to make yourself eat. My loved ones considered eating a chore; and they didn't want to do anything that felt like extra work. During chemo, the body

---

2 Please see https://www.livescience.com/31966-cells-garbage-disposal-crucial-processes-nigms.html.

3 "Now Entering Starvation Mode: What Happens to Your Metabolic Processes When You Stop Feeding Your Body," by Lecia Bushak, as posted on the Medical Daily website (2014). https://www.medicaldaily.com/now-entering-starvation-mode-what-happens-your-metabolic-processes-when-you-stop-feeding-280666.

isn't sending the same hunger signal you're used to recognizing, so you'll see no reason to eat. To help my family members, I wrote down what they could manage to eat and exactly when during the day was their best time to eat. I encouraged them to live on this schedule to heal. The intestines are going to have trouble digesting foods correctly, too. Read on how for getting help with that.

5. <u>Chemo can create myopathies in the body, which could last for years.</u> Myopathies are disorders of the skeletal muscle. Symptoms include numbness, fatigue, stomach problems, liver problems, and weakness. Please study this topic to really know what may happen to your body. If you ask the doctor how long will the chemo stay in my body, they will tell you it's a week for the drug to leave your body. They will not tell you the lasting effects of the chemo to the rest of the body. You think, "Okay, it will be gone in a week. I can do that." But the effects may last many years after the drug is gone. I am not telling you not to do it, but knowledge is key when asking questions.

6. <u>Chemo will leave you dehydrated.</u> You will be nauseated from even drinking water. How will you flush your kidneys and liver to help cleanse them? To flush the cells and release the chemotherapy from your body, you would need to have extra fluids introduced through IV feeding. If I had to go through chemotherapy, I would be paying for three IV bags of fluid a week to help cleanse my liver and kidneys. They will give you IV of fluids while having chemotherapy now, which is a new practice in some places, but I would pay for more and get in debt to do it. In California, we have IV fluid centers where you can pay for fluids to be administrated to you if you lack water in your system. Again, research them and make sure they are licensed and bonded to do so.

7. <u>Chemo is going to interrupt your normal digestion process.</u> You can be constipated and your colon is going to stop working

correctly, making you toxic from the inside. Here's a quick summary of the digestion process: the stomach holds food and it also mixes and grinds up the food. It secretes acid and enzymes to break down the food into a liquid or paste. The small intestine continues breaking down the food using pancreatic enzymes and liver bile. The colon, or large intestine, passes the waste left over from all the digestion that's been going on. It normally takes about 36 hours for all the waste to get through the colon. To understand digestion more fully, read the article "Your Digestive System" on WebMD.[4] If food isn't processed correctly, this may cause a bloating of the colon. The colon is the most important part of the digestive system. If it has waste stuck in it, this will cause many problems. You will feel sick as if you have the flu all the time. You need to watch how and when you eliminate waste in accordance with your food intake. If you are constipated even a bit longer than normal, I suggest you have colonic treatments. Make sure they are licensed and highly sanitary as you do not need more problems.

8. Chemo weakens your defense systems. You will be at a much greater risk of getting sick. Even the slightest malady can put you in the hospital. A sniffle unchecked can quickly develop into pneumonia. Your immune system will be weakened and depending on the severity of damage chemo has done to it, even a simple injury or illness will be difficult to overcome. If you develop a small problem with the implants, your natural healers—the white blood cells—will not be there to help you heal. Remember that on top of trying to heal from the mastectomy and implant surgeries, you are battling cancer cells.

When I was in Oregon to help my sister as she was passing away, I noticed she kept complaining about stomach pain. I lifted her shirt I saw her colon was extended. I asked her when was the last time she took a bowel movement.

---

4 "Your Digestive System," as posted on WebMD.com. https://www.webmd.com/heartburn-gerd/your-digestive-system.

She could not remember, nor could anyone else. She was becoming toxic from her own waste. I found a colonics person in her area and took her there right away. It was so amazing how much food was in her colon, as we watched in disbelief as it came out. When they were done, her colon was back to normal and the pain was gone.

I confronted the head of oncology at Scripps Green, a large and respected hospital in the Scripps Health network, with these questions. She confirmed that everything I found was accurate. If I decided on having chemo, I was really going to hurt my body for a long time—on purpose—even when I knew all the risks I was taking.

I also asked for any statistics they could give me. If I put my body through all of the above, what would chemo do for my chances of getting cancer again? I figured I'd have at least a 50 percent better chance of living cancer-free.

But when I heard the answer, I knew it clinched my decision. Chemo was only going to give me a 10 percent better chance of recurrence.

I asked the life-changing questions. I run, workout, eat organic foods, don't drink alcohol, don't eat red meat, mostly eat fish, don't eat sweets, and so on. Does my current shape give me a higher success rate when doing chemotherapy? But stats are not broken down into categories like this. We only have overall information to go on. We do not even have simple stats separating healthy people from sick people to see how chemo changes their chances.

If I chose not to do the chemotherapy and change my lifestyle instead would that give me the same 10 percent chance? I had multiple doctors say I was going to die. My own plastic surgeon said if I was his wife, he would make me do chemotherapy.

I am going to trust in my body and all God has done to protect me. The cancer was nowhere else in my body so I needed to protect my body against what they thought was true for every person.

Am I telling you not to do chemotherapy? **Absolutely not. Again, I am not a doctor!** There are so many factors you need to consider before you make that decision.

My genetic history, my body type, my circumstances, and my beliefs are different than yours. I believe you need all the facts before making such an important decision like this. Remember that there are many ways you can prepare for the outcome. You have control over making decisions that affect your body during and after chemotherapy.

One question to look at in making your decision is if the cancer has spread to your lymph nodes. Another is your overall health and strength going into chemo. I want to caution you: if you choose not to do chemotherapy, you will encounter people who will tell you they know how to save your life with their products. If I had a quarter for every person in 25 years who told me how to cure cancer naturally, I would be rich.

You and your loved ones need to make a plan and stick to that plan. People will try to take you off that plan to move you onto their plan or their best friend's sister's plan. Do they really know better than you what to do for you?

So, use one plan, no drifting around and changing on a whim. Cancer is a big business in the medical world and the homeopathic world alike. If there were a sure-fire cure in either world, these wouldn't be billion-dollar businesses, right? Yes, cancer is a business. If a cure was found, millions of people would be out of work.

Research everything before you do it. My key, as I have said before, was that once I made my decision not to have chemo but to use alternative methods to stay cancer-free, I did not let anyone pull me off my chosen path.

I may have added to my plan when research showed me a better way to eat and so forth, but other than these adjustments, I stayed on my path.

I am using what I discovered worked for me to help you to know the whole truth so you have the power to choose the path right for you.

I view my body as a gift from God and I always treat it like a gift. This is not easy, but I have stayed alive and cancer-free and I'm still counting the days and so will you. It is worth every extra day I have had with my family and friends.

Always, always, ask questions of your doctors. If they get upset, find a new doctor! You and your caregivers are your team that's keeping you alive. Study before you ask the questions. Don't ask to do things they cannot do. Know what questions to ask which type of doctor. I was so completely in charge of my decisions, the only person I could blame if anything went wrong was me.

And remember. We are all human—including your doctors—and everyone makes mistakes. Your doctor does not have the time to study everything on the Internet but you do. What you find could save your life. God has the first and last to say.

CHAPTER 11

Radiation

WHEN I WAS FACED WITH THE TREATMENTS that regularly go with having the type of cancer I had, the protocol was to do radiation and chemotherapy after surgery to make sure there were no rogue cancer cells missed.

I remember the oncologist telling me all the reasons why I should do both and the risks of not doing them. Keep in mind, in 1994, the Internet was still new and hard to use. I was not a person who could really research something as easily as we do today. So, all I could do was ask questions; a lot of questions.

Now, 25 years later I can look things up in an instant, I've researched what is going on with radiation advancements. It's now possible to pinpoint and direct the radiation to the exact area they need to radiate without nearly as much tissue damage as there was decades ago. This also helps in not damaging the surrounding organs as much. The amount of time needed to radiate the area has gone down, too.

Even with these advancements, is there any guarantee radiation treatments will not affect the other organs like the heart and lungs? No. In fact, since I started asking questions, there are still only two main types of radiation therapy: external beam and internal.

External radiation is just what you imagine it to be: a large and noisy machine aims radiation at your cancer.

Internal radiation either has a solid or liquid source. Therapy with a solid source (brachytherapy) allows for a higher dose of radiation in a smaller area than might be possible with external radiation treatment. The solid material is sealed in a small holder called an implant. It is administered in a private room due to the volume of radiation released. Therapy with a liquid source (systemic) is given by swallowing, intravenously with an IV line, or by an injection. The liquid travels in the blood system to tissues throughout your body, seeking out and killing cancer cells. Even with these targeted techniques, the radiation can affect your organs. You may need weeks of treatment.

While there have been refinements to these two types—and maybe the better targeting achievement seems like a lot—I am not so sure we should be celebrating. Compared to the horrible damage radiation does to the body, this effort does not seem like enough. And radiation treatments do nothing to guarantee you will not cancer again.

What does radiation do when you are fighting cancer? Please notice I did not say, "What does radiation do *not to get cancer again*?"

Many women are under the false impression that if they do chemo and radiation, they will not get cancer again. As a result, when something weird happens to their body, they do not research their symptoms to find out what is going on. A common claim is that radiation therapy can cure cancer, prevent it from returning, or stop or slow its growth. But there is not enough emphasis put on *can*, and the word "cure" is not explained as a temporary thing.

Radiation affects your cells and makes them *less able* to turn into cancer cells, period. Putting it in simple terms, it helps to stop the spread of cancer to other cells. However, if you ask your doctor for a guarantee that the cancer will not spread, they will have to tell you: no.

They might explain the radiation makes cancerous cells *less likely* to spread, since the cells surrounding the cancer site have been exposed to radiation making them *unlikely* hosts for cancer. Here is the bad news: cancer, if not fully encapsulated, does not stay in place. It spreads. So, the radiation is only *likely* to work if a tumor stays intact and doesn't break open.

If it has broken open, who knows where the cancer has traveled to?

As always, I am not suggesting you should not have radiation therapy. I am not a doctor. But when you are deciding on what to do, please research everything about the treatments so you can make a clear decision.

Once you understand the type of radiation you're being told to have and the risks involved, also consider the side effects. Here is an excerpt from an article on the drugs.com website, "Side Effects of Radiation Therapy."[1]

> **What are some of the side effects of radiation therapy?**
>
> The side effects of radiation therapy depend on the area of the body that receives radiation. Early side effects happen shortly after you receive radiation therapy. Late side effects can happen months to years after you receive radiation therapy. Late side effects of radiation therapy may be permanent. Early and late side effects may include any of the following:
>
> » Fatigue or loss of energy;
>
> » Pain in the area of the body that is being treated;
>
> » Skin changes such as a sunburn or red skin;
>
> » Hair loss in the area receiving radiation;
>
> » Nausea, vomiting, diarrhea, or indigestion;
>
> » Sores, pain, or dryness in your mouth;
>
> » Difficulty urinating; and
>
> » Sexual dysfunction.

Your doctors will, of course, have ways to help you deal with the side effects of radiation treatments. Remember that radiation therapy may prevent the bone marrow from making new red blood cells, white blood cells, and

---

1 "Side Effects of Radiation Therapy," as posted on the drugs.com website (updated 2019). https://www.drugs.com/cg/side-effects-of-radiation-therapy.html.

platelets. This may cause low blood counts, which your doctors will diagnose through regular blood tests.

This is so important: if you are unable to make white blood cells—do not take this lightly—a common cold could put you in the hospital for a week. Stay away from people and places likely to be high-germ areas—not only for yourself, but imagine how they will feel if they are the reason you're in the hospital!

Another side effect of radiation I discovered still shocks me. I knew this information 25 years ago and when I talk to people today, nearly all say they did not have this information. Here we are, decades later and the information is still hard to come by.

Radiation damages the skin and makes it thinner. First of all, it will feel like the worst sunburn you have ever had times a thousand. The skin is the largest organ of the body and is very complicated in its makeup. Even at its thickest point, our skin is only a few millimeters thick. But it is still our heaviest and largest organ, making up about one seventh of our body weight. As you know, just looking at someone's skin can already tell you a lot about their health. Once the skin has been damaged, it's very hard to restore. (Think about what the aging process does to skin: we have been looking for a cure for that for years to no avail.)

The repair or prevention of damage during radiation has not changed in the 25 years since I first started studying it. Here's what they may not tell you: if you have radiation treatments, you will probably not be able to have breast reconstruction at all. Why? The skin will probably become so thin due to the radiation damage, it will probably tear in the process.

What does this mean to you? You will have to stuff your bra with padding if you have a hole in your chest from the lumpectomy. If you have a mastectomy later on, you may not be able to stretch the skin to add implants.

My intention is not to sway you at all. I just want to give you information. With knowledge comes power and clear choices. Will the damage from radiation matter in comparison to saving your life? No. But study the pros and cons anyway. Ask a lot of questions. Do not make a move until you have the answers that you need, not the answers they are feeding you.

We need to keep imagining a world without cancer or the need for these brutal treatments. There has to be a better way. We have to join together to make one voice and demand them to find it.

Daily Life

The information and reference materials contained in this book are intended solely for the general information of the reader. It is not to be used for treatment purposes, but rather for discussion with the reader's own medical professionals. The information presented here is not intended to diagnose health problems or to take the place of professional medical care. The information is neither intended to dictate what constitutes reasonable, appropriate, or best care for any given health issue, nor is it intended to be used as a substitute for the independent judgment of a physician. All content and opinions of the author are for general information purposes, only. If you have persistent health problems or if you have further questions, please consult your healthcare provider.

The recommendations put forth in this book do not establish a doctor-patient relationship. Individuals should consult a qualified healthcare provider for medical advice and answers to personal health questions.

The information presented is not to be considered medical advice and is not intended to replace consultation with a qualified medical professional. The primary responsibility of your disease management plan is with your treating physicians and you should only follow your treating physician's advice. DO NOT change or modify your disease management plan on your own without consulting your treating physicians.

Some research needs to be completed and it is our voice that will make them complete it. How can we make decisions without complete testing? It is our job together to make them finish it. Then, and only then, can we choose what to do with our own bodies.

"Tell us why we're dying!"®

CHAPTER 12

Sleep

WITHOUT PROPER SLEEP, your life expectancy will go down by 12 to 15 percent. If you are going to live until you are 80 years old, **that is 12 years off your life.** What is worth 12 years of your life not to sleep? A TV show? I used to think so. When we are done with surgery and repairs, we start to return to normal life. You need to fully understand how to protect yourself in all aspects. We tend to take everything back on as though nothing happened—to prove to ourselves that we can still do it all.

Never take sleep as something not important.

I do not mean taking a nap to catch-up or sleeping late on the weekends. This will not allow the body enough time to repair and fight disease. If you miss one night of eight hours of sleep your body did not repair itself that night. **You cannot make up sleep, think about that, naps do not repair the body.**

When I first drafted this book, a friend quizzed me on why there was not a chapter on sleep. It is so funny, because I did not even think about writing about sleep.

I can say with complete honesty I do not do this enough: sleep. In the back of my mind I knew that sleep was important to healing but I disregarded it as being all that necessary. My mother would always tell me to get more sleep. *Okay, okay, I know. I need to sleep more.*

So, what I don't know, I study to see what experts are saying. Once I realized how much the body is working during sleeping hours, I added sleep to my priorities, to help me have a healthier life and to take care of the body I have been assigned by God.

God made every aspect of the body to work like a machine. Every part works together to keep the body healthy. In the Bible, we are told to rest on the Sabbath; Sunday. When the Bible was written, mankind was under extreme physical pressure. The body was taxed all week long. He did not make the body to not have time to rejuvenate itself. When we push the body while going through cancer, it is being pushed way past its ability to cope on a daily basis. **Without sleep, the body will break down faster.**

What I found out by studying the effects of sleep shocked me. It's amazing how much the body does in one night. I always tell my friends what I find out before I commit it to writing, and use them as my barometer to see if the information should be included in the book. When I told them what I discovered, they were shocked at how much they did not understand sleep and how much sleep is needed to stay healthy.

For one night of good sleep, the amount of time needed is seven to nine hours of uninterrupted sleep.

This does not mean you can add hours together here and there to equal this total amount. You need straight-through sleep time. Your body needs to go into REM sleep at least three times during this stretch.

I exercise in some way every day. Then I come home and walk my dogs for 15 minutes and pray during that time, too. I take a hot shower before I go to sleep. My problem is the time I go to sleep: it's too late. I am now trying to go to bed at 9:30 p.m. in order to get to sleep by 10:00. I was getting up at 5:00 a.m. (the alarm goes off at 4:30) to walk my dogs before work. Before, I was going to bed at 10:00 p.m. getting to sleep by 10:30 or 11:00, and that was only giving me five-and-a-half hours of sleep every night. That's not enough; **I realized I was not healing my body for 6 years!**

Read on and get ready to be shocked. I never knew this!

1. <u>Your body starts to jerk to relieve the stress your body has been under.</u> The stronger the jerk, the more tired your body is and the more work it has to do to relax.

2. <u>Your body temperature goes down during sleep to help save calories.</u> The perfect temperature for sleep is 69 to70 degrees. Your body goes into hibernation-mode like a bear; that's crazy. This is why it is so hard to wake some people up from sleeping— they are in hibernation.

3. <u>Your brain rejuvenates and toxins are released.</u> Without sleep, your brain truly does have brain fog. It is harder the next day to retain information because the brain has not dumped the toxins from the day before.

4. <u>You dump useless information at night.</u> Without sleep, the information stays in the brain and adds to the toxins not released. With both of these things happening, you can become confused. You have brain fog, but did you know how intense it really is?

5. <u>You become paralyzed while in deep REM sleep.</u> This is crazy, too. The brain is so active cleaning, dumping, and organizing information it cannot tell the muscles what to do. Think of the people you have tried to get to move over when they are in deep sleep and they do not move at all.

6. <u>All the cells try to repair themselves.</u> Your body starts repairing itself; not just your brain, but also your overall body.

7. <u>The discs in your body have time to regain the fluids they lost during the day.</u> They absorb fluid from your body. Crazy.

8. <u>Your immune system is on high alert, searching out any infections in your body.</u> If it does not have time to repair them, you will get sick more frequently. Your body produces a

substance called "cytokines" during sleep, this is used by the body to fight bacteria and viruses.[1]

9. <u>During sleep, your body produces two hormones, leptin and ghrelin, which control feeling full and hungry.</u> Without enough sleep, your body reduces leptin (full) and raises ghrelin (hungry), thinking you need more fuel since you are awake. This can cause you to snack at night or wake up hungry.

10. <u>Sleep helps keep your heart healthy, blood sugar low, and blood pressure low.</u> Sleep lowers your blood pressure to the rate of a person who is in a coma. This allows your heart to rest and repair. Lack of sleep can lead to cardiovascular disease and heart attacks.

11. <u>Lack of sleep can create problems with your endocrine system.</u> It can affect hormone production. Your hormones help repair muscle and tissue, which are both needed for repair from surgery.

12. <u>The aging process is worse without enough sleep.</u> Lack of sleep gives you less collagen in your skin and can cause wrinkles. Maybe this will get you to sleep?!

Researching sleep for this chapter changed my life in such a big way. If I don't get enough sleep on a daily basis, I can feel depression starting. I can also have crazy thoughts from so many things not being dumped from my brain.

I also realized that you can gain weight from your system not understanding why you are awake so much of the time, thinking you need extra fuel to keep you active. This in turn stimulates you take to stay awake more, creating patterns that can take months to change.

When you sleep too much you can also hurt your body. When you are on pain medication, the drugs create havoc on your sleep patterns. They

---

1 "What are Cytokines?" by Dr. Ananya Mandal, MD, as posted on News Medical Life Sciences website (2019). https://www.news-medical.net/health/What-are-Cytokines.aspx.

truly affect your brain. When you sleep all the time, the body does not set a pattern of repair.

Some people think if they sleep more, they will heal faster, so they stay in bed sleeping all day and not moving around. If you sleep all the time or drug yourself to sleep, the adverse effects on the body are also extreme.

While too little sleep is harmful, too much sleep can cause:

» Cognitive impairment;

» Depression;

» Increased inflammation;

» Increased pain;

» Impaired fertility;

» Higher risk of obesity;

» Higher risk of diabetes;

» Higher risk of heart disease;

» Higher risk of stroke; and

» Higher all-cause mortality.

The perfect amount of sleep is around seven to eight hours each night to help your body heal and stay healthy. Again, this needs to be uninterrupted sleep when you are healing. If you have children, they will need to be taken care of by someone else so they don't disturb you. If you are older you need to think about water intake and sleep, yes, I mean getting up and going to the bathroom. Plan to drink your last liquid two hours before you go to bed. This will stop you from interrupting your repair to go to the bathroom.

And after you've been through surgery and treatments and are fully recovered, you still need sleep to keep your body healthy all the time. This has to be a priority in your life like water, like breathing. You cannot force your body to do what it is not programed to do. Give it a chance to protect you and to save you in the only way it knows how to: through sleep.

CHAPTER 13

Stress

YOU KNOW WHAT STRESS can do to your body. Yes, to your body. But let's examine exactly what you are doing when you don't eliminate stress.

Here is an excerpt from the article, "Is there a connection between chronic stress and cancer?"[1]

> "Stress can speed up the spread of cancer throughout the body, especially in ovarian, breast, and colorectal cancers. When the body becomes stressed, neurotransmitters like norepinephrine are released, which stimulate cancer cells. That stimulation can help cancer cells evade death, expand, and adjust to new environments in the body, allowing them to grow in new places."

I am going to use myself as an example to drive home this point. I started to get eye migraines at the last job I had. What is an eye migraine? It is when everywhere you look the effect is like looking through a kaleidoscope. I thought I was having a stroke. I could not see clearly. It seemed as though I was looking into a tunnel. I went to the hospital and they told me when these eye migraines happen, I need to lie down for 30 minutes with my eyes closed until I can see again.

These were horrible episodes. I couldn't drive until they were over because I couldn't see straight. I also worried about the long-term effects on my eyes. I was starting to develop an eye twitch. I was so scared, and then I realized it was being caused by stress from my job combined with family problems. My body was warning me to stop.

---

1 "Is there a connection between chronic stress and cancer?" by Molly Peck, as posted on City of Hope's website (2018). https://www.cityofhope.org/living-well/is-there-a-connection-between-chronic-stress-and-cancer.

Was I hearing the warnings? No, not right away. I like to say this is like a fire alarm going off and I cut the cord, pretending there is no fire. So, do I keep letting the fire burn until there is nothing left?

What four-alarm fire warning is your body giving you? I know you can find one if you try. Are you covering it up with drugs? Let's name some off: headaches, shoulder pain, neck pain, stomach pain when you eat, extremely tired, brain fog, anxiety, lack of sleep.

I can't tell you how many of my friends are stressed every day. And now they are on an antacid every day. They cannot eat without it. They get horrible acid reflux every time they eat without it. They can't remember when it started, it has been years, but they continue to take the drugs to stop it. They are under so much stress but they would rather take the drug. Is their body now dependent on the drug?

All drugs have side effects on the body. When you change the natural digestive system with a drug, what does it do to the ability to digest and absorb your food? Has there been a study to see if you are absorbing your food correctly? I quizzed one of them and I asked if they have had studies done to see the effect. "No, the doctor just keeps telling me to take it," they answered. *What?*

Your body is trying to warn you. Don't just drug the warning away. Listen and review what you are doing differently to set this warning bell off in the first place.

We know stress is bad and yet, we do little to avoid it. Our mind tells us we can take whatever life throws at us, no problem. We convince ourselves the stress is not affecting our body in any way. When your body is constantly in stress it sees this as a fight-or-flight situation.[2] It's as though you are constantly under attack and ready to defend yourself.

---

2 "How the Fight or Flight Response Works," by Kendra Cherry, medically reviewed by Steven Gans, MD, as posted on the Very Well Mind website (updated 2019). https://www.verywellmind.com/what-is-the-fight-or-flight-response-2795194.

How does that affect your body? What does this mean to a person with cancer? It means everything to a person with cancer. You are fueling the cancer—making it stronger in a way. First of all, when you are stressed-out, your body does not truly rest and heal. That is really dangerous.

But you are asking, "How can I get out of stress when I am going through cancer? Cancer and stress go together, right?"

Just know that getting out of stress daily is part of your treatment. It has to be or you will not heal. Doing anything that brings you joy and makes you relax will help with the stress. Here are some things to try to do whenever you can.

1. Talking with God. Even if I am mad at Him, I still talk to Him. It may not always be a pleasant conversation, but He can take it. He knows all I am going through. He is fine with me talking, praying, crying… whatever is needed to work it out.

2. Exercise. I like to sweat out all the stress and the toxins caught in my tissues from stress. When I was first recovering, I walked my dog to workout, even when I could only make two blocks before I had to sit down. She didn't care. It was just time for me to get away from the situation I was in.

3. Breathing. This is something I have been working on myself right now. I catch myself holding my breath all the time. I don't know when it started but I think it was when I was expecting something terrible to happen. Or is it because my implants are tight on my chest so I only take short breaths all the time? Maybe when it hurts to take a big breath, I choose to take small ones instead. It is not that I can't take a large cleansing breath, I just have to think about it, stop, relax and do it. But if you train yourself to do it all the time it is amazing. I set my watch to remind me every hour and the stress clears away right when I am done, it is so easy to do now.

4. <u>Mindless TV</u>. For me (don't laugh) is "Animal Planet." The point is to let your mind go into a neutral zone or "alpha state" where you aren't overthinking everything. It's time to stop thinking and let yourself be entertained. Turn the mind off and tune-out the world. Half the time, I don't remember what I am watching. Obviously, too much TV is not a great idea, but an hour or two is fine when you are recovering and need to escape in comfort. Some people like the TV on in the background as white-noise or just to keep from feeling alone.

5. <u>Massage.</u> If massage is your relaxing point, it is so important to know that the person giving you the massage has worked with cancer patients before. Do not take their word for it! Ask for references and for any credentials from classes they have taken. When you start this, I highly suggest you drink a half gallon or more of water afterwards or you may feel sick (like the flu) from the chemicals being released. I remember a massage therapist who said she had worked with lymphedema patients and I did not research her, which was a big mistake… my arm took forever to heal.

6. <u>Stretching</u>. I have talked about sitting at a desk with our organs compressed all day and how it is affecting our lives. What if you took your lunch and stretched instead of sitting at your desk? What a gift to give your family if you stretched together a couple of times a week. What if you made it a priority to stretch three times a week? By stretching you create lengthening of your muscles and, if done with the mind relaxed, it can allow the muscles to relax, too.

7. <u>Heat.</u> Heat can be soothing, but use caution. Hot baths, showers, Jacuzzis, heating pads, and hot yoga should be avoided or monitored closely if you have had lymph dissection. Excess heat can cause lymphedema because the lymph nodes were removed and the fluids in your arms could have a reaction. I have lymphedema and you do not want it. I've tried to stay

positive and accept it, but it has severely changed my life. Please read the article, "Lymphedema risk after breast cancer treatment," and make an informed decision.[3] I am telling you right now, if I had this information before, I would never have put myself at risk.

How do you know when your body is relaxed? When your body has an "Ahhh" reaction. I know that sounds so weird. I know you have experienced this moment. It's when all your muscles just let go and your body says, "Ahhh, thank you!"

You need to fight for that feeling for at least 30 minutes, twice a day. And try to reach this moment more often if you can. This is when you honor your body for helping you get through everything you put it through. Remember, sleeping does not count. Your body has plenty of restoration work to do while you are sleeping. These "Ahhh" moments are conscious acts, where you actively train your body into relaxation.

It is almost impossible to relax when your body is constantly being stimulated with caffeine or sugar. Please, please know that learning how to relax out of stress will help save your life.

This article, "100 Ways to Relax, Unwind and Loosen Up," is a great starting place.[4] Why not try them all and mark them off as you go?

Many of you will be returning to work of some kind during or after your treatments. If you are working during your treatments, I am so sorry if that is what you are going through right now. You'll need to make stress-reducing time a priority. Remember to ask for help.

---

3 "Lymphedema risk after breast cancer treatment," by Patricia Nicholson, as posted on the Women's Health Matters website (2015). https://www.womenshealthmatters.ca/feature-articles/feature-articles/Lymphedema-risk-after-breast-cancer-treatment.

4 "100 Ways to Relax, Unwind and Loosen Up," as posted on The Daily Mind website (2008). https://thedailymind.com/stress/100-ways-to-relax-unwind-and-loosen-up.

In my case, I was expecting I was always going to be stressed. And I had to keep asking myself: at the cost of what? Me? Nothing tangible was worth getting sick over again. My expenses had to come down to a comfortable level to reduce financial stress. It did not matter what I had to sell to get there.

Sometimes, deciding to let go of stress comes when other people are trying to push us back into a situation that we know is not healthy for us in the first place. Consider your job. If you died because you kept working for your company, would the company go on? How long would they mourn your loss before they went back to business-as-usual? I quit and found out it took only two weeks for them to move on after 13 years with me. Once they adjusted to being without me, they did not look back once.

When it comes to your family, how long will you be the "everything-to-everyone" before you stop and let them be almost everything to themselves? I have personally witnessed many people getting sick strictly from the stress on their body that they might have avoided. Does this mean you sit around, doing nothing because you are scared of getting sick again? Of course not.

You have to be smarter about your life and know what your new body can handle. Yes, your new body. It will not be the same. It will have new limitations and to realize that means you cannot push it past the point it can now handle. It will warn you again as you go along. But this time, will you listen?

I personally have a hard time practicing this advice myself. Luckily, my body gives me signs I cannot ignore: my hands swell from the lymphedema and they simply will not work. Do I push myself? Yes. Do I pay for it all the time? Yes. But I realize when I am doing it and here is the key: I stop.

I thought I was "showing" cancer, "You did not get me, see? I can push myself and keep going." I told myself to push through the pain, push through the fear, push through the exhaustion. *Really, Karen.*

As if cancer cared. Yes, at first it made sense. In order to get through the ordeal, I had to think this way. But then I looked closely at my life after cancer and I wanted to set it up to win.

Now, I stop and think, *Oh well, the house is not vacuumed. The dust is pretty thick now, isn't it?* But I am not too tired to walk the dog a mile around the block, because that means healing. I always pick the dog and joy before something that might add to my stress.

Please listen to your body because if you don't, most of the time it will not keep warning you. One moment when it's had enough, it will put you down. If your support network is not there to help you, then pace yourself. It is easy for me to say quit your job, downsize your life, sell things, pay off things. But will those things matter if you are gone? I do not know one loving family member who said, "I am glad I have all these things instead of my loved one."

The last thing I will say is to consider the guilt you might leave behind. If they are without you only because you kept going too hard at yourself, this will cause them stress for a lifetime. And we know what stress will do to them.

Once I had a cancer diagnosis, I started to think about what I was leaving behind. What mess was I going to make of the people I was leaving behind? As I say over and over: cancer is a gift. I know that sounds crazy but think of it as a gift of the time you have to help others cope with what is happening to you. It is a time to be selfish and selfless at the same time.

You have to be selfish because you *have* to think of yourself to stay alive.

» Ask for help; don't be helpless;

» Know your limitations don't be limitless; and

» Listen to your body, don't tell your body what to do.

Write down what is stressing you out daily and handle what you can. Give the rest away to those who can handle it for you. And if you can't hand it off, take it out of your life.

Think back to when women tended to stay home instead of working. If cancer hit them, there were less stress factors. They had more time in the day to do the things demanded of "homemakers." Without a job to go to, there was a six-hour reprieve from the husband and children. What was it like while they were at school and he was gone?

Or was our world different when generations of people lived together and they all helped in the family, with nothing left to just one person? In some cultures, multi-generations live together. I don't know if I could have done that when my parents were alive. The house would have had to be really big.

If you downsized and sold belongs to pay off things, could you afford a housekeeper? Wouldn't that give you much more time of your own and weekends off from work to relax?

One **big thing** I was missing were regular vacations, where I was not in charge of anything and I didn't have to be a mom every second. Not a mom in a different location, just relaxing. I had one of those while I was healing; one vacation. It was amazing, I hired a nanny and she was in another room with my daughter. I went only 2 hours from my home to Palm Springs, but it was so relaxing. I don't have to worry about anything, just relax. Go local so the cost is low and spend the money on the nanny, or an older child of a friend, not a family member because they will still think you are in charge. I set the rules before we left, I was not to be asked anything about my daughter's care. I had all the plans as to where we went to dinner decided, amazing.

Just think about this is a perfect weekend: two nights in a hotel where no one can find you. You have time to relax, sleep, breathe your own oxygen, and not have it sucked out of you. Wouldn't this be great to do every month or two? Or a girlfriend weekend retreat is also perfect. We honor ourselves and rest, don't rush around, just relax and commit to doing. I'm not talking about a night out with the girls, but two days of absolutely no stress. **Set the expatiations ahead of time, no stress.**

Is going off by yourself worth it to your family? Yes. When you go on a family vacation, it is not a vacation if you are in charge of anything. If you have small children, go with multiple families and everyone can pitch in for a nanny to go with you. This is a real vacation.

Please. I know what stress can do. Take the time to keep yourself alive. There is nothing more stressful to those who love you than not knowing how to help you. You are doing nothing to help them by not telling them how to help you.

Your mind needs clear time to begin to think past the illness and onto envisioning the future. To get this space, this means having meetings to talk with each person about what their roles will be to help you heal.

When my sister was dying, I felt so helpless. I was a cancer survivor, so I should know exactly what to do, right? Wrong. I had no idea what to do to help her. If I suggested what she should do, she wanted to do something else. The stress of thinking I wasn't helping her enough has haunted me—and still haunts me to this day. I had to go through years of therapy to get over this. So, please know that the more of your stress you can give away, the less stress they will feel.

Don't misunderstand me. I am not saying to stop working hard to get your life back to normal. I'm only saying to give others assignments to help you in your quest. If it is your time to meet the Lord, this is so important. You want to leave healthy people behind.

Yes, it is your job to direct them. If you are thinking right now, "No, I can't find a way to ask anyone," then tape a message on your phone with a list of what you need help with and text it to everyone. Ask them to write out the list and present it to you in the meeting.

Meetings are so important. Professional people live by meetings. Why? Because meetings make them feel at ease because they know exactly what to do for the project, you are the project. There is power in bringing many people together to work on a task. They are trying to keep their emotions in check right now to be strong for you and all around them. You cannot expect them to go into your emotions and know what you need. Women are less stressed when taken out of their emotions and placed in a written-out world so they can focus on a given task.

Here is where you sit in silence and make a list of things that if they are not done, it would cause you stress. I always thought they should know because we have had meetings about this before, yet they did not pick up on it.

Now take the list and assign tasks to people, but be aware they are not going to do it like you would do it, ever! You have to let that go to stay alive. It will not matter if clothes are folded differently or things are not cleaned to perfection if they are trying.

Here is the biggest part: stop and thank them. Sometimes it's hard when you are under stress and it's a pain to thank people, but never stop thanking them.

Please remember to always include the children and the point is to be creative. This will help your children and loved ones to not be stressed about their role in your healing, but to feel now—and forever—that they truly helped you to live.

Stress is a killer. They will carry the stress of your illness with them if they feel they did not do enough to help you!

Daily Life

CHAPTER 14

Faith

IT IS IMPORTANT TO ME to include a chapter about God in my book. Many people told me to not make my book about God, because fewer people would buy it. It's so funny, because I did not write this book for the money, I wrote it to be a voice for women and people who have lost women in their lives. If I did not write about God, then I am not being true to myself or this book.

There has never been a day when I don't talk to God, my true Father. Talk is such a light word, because I don't just talk to Him, I have yelled at Him, gotten so mad I wanted to leave Him behind asking, *how could He do this to me?* He took all the women who loved me away from me and left me alone.

My sister, my mother, my best friend, my other friend, and then another friend, and another friend, and the list keeps growing to this day. I just had an amazing work associate die. I watched them die of cancer as I sat powerless to do anything. I thought I was the one who has all the answers, yet I sat there as they all made decisions for themselves and what was best for them.

I concluded it is their life and their journey with their God. The most powerful thing I could do for each one of them was pray. In a perfect world, as God planned this to be, there would have been no disease. But in what we have done to His world in changing His food, His atmosphere, His water… no wonder we are stress-filled. This world is not what He designed our bodies to endure.

I know we all have different aspects of beliefs and what gives us strength. I could not have done this without my belief in God and Jesus Christ. Many people tell me I am the strongest person they have ever met. How could I make so many decisions never made before? I was so scared so many times that I would die when my daughter was so young.

I found out when I am out of my element with nowhere to turn, I look to my true Father, God. I found out that relying on a human will most likely let me down because we are just that: humans with faults, limitations, and our own past experiences which lead us, so how can they know how to lead you when they have no experience in what you are going through.

But God is limitless.

I spent so many days talking to Him and leaning on Him, yelling at Him, crying to Him, asking Him what to do. Then, I just had to let go and trust in Him. I know that sounds crazy when it is your life and you are uncertain if you will live or die. I have learned through everything I've been through, there is only so much I can do as a human. Then, I'm out of options. There is nowhere else to turn, but up to the Lord.

I have been a part of so many miracles where the Lord personally intervened in situations that I have not included in the book but where the only explanation of what saved me was God.

I have stopped breathing and turned blue twice and I died. During those minutes, I have been past the Earth and gone toward the Lord, seeing the beauty He has and my best friend waiting for me. Only through the power of prayer—as a loved one shook me and prayed over me telling me not to go, to come back, Kasondra needs you, don't stay, she needs her mother—did I return to Earth.

Only hearing my daughter crying as she talked to the 911 operator, "She is not breathing! She is dying, help us," did I take a breath and come back.

I was so LOVED and in such a beautiful place. I will never forget the place the Lord has waiting for me. He sent me back to finish my task, this book.

The second time the Lord saved me I had fallen asleep in front of a space heater and I heard God tell me, "Fire! Get up. FIRE! Get up, now!" I woke up looking for a fire but there was no fire, only pain in my chest. I scratched under my shirt and skin was on my hand. I lifted my shirt to see the huge burn on my chest. I called my daughter back from a party and she took me to the hospital. I was not in pain. How could that be?

My daughter and her friend were in shock, not knowing what to do. I walked into the hospital and they asked me what was wrong. I lifted my shirt and they rushed me to a room. Packing the third-degree burn to stop it from burning more, I keep thinking, *why aren't you in pain? I don't know! Why didn't your polyester sweatshirt melt to your body? I don't know?*

I realized I was being asked these questions by the hospital staff. "How could you just walk in here? Do you know your name?"

Yes, the questions went on and on.

"You have to go to a burn center. This is too deep for us and too wide to close." I heard them giving instructions. "Burn center, we are going to have to skin graft this patient, it is too wide to close."

At the burn center, they explained what would happen. "We will take skin from your butt and attach it to the wound. This will take three surgeries."

I protested. "Can't you give me a chance to heal it on my own?"

"What?" they said, thinking I was crazy. "It is your body; we do not recommend you do that. It will not close if it's too wide, there is no skin left there."

I insisted. They gave me some cream to pack it with. In time, the wound started to close and get smaller. I went to my plastic surgeon to see what they could do to help me.

"If you can get it to close this much, I can pull it together and stitch it together" they told me. "It is so wide; I don't think you can do it on your own."

"Give me time," I said.

"If it gets red, or you see lots of fluid or anything strange, come back right away. I'll give you a month more."

I prayed, packed it, took the healing herbs I used for cancer and the burn opening got smaller. I kept praying over the wound telling God what needed to happen to be healed. I put myself on prayer boards and told everyone at my church what I needed to happen. When I returned, they told me they could, in fact, pull the skin together and they sewed it up in one surgery.

The Lord saved me again. I know He is there. Through all of these situations, I have never stopped praying to Him, learning about Him studying Him and what His plan is for me.

I actually went a little overboard when my sister passed away. I was trying to find out why I was saved and she was taken. But then I thought, *was she taken or was I left behind?*

I think you could also wonder about the same thing as to why your loved ones were taken away from you. So many situations you do not understand lead you to think He must be punishing you or your family.

The one thing I do know is God comes from Love. He has no ability to have negative thoughts toward you or your family. He is not capable of a negative thought. So, when you have a negative thought know it is not from Him. I have had so many negative thoughts about writing this book. Then I realize He did not put them there. Why would He? I put them there, others put them there. What force would not want me to succeed?

I know when I come from a punishing why-is-He-doing-this thought, that thought leaves me with a negative thought of my loved ones who have passed away, instead of thanking Him for the time I was able to spend with that loved one saying goodbye.

"Why doesn't God help my family with a miracle?" you ask. I truly don't have an answer for that. When seeking to find that answer, I would only have human responses, which have so many negative connotations, so, I just choose to think: *I am left behind. I am here to lead all of us to ask questions.*

I am looking at what we are doing to His body, knowing His body was not designed to handle what we are doing to it. His body was designed to live in a certain manner, honoring His creation and design. And, like anything, when you push the design past what it can handle, it will eventually break down.

My sister is now where my goal is to be: next to her for eternity. This time on Earth is only a blink of an eye compared to the life I will have when I am next to her.

Will I ever forget her, or all my family and friends who have passed away? No. I will carry them with me wherever I go. I try to live my life as a representation of how they would have lived their lives if they stayed; taking a piece of them and pushing myself to be more like them. They all taught me so much and have made me a better person. I am trying to take parts of them with me in how I treat others and how I *live* my life.

I am so sorry I don't have all the answers for this question. I wish I did. I know what it feels like to need those answers, to try to make sense of it all, but my conclusion is: I am not God. But I know in my heart that He would never hurt me, or forsake me, or leave me behind to suffer. I know He is with me all the time, helping me to process and live, never forgetting, but always moving forward.

Just please know God did not purposely create cancer. Cancer is a genetic mutation of two people coming together. It is a known fact that cancer has been around since Roman times, yet we still do not know why we get cancer.

If it has been around that long, how has it not taken over and killed us all by now?

Could it be because in the past, cancer was only genetic? Now, due to harm and advancements in our food and the environment, cases of non-genetic cancer have increased and taken over. We, as His people, are creating 75 percent of the cancer killing his people. Yes, we accept this on faith and blame Him without finding out what we are doing to kill ourselves.

Please know, God is not killing your loved ones. Please put the blame where it truly belongs. The more we blame the Lord for the deaths of our loved ones, the darker the world becomes. My prayer is this:

Dear Lord, we know you have embraced our loved ones and brought them home to you where you will unite us with them again. We will fight to keep your women where they belong, here, to show the world your LOVE.

CHAPTER 15

Water: Your Life Source

THIS BOOK IS A MUST READ: *Your Body's Many Cries for Water* by F. Batmanghelidj, M.D.[1]

People ask me all the time how I stayed cancer-free for so many years. I truly believe that this chapter will tell you the main reasons why I am. I see water as a lifeline for my body.

» Without water my body is dying every day. It's that easy.

» The only thing that cleanses your body from toxins is water.

» Up to 60 percent of the human adult body is water.

It's so funny because people say to me all the time, "I drink ice tea," or "I drink coffee," or "I drink Gatorade." Whatever they are drinking it isn't the same as water but they think since these drinks are made with water, that's all they need to do. What you're really asking your body to do is to use your liver and your kidneys to separate out the crap in those drinks so it can find water.

Others tell me they drink a glass of water with dinner or a bottle of water every day. Even though we've all been told most of our lives that we need to drink eight glasses of water a day, most don't do that, but assume they're doing that by drinking anything liquid.

So, I say to them: write down every time you drink a pure glass of water. This is so your body can use the water at once and without having to engage any other systems to process the drink. It shocks them when they really see

---

1 *Your Body's Many Cries for Water* by F. Batmanghelidj, M.D., available on Amazon. com (2012). https://www.amazon.com/Your-Bodys-Many-Cries-Water/dp/1452656975.

how much pure water they are actually drinking. I challenge you to start right now to write down how much water you drink. This truly going to save your life.

I'm not a doctor, but I know enough to know how to take care of my body. Water is there to clean our cells. Why is keeping our cells cleansed so important? When your body is toxic it creates disease. The more toxic your body is, the better breeding ground you've created for cancer or any other disease.

Your body warns you all the time that it needs water. As you become toxic you can get headaches, start to feel lifeless, get sleepy, get out of breath, your joints hurt, you get emotional… the list goes on and on.

Water feeds your skin and keeps it supple and beautiful. You will not get as many wrinkles if you are hydrated. Remember that skin is the body's largest organ.

Your colon controls so many of your organs and affects so many avenues of your life. Without enough water, food binds up and causes so many internal problems. The waste matter in your colon is an easy way for the body to get water. If you are dehydrated, the body will take water from it, leaving the stools hard and dry in your colon. That leads to waste getting stuck in the colon, and you know that constipation is painful, leaves you feeling bloated, and a backed-up system can lead to disease.

When you actually start to feel thirsty, you are already dehydrated. This shocked me when I first heard it. When you get thirsty, your body actually thinks it's in a desert. It's already starting to break down. Can you believe that?

Your body can last up to five days—depending on your girth—without food or longer. But your body can last only 24 hours before it starts to break down from lack of water. That is how important water is to your body.

Now, let's talk about the internal organs. Lack of water can seriously affect the cleansing organs: your kidneys and liver. These are the two organs we can't live without, yet we take them for granted every single day. We put so much crap into our body and we don't think twice about how these amazing organs are going to be able to deal with what we give them. We don't think about how drinking or eating certain things can negatively affect the organs that we cannot replace. Then we get all mad when these organs can no longer work for us. We then try to get a kidney or liver from someone else. That's horrible if we've deliberately done the damage to our own organs ourselves!

The Hospital

Have you ever wondered why the hospital makes you pee in a measuring hat? That's that plastic thing in the toilet used to measure the output of urine. Why are they measuring how much fluid you are extracting from your system? To find out how much fluid they need to put back into you and to see how your kidneys are doing with the drugs you're taking. Why would hospitals measure this if it was not important? They have to watch what your organs are doing.

Do you watch—or even take notice—how much you urinate compared to the amount of pure water you are drinking? There is no secret button your body can push as you start to get too low on water.

Here's a measuring trick I tell people: get a mental picture of your internal body swimming in fluids up to a high-water mark at the top of the head. In your mind, make the liquid red for blood because your blood needs water to move the blood around in your body. When you pee, imagine the liquid levels dropping from the high mark down to your eyebrows, then your mouth, and so on. Now, what are you doing to make the level go back up to the top of your head?

You also need water to mix with the enzymes to digest your food and push your food through your colon. Constipation is a warning sign that your body does not have enough water to digest your food correctly.

The blood in your body *has* to have water to move it throughout your body. Otherwise—in simple terms—you have thick blood. People have had heart attacks due to being dehydrated. If the blood is too thick, it can't move efficiently through the valves of the heart.

I hope you are getting the picture of how important water is to your system and the extra pressure that not drinking water can put on your system hourly and daily.

Medications

There are so many medications that deplete water from our bodies. If you have to take them, this is when you must drink more water. It's so important to know the side effects of any drugs you are taking, and many people don't understand that lots of pain medications are actually diuretics. Diuretics cause your body to purge water or use water very rapidly. I've heard many people taking pain medications complain of bad headaches, feeling lifeless, and wondering what was going on with them. I tell them, "You're dehydrated from your pain medication so you need to drink a lot of water." If they're in the hospital, I see if I can get them a bag of saline solution right away. And, lo and behold, they feel much better in a very short amount of time.

Alcohol

When you drink alcohol and you have cancer, you are causing a lot of extra pressure in your kidneys and liver, not to mention what alcohol does to the rest of your body. Do I drink alcohol? No. If you are going to drink "adult beverages" you really need to study what alcohol does to your system. Doctors will tell you not to drink alcohol if you're dealing with cancer. But if you're going to anyway, find ways to counter the effects by helping your system cleanse itself, all day every day. Please read the chapter on alcohol and cannabis and decide if these substances are right for you.

Chemotherapy

If you are doing chemotherapy, you need to drink water all the time. I remember when my mother was going through chemotherapy. There was no mention of water whatsoever. No one explained to her that chemotherapy stays in your system without water to flush it out. The liver and kidneys will work overtime trying to cleanse the chemicals out of your body; this puts an incredible strain on them. Many people have died, not from cancer, but from liver or kidney failure after chemotherapy. Can you imagine? They survived the cancer and died of organ failure. That is how important water is to your system.

After I had been diagnosed, people started asking me questions. One of the first things I would say to them if they are doing chemotherapy is to ask for an IV bag with saline or balancing fluids as you are taking the treatment, and that was more than 20 years ago.

With my mother, they also didn't tell her that water was going to make her nauseous during chemo. Who wants to do something that will make you want to throw up? They told her to add a little cranberry juice to make the water go down easier.

This is way before I started studying cancer and chemotherapy. There is a separate chapter on chemotherapy but just think about chemotherapy for a while. Think about what we've talked about at the beginning of this chapter about your cleansing your liver and your kidneys. You are putting a drug that can kill cancer into your body and if it's in a liquid form, it's being pumped into your bloodstream through your veins. It's going to circulate through your liver and your kidneys, leaving deposits in these organs along the way. And just like chemo's ability to kill cancer, it has the ability to damage your liver and kidneys.

That's why nowadays they give you saline solution with chemotherapy treatments to try to flush the chemotherapy from your liver and kidneys. They give you one bag of saline solution but is that enough? Is there a study on how much saline solution you actually need to help your liver and your kidneys? Maybe it's two bags or even three bags of saline solution or you may choose a balancing fluid instead to avoid the salt.

Here's what I do know: patients who have told me they are doing chemotherapy tell me they don't feel good. My answer is to tell your doctor that you want extra fluids right now. One of the most important things to help get toxins out of your body is water, period. I tell people all the time that if I had done chemotherapy, even if it cost $500 a month, personally I would pay to have balancing fluids with electrolytes given to me once a week to help flush the chemo drugs through my system. And not just during chemo treatments but to have extra fluids given to my system as much as I could afford to pay for. Doctors have told me it is not necessary to do this. My answer is: if you have test results or statistics showing this does not help the body cope with chemotherapy, let me see them.

If you asked years ago if they gave saline solution with chemotherapy treatments, they would have to say no. Then why do you give it now? Do you know exactly how much to give per person? Again, they will say no. I say, *give me the extra bags*. You're thinking how many bags is extra bags? I wish we all knew the answer to the exact amount to save your organs. If I were to do chemotherapy I would want to flush it from my system without hurting my body. I'm not a doctor, but I personally would start with two bags and see how I feel. I would check with the doctor the exact amount of time chemotherapy is expelled from the body and ask for the extra bags after that to help it. Doctor, is it one day? Two days? Then ask for the extra water after that.

The next chapter is about shower filters, make sure to read it next, it could save your life.

CHAPTER 16

Chlorine in the Water—Filters

FOR YEARS, I have been trying to see what we could all be doing the same across the country—no matter where we lived—that is causing breast cancer. *There has to be a common link.*

As I started writing this book, I found that there are so many things linking us together that could be the cause of cancer it was incredibly concerning. They just kept mounting up as I studied.

I've now seen studies researching the chlorine in our water and I've added this as another potential link to the high rates of non-genetic breast cancer. We need to know if this is one of the things causing breast cancer in order to save the lives of our daughters, our loved ones, and ourselves.

Breast cancer, which now affects one in every eight women in North America, has recently been linked to the accumulation of chlorine compounds in the breast tissue. According to this 2010 article in Scientific American,

> "A recent study conducted in Hartford, Connecticut found that women with breast cancer have 50–60 percent higher levels of organochlorines (chlorine by-products) in their breast tissue than cancer-free women."[1]

For the last 25 years, I have been telling people I think one of the links to cancer is the chlorine added to our water. It makes sense: so many of us bathe and take showers in public water treated with chlorine there has to be a link.

---

1 "Tapped Out? Are Chlorine's Beneficial Effects in Drinking Water Offset By Its Links to Cancer?" as posted on the Scientific American website (January 2010). https://www.scientificamerican.com/article/earth-talks-tapped-out.

Let's take your shower water for another example. You are standing under a lovely hot shower because it feels so good after a really long day at work. In the steam coming up all around you, you realize you are standing in a chlorine cloud. Your skin is one of the biggest organs of your body and when it's hot, it absorbs everything that touches it.

Because we all know your nipples firm up when they get cold, but what happens to them when you are in a hot shower? All the pores of your body open up. We are now finding out steam cloud of chlorine could be one of the reasons we are getting cancer! I thought this for years, it only made sense.

Living in San Diego, I would often smell a strong chlorine scent when I took a shower at certain times of the year. I would step in and the water smelled like a swimming pool. I called the water company and they told me it was because they clean the pipes at certain times a year by adding more chlorine. *What?*

As I took my shower I would think, *what is this steam doing to my lungs? Didn't they use chlorine gas in war a long time ago?* Then my skin started to itch, dry up, and crack. The chemical was attacking my body all the way around.

From that day forward, I started to research water filters. Since this was decades ago, there weren't many companies to choose from. Luckily for me, one of the chiropractors I worked with, Dr. Howard Cohn, was a fanatic about looking at the overall body.

Dr. Cohn and I looked into the different kinds of filters that were on the market. As I studied water with him—yes, we studied water—I found out about all the additives that are allowed in the water coming out of our taps. If you want to understand this more yourself, look up your water district online as there are laws requiring them to give you this information.

You can also test the water yourself. There are affordable at home tap-water kits that will test for lead, bacteria, pesticides, chlorine, nitrates, and more. Some cities in the United States have been found to have traces of pharmaceutical and antidepressant remnants in their tap water. It's not worth the risk to ignore this, and you should find out if there are harmful elements in your water. Remember, knowledge is power and not fear. First, know what you're dealing with and then work to change it.

Dr. Cohn started carrying water filters in his clinic and since then, I have used a water filter in my shower wherever I have lived.

When I had my daughter, I knew I wanted to protect her. I would use the shower filter to fill up the tub for her before I gave her a bath. She has never had non-filtered shower water; even in college I sent her a shower filter. Her skin is so used to filtered water, when she washes her hands at work her hands turn really red.

I know you are thinking: *Karen, with so many filters on the market it is so hard to know which filter to use to protect my family.*

I feel the same way. That is how it's gone with so many things to sort through while I was writing this book. But in this category, I did not have to do much research. Thankfully, there are programs in place to do it for all of us.

It starts with water filter certifications.

Here are two independent organizations that test and certify water filter systems and components. Water filter systems that carry these logos are proven to deliver on what they say their filters are able to do.

Water Quality Association (WQA). This has a gold seal with the words, "tested and certified under industry standards" and is easy to see so you know you are getting exactly what you want. You can find more information on their website at wqa.org.

NSF International. Products with the NSF blue-and-white seal with the words, "independently certified" have been rigorously tested to comply with all standard requirements. You can find more information on their website at nsf.org.

The website, Water Filter Answers, explains these certifications, and lists several different filters.[2] The one I use I really like. It is easy to replace the cartridge on the shower filter and you can take it with you if you move homes. And the best part is that it has the gold WQA seal so I do not have to worry.

I have personally never used a whole house system; I only filter the water at the source coming into the shower or sink. I was married to a plumber for years but our house was old and the pipes were old so I can imagine what was in them. I decided to put the filters on the end user area. If I was going to use a whole house system with older pipes, I would still put a filter directly on the shower and the sink as an extra measure.

Next to consider are the filtration methods. The most marketed shower filters use carbon to take the chlorine out of the water. There are different kinds of carbon filters.

A solid carbon filter that the chlorine passes through. The problem with this kind of filter is that once the water makes a river through it, the filtration is probably less effective.

A bead-type carbon filter. With this type of carbon filter, the chlorine has no chance to make a river so it's thought to be more effective.

The shower filter I currently use is Rainshower's "Restore" filter which has a changeable filter cartridge.[3] From their product information, here is the description of how that filter works:

---

2 WQA & NSF Certified Water Filters information as posted on the Water Filter Answers website. https://waterfilteranswers.com/water-filter-certifications.

3 The Rainshower Restore filter can be found online at https://www.rainshower.com/new/restore.html.

Stage 1: Polyester Pre-Filter. Traps particulate matter that would otherwise mix with the medias and reduce their effectiveness.

Stage 2: KDF-55. This stage destabilizes the free chlorine and turns it into a harmless chloride.

Stage 3: Crystal Quartz. This stage "energizes" the water by reducing the water's surface tension, giving the water a "lighter" feel.

If I decide to change from this water filter, I will update you on my website or through my social media accounts.

When I cook, I use bottled drinking water every time. Please read about what drinking water I use in the chapter on bottled water. To rinse my vegetables, I use a PUR water filter that hooks onto the facet. Who wants to pay for organic vegetables only to rinse them with chlorinated water?

What about apartment buildings, and homes new and old? If the nation knew the importance of filtered water, and the overall benefits that contribute to our body's health both inside and out, would apartment amenities include water filters? Would new homes be built with whole house water systems? Would pipes and water quality be involved in home buying inspections?

We need to press the government to complete testing to see if chlorine is a significant cancer-generating problem. If it is contributing, even a small percentage, to the cause of cancer as a worldwide epidemic, we need to find a solution and notify the public that extra filtration is an effective prevention measure.

CHAPTER 17

Bottled Water

Personally, I am a water freak. Or maybe I should call myself a water snob. I have actually studied water companies; I know, kind of strange, right? If you think of 10 people in your life, I'll bet not even one of them have studied up on water companies.

Unbelievably, not all bottled water companies are alike and even water filters are not alike. As with everything else you put into your body, you have to know how your bottled water is being filtered. Otherwise, you might as well drink water straight from the tap. Which, in San Diego County, is like a death wish. There are chemicals, metals, particles, pharmaceutical drugs, and other properties in our tap water. I won't even give it to my dogs and I feel bad about giving it to my plants.

The water company that I found to be the best in my area is Palomar Mountain Premium Spring Water.[1] (No, they don't give me any kind of kickback for saying that.) This water had the best test results I could find. The quality depends on how many different filtration systems they use before they bottle the water. It also matters what type of bottles they put their water in and how long they let the water sit in their warehouse. They should rotate their stock and keep track of bottling dates.

The one thing you never want to do is to let the bottled water sweat inside the bottle because that is where bacteria grows. In plastic bottles the plastic leaches into the water. Palomar is really into the carbon filtering of their water. Most of the filters that you can attach to your tap have one

---

1 Palomar Mountain Premium Spring Water is delivered to homes and offices throughout San Diego County. Visit their website at https://palomarwater.com.

filtration system and that is carbon. Carbon erases, for lack of a better word, the chlorine in the water. But that is not the only chemical or property you have to worry about. So, the more filtration systems you can put your water through, the better. Some water systems use clay filters that trap the other particles that are in your water.

It's so funny, I had the biggest realization of my life before I really started becoming a water snob. When I was buying organic vegetables, I was using tap water to steam them with. When you heat water to a boiling temperature, the property released in the steam is actually like a chlorine gas. So here I am, spending all this extra money on organic vegetables only to find out I'm later gassing it with chlorine steam before eating it. I hope you got a laugh out of that, too.

Okay, so this is what I personally do, now that you kind of understand my feelings about water, in terms of how much water I drink. I have a Yeti bottle which holds 32 ounces of water. I fill it full of Palomar Mountain Spring Water every morning before work. I drink all of that before I come home. Then I fill it again when I get home and drink that before I go to bed. That equals a gallon of water a day. That bottle is my goal bottle. That bottle is my life bottle. I drink that much water every day, no matter what. Anything I drink above that gallon of water is just extra.

Do I drink other things? I would be lying if I told you I didn't. I drink carbonated water, but pure water is what I drink 85 percent of the time. I know it sounds really boring but drinking pure water and eating organic food is what I do for my body. For me, a healthy body is fun, not boring. I hope this chapter helps you understand how important water is for your body.

Please teach your children at a very early age that water needs to be their drink of choice. Children only know what they are taught. My daughter never drank milk, juice, or soda. She was raised on water. She never put that other stuff in her body until she was old enough to make the choice herself.

And when she doesn't drink enough water, her body lets her know it and she'll end up really sick.

I am so blessed to see that she realizes just how important water is to her body. She also carries around a Yeti bottle filled with water everywhere she goes. Why? Because I bought it for her. I knew she would not spend the money for herself and this way I know I am doing a small part to keep her healthy. I hope you train yourself and everyone you know to be a water snob. To be water snob you need to know where your water is coming from. Knowledge is power and the minute you pick up a case of water to drink you should think about it and what it is doing to your body.

Not All Bottled Water Is the Same

According to this article, "Should We Break Our Bottled Water Habit?" in 2018, Americans spent $31 billion on bottled water.[2] That translates into billions of gallons of water each year. And the amounts are growing every month. Maybe that is a good sign, since we all need to drink more water!

We also want to drink the best water we can find for our body. Unfortunately, that cannot come from our tap anymore. So, we have to buy water from a manufacturing company. When my father was growing up, he would think I was nuts asking about bottled water. "Just drink from the hose like we did when we were kids," he'd say.

You have to read the labels when you buy water. Yes, I said read the labels. You need to know what the water company is selling you. You would be amazed to see how much bottled water is not from clear mountain streams, it's actually "purified" tap water! We think it is easier to just buy water from the store, but is it? What are all those plastic bottles doing to the environment? Even if half the people try to recycle them, it's still too much plastic.

2 "Should We Break Our Bottled Water Habit?" by Ryan Felton, as posted on the Consumer Reports website (updated 2019). https://www.consumerreports.org/bottled-water/should-we-break-our-bottled-water-habit.

I buy my Palomar water in big bottles and I started to think about the water dispenser they sell you to dump the water into. How often do I clean the machine? Not often as I should. It's time to get a new machine or figure out how to clean this one without leaving a chemical behind!

Just remember, there is no water police anywhere checking to see if what the company is saying about their water is true. I just spent an hour watching videos on water and learned that most bottled water is acidic. *Wait. Aren't we trying to get away from acid?* Some water is rated as being acid-based when tested. Later, I discuss each water company by brand.

But before you read on, know that it is not just the water you are buying but the container it is stored in. Does it leach into the water? Does the company rotate their stock of water, or does it sit there for months on end leaching the container's plastic into the water? Some of the top water companies allow their pre-bottled water to sit in a warehouse for up to two years. And stores don't always rotate the water like food. It probably just sits there until someone buys it. How many months can that be?

There was a makeshift law in New Jersey that dictated water is not to stay on shelves past the two-year mark. They forced manufacturers to put a date on their bottles. But is anyone checking to see if the date is accurate? No! But if you see an old date, that should be a clue to walk away. Some brands only put the year. Twelve months is a long stretch to be accurate. The water from Palomar gives an exact date: 04/20/2019. Thank you, Palomar Mountain Premium Spring Water.

They also put the date on the bottle when they pour it into the 5-gallon jug. I do not know another company that does that. I buy their small waters for the gym and they date the small bottles of water, amazing. Palomar is amazing. I love the water. Their customer service and marketing efforts need a lot of work… you can't have it all.

As cancer patients, we want to keep acid out of our bodies in order to keep our internal organs working to protect us in the best way they can. Acid has a negative effect on all the internal organs, creating a toxic environment to the organs that function to keep our entire body well.

If you are going to choose a water company, it's best to pick the most natural water you can, hopefully from a source filtered by God, not man. You can get a pH testing kit from the health food store to see what is going on with your favorite water. You can also use this kit to test your shower water to find out what you are bathing in.

The best thing about studying up on this is that when you're done, you can keep buying the best water you have around, once you know what that is. Okay, here is the breakdown of some of the top brands:

Dasani. This bottled water is from Coca-Cola and it is purified (by reverse osmosis) tap water re-mineralized with magnesium sulfate, potassium chloride, and salt, which gives it a clean and fruity taste.

Aquafina. This purified tap water is another extremely popular brand of bottled water that comes from PepsiCo. It goes through a seven-step filtration process called HydRO-7. The filtration process includes reverse osmosis, ozone sterilization, and ultraviolet.

Evian. Evian claims their water is a geological miracle. It goes through a 15-year process where rain and snow go through an underground spring and is harvested full of electrolytes and minerals.

Fiji. Fiji water comes from the tropical rainfall on the island of Viti Levu in Fiji. It is filtered through volcanic rock where it naturally picks up electrolytes and minerals before welling up in an underground aquifer.

Arrowhead. The company states it comes from a natural spring and is not changed when it is bottled. I personally do not like the taste of the water; I would probably pick any water other than this water.

Crystal Geyser. This water claims it comes from an Alpine spring with balanced pH and some electrolytes.

Nestle Pure Life. As a purified water, it comes from a municipal source or well and is then carbon filtered, softened, demineralized, and then re-mineralized.

It would take pages and pages to write up every water brand you can find on the shelf for you to reach and put in your cart.

If you have a favorite water you reach for every time you go to the store, I would suggest you research what you are drinking. Here are the questions to find out before you buy your next 24 pack of water.

- » Does the company use BPA free bottles to store it in their water in?
- » Does the company date the cases of water before they send them?
- » Does the store date the cases when they come in?
- » Does the seller of the cases watch the heat they are storing the bottles in?
- » Do they come to the store directly from the manufacturer? Where do they store the water for shipment?

Without this knowledge, you are probably drinking a byproduct of plastic which has been known to cause all kinds of health problems including some cancers.[3, 4] We all think we are doing right by our bodies by drinking water, but know what you are giving your body to overcome.

Is it a pain to carry refillable water bottles? Yes, but I know exactly what water I am drinking all the time. We all think we are doing right by our bodies by drinking water, but know what you are giving your body to overcome.

---

3 "Plastic Water Bottles Exposed to Heat can be Toxic," as posted on this website, https://drgeo.com/plastic-water-bottles-exposed-to-heat-can-be-toxic.

4 "The problem with all the plastic that's leaching into your food," by Julia Belluz and Radhika Viswanathan, as posted on the Vox website (updated December 4, 2018). https://www.vox.com/science-and-health/2018/9/11/17614540/plastic-food-containers-contamination-health-risks.

CHAPTER 18

pH Balance Your Body

IT IS AMAZING HOW MANY RESULTS came up when I started researching the body's pH levels. The pH, which stands for "potential of hydrogen," levels are designated on a scale of 0 to 14. The lower the number, the more acidic you are, and the higher the number, the more alkaline you are.

There are so many opinions on each subject I write about it's crazy. How do you make heads or tails out of all the information? And on top of this, you have to consider what your doctor tells you. A person could go crazy. I am kind of glad I didn't have access to all of this advice at my fingertips when I was going through all my decision-making processes. It was me, God, a lot of prayer, and common sense that got me through.

Let's look at the way God made our bodies. First of all, He did not expect us to put so many disruptive things in them, period. He only made so many enzymes to digest things because He thought that is all we were going to eat. Those enzymes digested the food He put on the planet for us to eat. We are the ones trying to change His perfect body by eating whatever we want and then getting upset or blaming God when the body fights backs and we end up sick.

The blood in our body is the life force God created to keep everything alive and working in our body. The oxygen we breathe feeds our blood supply and the water we drink helps move our blood supply from place-to-place. I think it only makes sense to keep the blood the way God intended it to be in my system: as clean as I can possibly make it.

If the body needs oxygen in the blood to keep all the organs functioning at their best, why not help the blood do that with what I eat? I decided to bring as much oxygen into the body that I could find. I studied fruits and vegetables and I found I did not like to eat fruit. Fruit did not make me feel healthier when I ate it. But when I ate a lot of vegetables I felt better. When I added a lot of green vegetables and pH-balanced vegetables, I had more energy.

All the choices were based on the blood and its ability to reach the cells to help kill the cancer. I had heard that cancer likes to live in an acid-based blood. Cancer is not something meant to happen to the blood; it is a mutation of the cells of the body. If I could make the blood going to the cancer toxic, could I make it harder for cancerous cells to grow? Or even stay alive?

When you think about it, this is exactly what doctors are doing with chemo drugs. Unfortunately, that substance is foreign to the blood so as it goes to kill the cancer it leaves behind other things to fix in the body.

If I could find something that does not hurt the body but makes it harder for the cancer to grow… hello, let's try that. If cancer likes acid and low oxygen to live in, I was going to give it the opposite to live in. I was going to give it high-pH oxygen-based blood to piss it off. I ate everything I could to make my body pH balanced.

I discovered foods that help make your body pH-balanced. And this is exactly how I have been eating for more than 25 years. The list of high alkaline foods is at the end of this chapter and will make your body as clean as you can make it—and the worst place for cancer to live and survive. I know how I've been eating for decades has a lot to do with why I am alive today.

Alkaline Water: The Newest Fad to Keep Your Body Alkalized

I went to a pH water machine seminar because I had so many friends asking me if they should get such a machine to help keep their body pH balanced. I knew nothing about it so I decided to go to the seminar and ask questions of the experts selling the water machines.

I have said this many times: even things that are good for your body can be bad for your body if not studied first. The body can go into shock if given too much of a good or bad thing too fast. So, I asked the questions I would want to know before starting any program.

> » How much alkaline water is too much for my body?
>
> » How do I know my body needs this water?
>
> » What is the effect on my body if I have too much water?
>
> » What is the effect if I do not drink enough water?
>
> » Do I need to know the pH of my body before I start drinking alkaline water?
>
> » If I drink alkaline water in combination with acid-based foods or drinks, will they cancel each other out? Would I have to start all over if I did?
>
> » Once I start using this program, will this then be a lifelong commitment to keep my blood acid-free?
>
> » Once my body has changed to a high-alkaline body, how will I know that?

The seminar people where not happy when I showed up. They sold no machines that day because they could not answer a single question I asked.

In researching this book, I went online trying to find answers to my questions. After countless websites and reading for hours, the only thing I found out was that too much alkaline can cause problems in the system, as can anything when done to the extreme.

It is so hard to find answers when the experts don't study something all the way to the end. They tease us, as with the studies referenced in this article, "Is alkaline water good for you?"[1]

If nothing has been proven, why not?

What I find interesting in this article is that they say, "One study has suggested that an alkaline diet, but not specifically alkaline water, may enhance the action of some chemotherapy drugs used to treat cancer." This is in the same article mentioned above.

The article references other studies that claim alkaline water lowers blood pressure and helps with acid reflux by reducing the acidity of the stomach contents. However, the author also points out this about the acid reflux study:

"The work was done in a laboratory rather than in humans. More research would be needed to support these findings. Moreover, stomach acid exists for a purpose. It kills bacteria and other pathogens, and it helps our bodies to digest food and absorb nutrients."

And this about the blood pressure study:

"It is worth noting that the study was sponsored by Essentia Water, who also provided the alkaline water used."

And the article ends with this takeaway:

"The Cleveland Clinic... advise people to drink water, but make it plain water, because too much acidity or too much alkalinity can cause problems. They point out that the human body is designed to find its own balance. People should think carefully whether it is worth investing in expensive equipment that is unlikely to make a difference."

I could not find any studies that absolutely state whether drinking alkaline water is good or bad, or even what amounts to drink. I don't understand

---

1 "Is alkaline water good for you?" by Markus MacGill; medically reviewed by Natalie Butler, R.D., L.D., as posted on the Medical News Today website (2017). https://www.medicalnewstoday.com/articles/313681.php.

why, if the public wants proof of something and we are reaching for facts, something can't be proven right or wrong. Please don't keep us guessing!

I do know that research has confirmed that cancer tumors create the acid around them they live in and we cannot drink water to change the surrounding acid.

Common sense says if you know cancer creates acid, study how to inject the right pH into the surrounding areas to make it pH balanced. Right? If we don't give cancer a healthy place to grow and thrive, would the cancer die? Why aren't we studying these kind of things?

We can kill it. What's more, if we simply balance pH in the body, this isn't introducing foreign substances to the body. The body would not have a negative response as it does with chemotherapy.

Why aren't we looking into things like this? We need to fight to get common sense research underway instead of accepting what has been done for years with little change.

There are many different ways to alkaline your water including drops, with a machine, pills, or buying off-the-shelf alkaline products. I like the taste of most of the alkaline water in my health stores. Would I buy a machine and spend thousands of dollars? I don't think so at this time.

After considering the health benefits studies have shown, I don't think the expense is worth adding it daily to my routine yet. I don't have any stomach or reflux problems at this time. Until they have clear studies how much to use and the effects on the body, I think I will pass.

What I think I will do is watch how I am countering that intake with things like coffee. The following list will help you make better choices on how to help your body balance acid and non-acid foods until we know more about what is better to do. As I started to research the vegetables that would help with the acid levels in my body, I realized this is what I am already eating every day. The only products I needed to add were bananas and watermelon! As I mentioned, I do not normally eat a lot of fruit. Even though it's natural sugar, fruit has a high sugar content and I try to stay away from sugar because of the (again, non-conclusive) studies linking sugar and cancer. Why take a chance? Plus, I don't really like fruit. I know, I know… it's a personal choice.

The way I am normally able to eat so much salad is that I make a super food salad once a week. I use Sunday as a prep day. I have done this for more than 25 years. I started when I was pregnant with my daughter. I make a large organic salad with the super foods listed below. I have a large stainless-steel bowl and use a steaming grate you use in a pot to steam vegetables at the bottom to keep the water drained so they don't get mushy.[2] I also use a salad spinner to get as much water off the salad as I can before I put it in the bowl. I wash all the vegetables in filtered water using the water filter on my faucet.

I put foil on the top to keep it fresh. It's very important to leave a slot open on the top to let the gas from the vegetables escape.

I then make an organic relish tray weekly with broccoli, celery, small tomatoes, small bell peppers, and snow peas. I change to other vegetables as they look good to give it variety.

My daughter could grab this at any time and eat it with hummus, dressing, plain avocado or guacamole, salsa… there was always a dip of some kind ready to go.

Okay, here is an easy list of the "10 Best High-Alkaline Foods" from the Facty Health website:[3]

1. <u>Cucumbers.</u> Eat these with every meal. They are also in my relish tray and super food salads.

---

2 Stainless Steel Norpro Steamer Vegetable basket as posted on the Walmart website. https://www.walmart.com/ip/norpro-steamer-vegetable-basket-ss/47713807.

3 "Best High-Alkaline Foods," by Trista, as posted on the Facty website (2019). https://facty.com/lifestyle/wellness/10-best-high-alkaline-foods.

2. <u>Seeded Watermelon.</u> I do not eat much of this and I'm not sure how easy it is to get organic ones.

3. <u>Avocado.</u> As a California girl, these are a must for me. Go Avos!

4. <u>Cayenne Peppers.</u> This is new to me and I'll let you know if I like them.

5. <u>Bell Peppers.</u> I eat these at least once a week and in my relish tray. It's easy to get organic peppers.

6. <u>Spinach.</u> I eat a Super Greens mix every week in my super food salad that I explained earlier.

7. <u>Kale.</u> This is one of my favorite super foods. I don't like the taste by itself but I put some in my super food salad every week.

8. <u>Bananas.</u> As you know, I am not a fruit person. This fruit is loaded with sugar and carbohydrates which turns to sugar: 14 grams of sugar per banana. I'm going to skip this and not add to my routine!

9. <u>Broccoli.</u> I do not go a day without eating broccoli. I put it in salad, I steam it, bake it, or I sit on the couch with a relish tray and eat it with hummus while watching TV at night. This is definitely one of my super food products.

10. <u>Celery.</u> Not only is celery alkaline, but it also has extremely high-water content and lots of vitamin C, which helps support the immune system. It is known to reduce inflammation so I eat this to help with lymphedema and add celery sticks to the relish tray.

For a complete list of alkaline and acid foods, see the "pH Balance Diet Food List."[4]

---

4 "pH Balance Diet Food List," as posted on the Simplex Health website. https://www.simplexhealth.co.uk/ph-balance-diet-food-chart-cms-33.html

CHAPTER 19

Roasted Coffee

I AM ALWAYS WONDERING, *what are we all doing the same—across the country—to cause cancer?*[1]

If we look at cancer and the changes to our environment which we now know is causing cancer, we also have to look at all the states and all the things we do together, right? When I was first diagnosed with cancer, the biggest concern was smog. I remember thinking I was doomed because I lived in the Inland Empire and we had Stage Three Smog Alerts all the time when I was growing up. What are those? Days when the smog is so bad, we did not have to go to school, we had a smog day. Can you believe it?

But as I got older and I started to study cancer I decided that did not make sense. Why? Because people were getting cancer in places where there wasn't any smog. Then one day, I drove by a Starbucks and it hit me: coffee. We are all being programed to drink more coffee. It is crazy the amount of coffee we drink. Maybe that is the link.

I read an article about a survey done in 2018 that found the number of Americans who drink a daily cup of coffee was the highest it's been in six years.[2]

It's interesting that at the end of that same article, they link to another article referencing studies saying that drinking coffee might help you live longer! Coffee consumption is the highest it has been in six years. Could there be a correlation between the two?

---

1 "Acrylamide and Cancer Risk," as posted on the cancer.org website. https://www.cancer.org/cancer/cancer-causes/acrylamide.html.

2 "Americans Are Drinking More Coffee Than Ever," by Elisabeth Sherman, as posted on the Food & Wine website (2018). https://www.foodandwine.com/news/americans-drinking-more-coffee-ever.

The National Coffee Association interviewed 3,000 Americans and found coffee consumption was at 62 percent in 2017 and by 2018 it was up to 64 percent and climbing. Also, out of the people surveyed, 79 percent said they drank coffee at home *before* they bought coffee out in the public. I was surprised the survey said only 39 percent bought it outside the home. How does Starbucks make all their money? Does this mean a vast majority of Americans are drinking two or more cups a day?

It's shocking to think that **Americans consume the most coffee in the world overall**. This is something we are all doing and coffee has a known link to cancer.

The link comes from roasting the coffee. This has not been explored in its entirety, but there are many independent studies linking roasting coffee to carcinogens, and carcinogens cause cancer. The studies, again, have been around for years and concerned researchers say they need to be studied closer. **But where is the continued study?**

This report from 2007, "Acrylamide, Furan, and the FDA," explains how acrylamide is a known animal carcinogen and human neurotoxicant.

> "Acrylamide is an industrial chemical used in products for water purification, grouts, packaging, and scientific research. So, what was this substance doing in food? Scientists soon discovered that acrylamide was forming in food as a result of a heat-induced reaction between two naturally occurring ingredients, the amino acid asparagine and reducing sugars. In other words, acrylamide resulted from the cooking or thermal processing of foods." [3]

After discovering acrylamide, scientists found furan, another cooking-related chemical. And that was found in larger amounts and in a larger variety of foods than had previously been reported. During the coffee-roasting process, acrylamide and furan are formed. Different techniques have been

---

3 "Acrylamide, Furan, and the FDA," by Lauren Posnick Robin, Sc.D., as posted on the Food Safety Magazine website (2007). https://www.foodsafetymagazine.com/magazine-archive1/junejuly-2007/acrylamide-furan-and-the-fda.

tried on other foods, including lowering cooking times and temperatures. But, so far, "No good techniques have been identified for reducing acrylamide in coffee while preserving taste."

Maybe the reason is because coffee, like sugar, is a giant consumer industry. If Americans stopped drinking coffee it would be devastating to the industry. I searched for hours trying to see if we could have our precious cup of coffee without roasting it first. All I found was that it could *not* be done. People have tried and failed because unroasted coffee beans makes terrible-tasting coffee. So, we aren't told we shouldn't drink coffee.

The average American spends about $1,000 a year on coffee. The coffee industry is a $20 billion dollar industry. Can you imagine if it was published that coffee is causing cancer—as it was with cigarette smoking—what would happen to the industry?

If nothing less, it would cut consumption down maybe by half, which equals $10 billion dollars. Do you think they are going to tell us? Probably not. But we need to know. We deserve to know. How can we make decisions if we do not have all the facts?

There needs to be more studies done now. I see children coming out of Starbucks all the time, and high schoolers are drinking loads of caffeine. Even if the youngest ones aren't drinking coffee now, they are being groomed to want it when they get older. Are they cutting their lives short without knowing it? Are parents buying them their favorite drinks not knowing what they are doing? Not to mention we making them coffee at home before they leave for the day, with no idea of how many more cups they will drink by the end of it.

How much is too much coffee? Is there a limit? Do the carcinogens linked to coffee accumulate in our body? How can we work so hard to stay alive and the lack of knowledge—or the redirection away from knowledge—is killing us one cup at a time?

We need studies. Knowing what you know now, are you going to cut coffee out of your life? Are you going to cut it back to one cup of coffee a day?

A Challenge

I have a challenge for you. If you had to drink your coffee black with nothing added to it, would you still drink it? Have you ever studied what's in the sweeteners at Starbucks? If you are drinking the coffee for the additives that make it taste good, why not switch to something that does not have a cancer agent in it? Tea. Why not drink green teas, which actually can help your body.

We know coffee is made with a byproduct that is leading to cancer. Then we add sugar, which has studies it helps cancer grow. What are we doing to our bodies? The studies we need are independent studies done by people who have nothing to lose by telling us the truth. Unless we press the government to do it, the coffee and sugar lobbies will squash the results of any independent studies. Why do you think we see mass-media articles on the benefits of coffee and sugar so often?

Is that why we are dying? Because the small voice can't be heard over the loud voice that is telling you, "Don't worry about it, studies say coffee helps cancer." We hear nothing said about the link between coffee and cancer. We are distracted by another "look over here" magic show.

We will not sit and wait any longer.

CHAPTER 20

Sugar

THIS IS ANOTHER CHAPTER YOU MUST not pass up. There is a huge link between sugar and cancer. Start with this article, "The Deadly Link Between Sugar and Cancer."[1]

I had heard that sugar was something to avoid when you have or have had cancer. A friend of mine in a holistic center said this in passing. I am not a big sweet eater so this pretty much went in one ear and out the other at the time. I don't have anything sweet in my house. Sweets are for special occasions like going to the movies (then look out). I did not allow my daughter to have sugar but when she was two, a neighbor gave her a piece of cake. Luckily for me it was soon forgotten and never asked for again. I had to make my parents promise not to feed it to her and I wrote instructions on all daycare paperwork to not give her any sugar.

Did she live her whole life without sugar, no. I allowed her to have it after dinner like a normal child when she was 3, but her body did not crave it like the drug that it is, yes, it is a drug. I only gave her organic cookies and one or two cookies after dinner only. All sugar was monitored by me and the amount allowed her whole childhood.

When I turned 60, I decided to really look at all aspects of what I'm eating. My last job had sugary food all around me every day. For the first time in my life, I was not realizing every time I passed by it, I grabbed one piece. *It's just one piece of candy, what's the big deal, right?* Well, I worked there for more than six years.

1 "The Deadly Link Between Sugar and Cancer," by Clifton Leaf, as posted on Fortune's website (2017). https://fortune.com/2017/10/16/cancer-sugar-link-study.

In that six years, my eyesight had changed and become foggy. My mental capacity had become less clear by the end of the day. I was not sleeping through the night and waking up all the time.

Then I had blood work done and my whole body was off for the first time in my life. They told me I was pre-diabetic. *What?* I work out three times a week (elliptical machine for 40 minutes at level 10), lift weights, jog with my dogs for 15 or more minutes twice a day, eat organic foods, eat small meals throughout the day, and wear a size 12–14 in clothes. So, of course, the doctor did not believe me when she told me the pre-diabetic news. The look from the doctor made me feel like I was crazy. I wanted to take a video to show her everything I do.

I had to look at what I was putting in my body that I wasn't accounting for and what it was doing to my body. Then I reached for the piece of candy one day and thought *oh, man, there it is… sugar! What are you doing to my body?*

I needed to research what sugar is really doing to me. How much sugar is in my life? All I have to do is stop eating sugar at work, right? I mean, I do not eat sugar at home and I don't have sweets at home. So, I started looking at food labels.

Four milligrams of sugar per-serving is no biggie, right? *Wait. I am eating three servings of 12 milligrams of sugar.* What does that mean anyway, in just one thing I eat? The company put that in my food and I did not even ask for it. The company gave it to me without my permission. How many companies are doing that to me based on everything I eat in a day?

As I started to look at labels—really studying ingredients and daily levels—it was crazy. Everything I'm eating probably has sugar added to it. That is when I started to ask myself, *why?*

There are so many things hidden by just the way it is labeled on the box, bag, can, or bottle. My new favorite saying is "The Magic Trick." They have you look over there while they do this over here—and sugar is one of the tricks. Here's how they try to hide the amount of sugar:

Amounts. **4 milligrams of sugar = 1 teaspoon of sugar. A milligram sounds tiny. A teaspoon, not so much.**

Portion size. **You read a label and figure, "Okay, that is not that much sugar. No biggie." But on closer examination, "Wait, wait, wait. That is a one portion-size amount."**

Please look closer. You'll see that there are 4 servings in the portion size of the product. How many servings do you eat in one sitting of that product?

Here is an example. A jar of spaghetti sauce has 16 grams of sugar per serving. But I do not eat one serving of it, I eat half the jar (I like a lot of sauce). **That means I just ate 32 milligrams of sugar or 8 teaspoons of sugar!** Please make sure to read the chapter on carbohydrates to find out what carbs add to the amount of sugar in your food.

The Challenge That Could Save Your Life

The challenge is to look at what you are eating. Go buy a big box of single-serving sugar packets. Write down the grams of sugar in grams you eat in a day, if you can find it all. Then count out the sugar packets and put them in a jar. At the end of the week you will see the amount of sugar you eat in a week.

Let's Look at What Sugar Does to a Cancer Body

When I started to research what sugar does to a body with cancer, wow, did I get mad. After reading numerous articles, I found out a biochemist, in 1920, is credited with being the first to find the coloration between cancer and sugar. That's 100 years ago! Here is an excerpt from the article I mentioned at the beginning of this chapter.

"A German biochemist named Otto Warburg in the 1920s, was the first to observe these oddball, counterintuitive facts about cancer cells, which he blamed on a defect in their mitochondria, the cell's energy factories… Indeed, the biochemist believed this aberrant aerobic glycolysis—which later became known as the "Warburg effect"—actually caused cancer, though it wasn't clear how or why."

Why wouldn't anyone want to study the effects further? And if they didn't want to study it, at least give cancer survivors the information so we can do our own studies and make our own choices based on our findings. Give us the chance to protect ourselves!

Basically, what I found out is that sugar is the exact fuel cancer uses to help keep it alive and growing rapidly. Cancer uses the fermentation of the sugar as fuel to help it grow.

What? No one told me this.

I went through so many things to stay alive and my doctors did not share this with me.

True, there is not a conclusive study that proves excess sugar is causing cancer. But I would like to insist that they continue the study to see if processed sugar is what is giving all of us cancer.

Could this fact alone be part of the reason why 75 percent of us are getting non-genetic cancers? We need to insist researchers start spending as much money on finding the cause if we want our children to live.

Back to my study using my body. *Every* packaged food product I picked up had sugar in it. As I am doing this study on cancer, I was thinking about people who develop diabetes. Did too much sugar in our food give it to them? When the doctor says you are pre-diabetic, they tell you not to eat sugar, so you think they mean don't eat sweets. But do they tell you to look at how much sugar is in the foods you are eating every day?

On a recent trip to the grocery store, I saw a can of chili. It was a cold day and that sounded really good. I was thinking that was safe. It's beans, right? But no, it had added sugar. In one can, there were two teaspoons of sugar.

I have taken sugar out of my diet all together and I have lost so much weight, without trying. As you read before I used to wear a size 14. I have lost 4 pants sizes to a size 8 pants in just 4 months. I know taking sugar and carbohydrates out of my diet is a large reason why. My body has the exact food it needs to work the way God intended it to work so it is not storing any food in fat. What's more, my whole body is changing without sugar. If I had silent cancer growing in my body, I could have been feeding it, actually helping it grow for years because of this lack of knowledge.

Here is the clincher: in the PET scans radiologists give you, they are able to see cancer because of the effects of sugar. What? They knew this for years? From the article:

> "What's more, cancer cells need gobs of energy to fuel their mad rebellion; rapid cell division, after all, requires plenty of biochemical fuel. And cancer cells gobble up sugar like nobody's business. (That's why we're often able to see tumors on a PET scan, which highlights tissues that rapidly take up an injected sugar called FDG.)"

Why aren't millions of dollars being spent to further study cancer and sugar when they already have proof there is a connection? If you are not going to protect me, tell me what you know so I can protect myself. When I shared this information with cancer survivors like myself, they did not know this, either. Why? It's crazy not to give us all the information so we can make life changes.

If you knew cutting sugar would result in a high percentage of never getting cancer again would you change your life habits around sugar? If this is what is helping cancer grow, shouldn't the government and healthcare lobbies make a campaign to let the public know?

I watched a mother in my holistic grocery store (Sprouts) looking at the milk selections and she picked the sweetened almond milk for her children. I wanted to tell her, *look at the sugar amount you are giving your child… that's like a candy bar!* Then I watched the next mother pick soy milk with estrogen and sugar. They both thought they were making healthy choices for their children. My milk of choice for cereal is walnut milk. It's more expensive but free of estrogen and sugar.

And what about sugar addiction? This is a big deal. I just watched a video online showing a child screaming for sugar. We all laughed and thought it was funny. Millions of people shared the video. But how many saw it for what it truly was? It was an addiction video. It was not funny. My daughter does not crave sweets because I did not train her to eat them or want them. Her body has no memory of them. They were only allowed on special occasions. Her friends used to bring their own cookies when they came over because they could not believe we had no sugar in the house.

I did occasionally buy cookies but they were organic and not too sweet. Her friends would wrinkle up their noses after a bite and refuse to eat them. Is sugar the reason Americans are in the top 10 in the world for breast cancer? What sets us apart? What makes us the same as the others in the top 10?

Let's start asking more questions! Let's start demanding more answers! Why is this not being asked and why isn't more research spent on finding out?

There is a petition on my website, telluswhyweredying.com. Please sign it and ask your friends to sign it. To demand change we need an army demanding it. One of those changes needs to be to demand the non-use of milligrams as a measurement on food labels and require they measure sugar in teaspoons.

The sugar lobbyists are very powerful. To make changes we will need a lot of signatures and a lot of press. So, before we can make this change a reality, please read the labels, and know what you are buying when you buy it so you don't eat something you didn't intend to. We need to protect our bodies at all costs, even the sweet ones!

CHAPTER 21

Carbohydrates

I WAS STUDYING HOW SUGAR CAUSES cancer growth and looking at all the sugar in my food when the thought came to me, *carbohydrates change into sugar in my system, right?* I hadn't thought much about carbohydrates as I do not eat a lot of them, mainly because I do not eat a lot of gluten. I do not eat bread or pasta and they don't matter to me, but I have many friends who can't live without them.

Am I a saint? That is a big fat no. I crave California carbohydrates—our famous chips and guacamole. I was raised with a chip in my mouth. They are my downfall and, no, I can't just eat one.

When I started to study carbohydrates, I began to realize why my friends cannot live without them. It blew my mind what I did not know.

Carbohydrates mean they contain carbon, hydrogen, and oxygen. Most of the food we eat contains carbs so we have to be able to know the good ones from the bad ones. For example, fruits and vegetables are quality carbohydrates that are loaded with fiber. Refined and processed carbohydrates, such as white bread and white rice, strip away the food's natural beneficial fiber when they are manufactured.

If you remember nothing else, please keep this in mind when you are buying food for the family and reading labels. Manufacturers are tricking you by using milligrams as a measurement and then not providing you with any analysis of what that means for you. Then, to make it even harder, they add a measurement for sugar on the label, so you do not know what is what, even though you have both listings which are basically sugar to the body.

This is why Americans are getting heavier every day and why we, as cancer survivors, have to really study the labels on everything we eat.

Remember the sugar challenge where we put one package of sugar in a jar for every teaspoon consumed in a week? They added up so fast, didn't they? Well, now you need to add the amount of carbohydrates to the jar because they transform into sugar in the blood. Once you add carbs, it will scare you how much sugar your body is trying to process.

5 grams of carbohydrates = one teaspoon of sugar.

The experts tell us there are two kinds of carbohydrates—simple and complex—and I will explain the difference but it is so easy to know the difference. If the carbohydrates are coming from God in His form, He has made a way for the body to break them down for us.

What does the body do with carbohydrates? It breaks them down into smaller sugars, such as glucose and fructose. Then, they go into the small intestine where the sugar is absorbed. From there, it goes to the bloodstream and it ends up in the liver.

The liver changes the sugars into glucose, which the body then mixes with insulin so the body can easily use it as energy.

Here is the crazy part: the body can store up to 2,000 calories of the mixture above in your liver and skeletal muscles in the form of glycogen.

Once glycogen stores are full, carbs are stored as fat. The body needs a carbohydrate to use as fuel quickly—that is why God made them to help the body. If you have insufficient carbohydrate intake or stores, the body will have to consume protein for fuel. Although our body will be craving protein, many of us mistakenly reach for any man-made carbohydrate to get an instant boost and suppress the craving.

We have all grabbed a sugar-based simple carbohydrate when we feel hungry, often reaching for what we think is a good sweet tooth substitute for a candy bar, such as a protein bar. But what is the difference between the two if the ingredients in the protein bar are sugar-based and full of simple carbohydrates? Very little.[1]

This is our problem. We are eating a lot of man-made, simple carbohydrates. We are also now sitting in one place for longer amounts of time, which will cause the body not to use them, so they are stored as fat. Ever wonder how we are getting heavier and heavier? We are storing these man-made carbohydrates as fat because it is harder for the body to use them.

If you use all your protein for fuel instead of using carbohydrates, this can become a problem because the body needs protein to make muscles. Using protein instead of carbohydrates for fuel also puts stress on the kidneys.

I studied this for hours and hours and got more confused with every article. Why? Because some carbohydrates are good for us so I cannot just tell you, "Don't eat this."

The problem is manufacturers take the complex carbohydrates as they were designed and strip them of the essential things needed for them to be digested in our system. Take an orange, for example. When I eat a whole orange, it has fiber to counteract the sugar and carbohydrates so it evens out. But if I juice an orange, I remove the fibrous pulp so the orange becomes a simple sugar. But eating the whole orange is a good, complex carbohydrate the body can work with.

I tend to think of it like this: if humans are processing the food that I am eating—if they are simplifying it—it probably isn't going to be used properly by my body. So, I look at the body and how it was designed. I realize it has to break down whatever I am putting into it. *Does my stomach have a digestive enzyme that can break down this food and use it?*

---

1 "What is the difference between simple and complex carbs?" as posted on the Medical News Today website. https://www.medicalnewstoday.com/articles/318615#not-all-carbs-are-created-equal.

I try to limit my intake of carbohydrates because I count them all as a sugar. Otherwise, I would go crazy trying to figure out what are good carbs and bad carbs. If the packaged food I'm eating has carbs, I try to select products with a very low number of carbohydrates on the label, and that product has to be in as natural a state as possible.

I decided to look on YouTube for other videos to see what else I could find out. There are so many videos on this subject that if you search for "carbohydrates and brain patterns" you will be amazed. A video came up as I was studying carbohydrates that said man-made simple carbohydrates can create the same brain pathways as cocaine! You can become addicted to carbs when they are simplified into sugar and this is one of the reasons we have become more overweight than ever before as a society.

How many other things will we find we are addicted to once we start to study how our food is processed? Remember, knowledge is power. You have to choose your battles, and this is one challenge I decided to take on using myself as the guinea pig. I decided to cut all carbohydrates and sugar from my life, as well as caffeine. I have now made my body a body from God, eating as He intended us to eat.

So far to date I have dropped four pant sizes in four months; yes, four months. And I eat all the time, but only what God has an enzyme for me to eat. Though here is what has been blowing my mind: I still crave carbohydrates and sugar all the time. I don't know when or if the cravings will go away, but I don't want to ever go back. Ever since cutting those three things from my diet, I am amazed at the energy I have all the time. My bowel movements are easy now and my skin looks like I am 45 instead of 61. The next phase of this challenge is learning how to cook more meals this way, and sustaining a natural, whole food diet.

I hope I motivate you to look at what you eat and know God's machine needs His fuel.

CHAPTER 22

Dairy Products

Milk

IN MY RESEARCH ABOUT DAIRY PRODUCTS and cancer, I was led to this report: "Usual Consumption of Specific Dairy Foods Is Associated with Breast Cancer in the Roswell Park Cancer Institute Data Bank and BioRepository."[1] A summary article reports:

> "Dairy products including cow's milk may be associated with an increased risk for breast cancer, according to a new study funded by the National Cancer Institute. Researchers looked at the dietary intakes of 1,941 women diagnosed with breast cancer and found that those who consumed the most American, cheddar, and cream cheeses had a 53 percent increased risk for breast cancer. Those with ER- breast cancer (a designation of estrogen receptor status) who drank the most fluid milk had a 58 percent increased risk for breast cancer. Components in dairy such as insulin-like growth factor (IGF-1) and other growth hormones may be among the reasons for the increased risk for cancer."

As I continued to search, I couldn't find any studies that said with 100 percent certainty that milk causes cancer or helps cancer grow. Why not ask who stopped the tests? Were they independent tests? Will there ever be a truly completed study when a billion-dollar industry is at stake?

---

1 "Usual Consumption of Specific Dairy Foods Is Associated with Breast Cancer in the Roswell Park Cancer Institute Data Bank and BioRepository," by Susan E. McCann, et. al., as posted on the Oxford Academic website (2017). https://academic.oup.com/cdn/article/1/3/e000422/4555132.

We use animals to study disease all the time. Why not give a heifer calf just breast milk and see what happens to it? Can it get udder cancer? I know that sounds crazy, but we are drinking its breast milk, right?

So, what do I do? This is me personally and not based on what I have read recently. I chose not to give my daughter milk. I was raised on milk, my mother made me drink it with every meal for the calcium for my bones. The marketing for milk has always been strong. For as long as I have watched TV, I'd see at least one milk commercial every time I turned it on. But I chose not to give milk to my daughter. Why? It never made sense to drink another species' breast milk. We are the only species that drinks another species' breast milk. Did I get pressure from my mother, other mothers, and her doctors that I was going to affect her body and make it weak if I didn't give her milk? Yes, all the time.

All her friends would ask, "Where is the milk?"

"We do not drink milk," she would say.

"What? Why not?" They couldn't believe it.

"It's just our choice," I would tell them, adding, "We have unsweetened almond milk."

"What is that?" they'd ask, as though it was poison.

Never mind.

I knew calcium was important for my daughter and so I found another way to give it to her. I started to select vegetables with calcium. Yes, vegetables. I started to give her the green drink. I made a smoothie that her friends started to call, "the green goo." I designed it to cover anything she would not eat. She was rarely sick and never went to the doctor for even a cold her entire life and she is 27 years old. She has never had an antibiotic in her life, an ear infection, or strep throat and she still has her tonsils.

Have you ever wondered why so many people are allergic to milk? Why do dairy manufacturers keep changing the formulas to make it easier for us to digest? Because we do not have a digestive enzyme created to digest milk. We have one to digest protein but that was created for meat.

As I researched milk for this chapter, I wanted to know how are you supposed to get calcium for your bones. I found out God had us covered in the vegetables He gave us. All along, He had His body covered for everything it needs in the plants He gave us. I was amazed at how little I knew.

A wonderful resource for what's in different fruits and vegetables can be found on the My Food Data website.[2] Search for calcium in vegetables to bring up an entire list. There are so many vegetables that have calcium: collard greens, spinach, turnip greens, kale, mustard greens, beet greens, bok choy, okra, swiss chard, and broccoli rabe.

If you want to see all 200 foods high in calcium you can use the Nutrient Ranking Tool on the My Food Data website.[3] It will blow your mind.

Why eat dairy products for calcium? Why because we have been programed to need it.

Milk is an easy source for **other cultures** who do not have any other way of getting protein and calcium. And it makes sense if that was the only source we had but we are fortunate in the United States to be able to make other choices.

If your children will not eat vegetables, there are organic chewy supplements with the same properties. It's not a great substitute but it's better than not giving their bodies what they need. Just make sure the brands you buy are only using natural ingredients to make them.

---

2 "Find Better Foods: Organize and Understand What You Eat," as posted on the My Food Data website. https://www.myfooddata.com.

3 The Nutrient Ranking Tool on the My Food Data website. https://tools.myfooddata.com/nutrient-ranking-tool.php.

Now, let's look at the animals we are getting our milk from. I think this information will make you look at milk in a totally different light.

Can cows make milk when they are not pregnant? No. This means we are drinking a cow's breast milk!

Please take a look at this website: https://mercyforanimals.org/hereswhat-farms-do-to-cows-who-no-longer.[4]

They make the cows have baby after baby for years to produce milk. They can give a cow hormones to produce more milk during their pregnancy which gives them a higher yield of milk. After they have their baby, the calf is ripped from the mother cow and she can scream out for her baby for weeks. When the cow's body starts to break down from the strain, they kill it and throw it away or grind it up. It can't be sold for meat so this cow is literally a living milk machine.

I think of my own body and all it took to make milk for my daughter. Could I do it over and over, never stopping? Do we ever think about cows? I know I never did until I read this.

What happens to the baby they rip way? They become the veal we eat, which is young cow calf. Most veal comes from the male babies which can't be used for breeding, so they butcher them and get paid a high price for their meat.

The abuse cows go through to make milk for humans is insane. When I read about this, I got sick and cried. I am not writing this book to raise awareness about domestic animal cruelty but I understand why so many people are fighting for change.

---

4 "Here's What Farms Do to Cows Who No Longer Produce Milk," as posted on the Mercy for Animals website. https://mercyforanimals.org/heres-what-farms-do-to-cows-who-no-longer.

What I am focused on here is the link between milk and cancer. This study from the Iranian Journal of Public Health opened my eyes.[5] From the introduction, you can see the concerns:

> "The presence of hormones in dairy products that have the potential to disrupt the physiological function of endocrine systems has raised great concern worldwide…. The naturally occurring hormones in dairy foods have biological effects in humans and animals, which are ranging from growth promoting effects that related to sex steroids, to carcinogenic properties that associate to some active metabolites of oestrogens and IGF-1 (insulin-like growth factor-1)."

Medical professionals and researchers have long understood the effects of animal milk on the human body. I have been asking about this for years. What does drinking a cow's natural hormones do to me? And if cows are given synthetic hormones to make them produce faster, what is that doing to me? What if I am drinking their milk and then producing my own milk to feed my children?

Can cow's milk affect the hormones I make in my breasts? **The answer is yes!** They found traces of the hormone they give cows to produce more milk in human breast tissue, but they have not studied all the facts about what it's doing to us.

We must insist they study this and give us simple answers. This one of the strongest lobbyists in the United States and millions of dollars are at risk. It will not be easy to do but we can join together as one voice, one loud voice.

I went through years of people looking at me as though I was crazy for asking these questions. But no, I was not crazy.

"What am I supposed to do, Karen," they would ask, "not drink milk, not eat cheese? Should I give my kids soy milk instead?"

---

5 "Hormones in Dairy Foods and Their Impact on Public Health," by Hassan Malekinejad and Aysa Rezabakhsh, Iranian Public Health Association and Tehran University of Medical Sciences, as posted on the National Center for Biotechnology Information website. https://www.ncbi.nlm.nih.gov/pmc/articles/PMC4524299.

No! Soy has estrogen which can also cause problems, especially in cancer patients with estrogen receptors. I now drink walnut milk if I have to have that type of liquid. I really do not drink milk of any kind. Do I miss it? Yes, I do. I was programed by my mother to drink a lot of milk. But just like anything else, I can reprogram myself if it means staying alive—if it means the chance of not getting cancer again. Your children will not miss it if they are programed from the beginning not to drink it. My daughter does not drink it to this day.

Cheese

Let's look at cheese. Start by reading this article, "This Is Your Brain on Cheese," that looks at cheese addiction.[6]

> "It turns out there's a reason behind our cravings. Cheese contains casein. It also contains casein fragments called casomorphins, a casein-derived morphine-like compound. Basically, dairy protein has opiate molecules built in. When consumed, these fragments attach to the same brain receptors that heroin and other narcotics attach to.
>
> 'These opiates attach to the same brain receptors that heroin and morphine attach to. They are not strong enough to get you arrested, but they are just strong enough to keep you coming back for more, even while your thighs are expanding before your very eyes.' —Dr. Neal Barnard, author of *The Cheese Trap*."

Writing this chapter made me yell out more than all the chapters. What is going on? How can I have been so fooled? What else are they making me crave?

I started thinking about digestion again. If I do not have an enzyme to break it down because God did not make our bodies with one, how can

6 "This Is Your Brain on Cheese," by Michael Pellman Rowland, as posted on the Forbes website (2017). https://www.forbes.com/sites/michaelpellmanrowland/2017/06/26/cheese-addiction/#a53ab7a35830.

I expect that food to be healthy for me? He made me an enzyme for meat protein but this is not a meat. How is my body supposed to deal with it?

Okay, you are going to laugh, but I really started thinking about cheese when I could not get it off my sponge when I cleaned a pan that had some melted cheese on it. I looked at the gross stuff stuck on my sponge and wondered, *what does this look like when it cools in my stomach and then goes through my colon? Will it stick to my intestines like it does on the sponge?* I had to throw the sponge away, it was so gross. *If it sticks to my colon like it does to the sponge, what can I eat that is strong enough to get it off?*

Colon cancer is a top killer in the United States and I have seen it up close and personal with people wearing bags attached to their belts to empty. There is nothing I can point to with a clear answer on how long cheese stays in your colon if you eat it by itself. It is usually mixed with a white flour product (pizza, pasta) that remains in your colon like putty.

The answer to keeping your colon healthy is to get enough fiber in your diet which is done best by eating raw vegetables. I guess they are the equivalent of the sponge?

To me, cheese is not worth the hassle of cleaning up after. Do I eat cheese? Yes, on occasion, typically when it is in a recipe that someone else has made. Do I have it in my house? Sometimes. I am human and I was raised on it. Is it a snack I reach for all the time? No. Do I crave it? Not at all. When I see the cheese section in the store I think of that gross sponge and I walk away.

Cheese cannot be made without milk, just remember that. Always side on abstinence or moderation for foods that can make your body work too hard to digest. But can you have moderation in the things you crave? Why are you craving such a thing in the first place? What is your body telling you? You might just need something else, so don't react too quickly.

I certainly did not want my children to be addicted to anything. Remember, their appetites are largely trained by the foods you give them.

CHAPTER 23

Alcohol and Cannabis

Alcohol

WHENEVER I'M IN A SOCIAL SITUATION where alcohol is being served, I get ready for the questions: "Why don't you drink?" "Did you used to drink?" "Did you stop drinking because you had a drinking problem?"

Did I have a drinking problem? NO, I could take it or leave it. I drank when I was younger and before I had my daughter. After I had my daughter, I had a hard time with alcohol. It made me very sick. I had trouble breathing, got flushed, became dizzy, and all this told me I was having an allergic reaction to alcohol. I decided it was not worth it so I just stopped drinking.

Alcohol never really did that much for me. I had also seen people I loved battle with alcohol only to lose the fight. I could see alcohol breaking down their bodies right in front of me: to the point where they had to have the scar tissue from drinking stretched in their throat just to be able to eat and to the point where their doctor told me their DTs (delirium tremens, which are the rapid onset of confusion caused by alcohol withdrawal) would probably kill them.

Then I studied the effect of alcohol on cancer patients and I knew I had made the right decision not to drink. Many people insisted there must be a way I could drink. "You research all the time; can't you find a way?"

As with so many of my personal choices, I am not here to tell you to do things one way or the other but to lay out the information so you can choose which path is right for you. I know alcohol can relieve or enhance the reality of a situation and it seems like the right escape or enjoyment at the time.

Here are some things to think about from an article that asked if as little as one alcoholic drink a day could raise your risk of getting breast cancer:[1]

"More than 100 studies have looked at the association between alcohol consumption and breast cancer risk in women. These studies, although observational—meaning they draw on inferences from researchers—have consistently found an increased risk of breast cancer associated with alcohol intake.

Reasons why alcohol consumption may lead to breast cancer include:

» Alcohol has empty calories and can lead to unwanted weight gain. Excess fat can lead to increased cancer risk.

» Alcohol can increase levels of estrogen and other hormones associated with breast cancer.

» Alcohol users are more likely to have increased amounts of folic acid in their systems, which can lead to increased cancer risk.

» Select low-calorie options to avoid unwanted weight gain Stay away from 100-proof liquor. Researchers believe that it's the ethanol or alcohol in beer, wine and liquor that causes increased cancer risk.

» Avoid alcohol as often as possible.

In the studies I have looked through, alcohol increases your risk of getting breast cancer by 10 percent, which does not sound like a lot, but add that to the other things you are doing to keep your chances low. How much more are you willing to do to be able to drink and not increase your odds?

Cannabis

Cannabis was not legally available in California when I was going through cancer surgery. I have thought about it and wondered if I would have used it to help with pain. My brother (the straightest person I know) started to grow medical cannabis on his ranch in Oregon. I have had numerous talks with

---

1 "Alcohol and breast cancer risk: What to know," by Kellie Bramlet Blackburn, as posted on the MD Anderson Cancer Center website. https://www.mdanderson.org/publications/focused-on-health/alcohol-breast-cancer-risk-what-to-know.h30Z1591413.html.

him about the positive effects of cannabis on cancer patients dealing with pain and how much better for the body it is compared to pain medications.

This article, "Marijuana and Cancer," points out the pros and cons, and I've summarized their points.[2]

Positive effects:

  » Decreased pain without the harsh side effects of opiates.

  » Dronabinol (a trade name for a specific form of tetrahydrocannabinol or THC, the principal psychoactive property of cannabis) can be helpful for reducing nausea and vomiting linked to chemotherapy.

  » Dronabinol has also been found to help improve food intake and prevent weight loss in patients with HIV. In studies of cancer patients, though, it wasn't better than placebo or another drug (megestrol acetate).

  » Nabiximols (another cannabis extract) has shown promise for helping people with cancer pain that's unrelieved by strong pain medicines, but it hasn't been found to be helpful in every study done. Research is still being done.

Here are the negative side effects:

  » Weight gain can occur (see the chapter on weight and cancer), which can increase your chances of getting cancer again due to the estrogen produced and retained in the body.

  » Like many other drugs, the prescription forms of cannabinoids can cause side effects and complications.

  » Some people have trouble with increased heart rate, decreased blood pressure (especially when standing up), dizziness or lightheadedness, and fainting. These drugs can cause drowsiness as well as mood changes or a feeling of being "high" that some people find uncomfortable.

---

2 "Marijuana and Cancer," as posted on the American Cancer Society website (last revised 2017). https://www.cancer.org/treatment/treatments-and-side-effects/complementary-and-alternative-medicine/marijuana-and-cancer.html.

» Cannabis can also worsen depression, mania, or other mental illness. Some patients taking nabiximols reported hallucinations. The drugs may increase some effects of sedatives, sleeping pills, or alcohol, such as sleepiness and poor coordination.

» People who have had emotional illnesses, paranoia, or hallucinations may find their symptoms are worse when taking cannabinoid drugs.

» Patients have also reported problems with dry mouth and trouble with recent memory.

» Older patients may have more problems with side effects and are usually started on lower doses.

This information didn't lead me either way as to whether I would take cannabis for cancer pain management. I am a control freak and like to know what is going on at all times so I am not sure I would take it. I have enough problems as I get older remembering what was said to me. I only want to give you information you may not know. As always, I am not trying to influence you one way or the other. You should weigh out what you are willing to do to keep cancer from your life. If you add up all the small percentages of what you are doing to help cancer have the perfect place to grow, you'll know which practices and preferences are worth it and which ones are not. Cut these down as much as you are willing to do to stay alive.

To me, nothing is worth the risk of another battle with cancer.

CHAPTER 24

Eating Meat

DO I EAT MEAT? This is a big question I get asked a lot.

Yes, I eat meat. I do not think eating meat is bad for the body. But here are the main things you have to ask yourself if you are going to eat meat:

1. <u>Am I combining my foods correctly when I eat meat?</u> Meat takes the longest to digest in the body. There are certain natural enzymes we have (made by God who put them in the stomach) to digest meat. When eating meat, we do not want to cause hardship on the body while it is trying to heal. The last thing we want to do is put more pressure on the body. We want to relieve the body of strain. If you eat fruit with meat at the same meal, the fruit will sit in your stomach waiting for the meat to digest. The fruit will ferment as it waits for the meat, causing bloating and a hardship for the digestion process. Meat is best digested with vegetables only and no water so the enzyme is strong and able to process the meat. In the perfect environment, the meat should pass through the first phase of your digestive system in no more than six to eight hours. To complete the entire meat digestion, it should take 24 hours, if healthy digestion is taking place.

2. <u>Lunch meat and packaged meats.</u> As we know from previous chapters, additives and chemicals are found in the foods we buy. We did not go over all the chemicals put into packaged lunch meat to keep it fresh. Without those preservatives, the meat would only stay fresh for a few days before it has to be thrown out. Always be thinking: could that be good for my body? If a chemical is allowing meat to stay longer on the shelf,

what is it going to do once I eat it? The controversy is in the nitrites that keep meats fresh. They have been thought to cause cancer.

3. Natural Meat. You'll see many meat products with labels saying they are "natural" products. This is marketing speak to make you feel you are buying something healthy. Or, the package will claim the meat is "hormone-free" with "no antibiotics given to the animals." But does this mean free of growth hormones? In other words, hormones and antibiotics may not have been added to the meat, but what did the animals eat while they were being raised? Are they eating corn loaded with growth hormones which is transferred to you? Are they eating food heavily sprayed with pesticides (chemicals) which is then transferred to you through their meat?

Organic Meat

One reason I do not eat a lot of meat because to do it right, I have to buy truly organic meat, from sources where the meat is as pure as I can get it. Raising beef cattle on an organic farm in the United States is very costly.

If it is marked "organic" everything that comes in contact with that cow has to be organic. It will not get shots with antibiotics of any kind, all food it consumes has to be organic. All of that care comes with a high cost. And a grass-fed organic cow is a healthy cow and the meat it produces is pure and exactly what we should be eating if we are eating meat.

Before you read on, let me explain the digestion of a cow. It has multiple stomachs given to it by God. To digest what? Grass. Yes, just grass or hay. When you put anything but grass into its stomach it becomes a very sick cow because it only goes through one stomach instead of three. Read the transcript, "Frontline: Modern Meat, interview with Michael Pollan," as posted on the PBS website and please read it all.[1] You will find out why you should not eat meat if it comes from a very sick cow.

By contrast, take a look at what is fed to non-organic cows as reported in this article, "They Eat What? What Are They Feeding Animals on Factory Farms?"[2] The author takes a look at what they feed to cows, chickens, turkeys, and pigs. When I think of the chicken and beef I eat in restaurants that I don't know where it is coming from, I think I will stick to salads when going out. When I read this, I almost threw up. Ready? Here's the list:

» Same species meat;

» Diseased animals;

» Feathers, hair, skin, hooves, and blood;

» Manure and other animal waste;

» Plastics;

» Drugs and chemicals; and

» Unhealthy amounts of grains.

Are these ingredients legal? Unfortunately, yes. Nevertheless, this has to raise human health concerns. There are many reports on what is being fed to livestock raised for mass food production. Even if it's not this bad, the standards are very low when it comes to mass-feeding these animals. As a society, we have lost sight of the appropriate way to raise food animals.

I cooked an organic steak for my dad and when he bit into it, he said, "Wow, this is like the old days, incredible. It tastes like real meat." If you have never had one, buy just one and see what you think. In restaurants, they add lots of seasonings and marinate the meat for a day to make it more tender

---

1 "Frontline: Modern Meat, interview with Michael Pollan," as posted on the PBS website. https://www.pbs.org/wgbh/pages/frontline/shows/meat/interviews/pollan.html.

2 "They Eat What? What Are They Feeding Animals on Factory Farms?" as posted on the Organic Consumers Association website. https://www.organicconsumers.org/news/they-eat-what-what-are-they-feeding-animals-factory-farms.

and to hide the true flavor. But a real organic steak tastes so much different. It only needs to be cooked with salt and pepper to taste amazing.

Chicken

Chickens are raised very close together and they catch diseases from each other very easily, like a kindergarten class. This makes it costly to keep them all healthy. Workers are tasked with "plucking" the diseased birds from the crowd all day long, but they can never stop the contamination. That is why they are given so many drugs as a precaution against an outbreak of some kind.

You really have to look at the package information very closely because they will fool you with terms such as "cage free," "all-natural," "happy birds," "steroid-free" and other healthy-sounding phrases. If it does not say organic, they are letting so much get by to bring the costs down.

Several companies do a great job with this clever phrasing. But they do not mention anything about the genetically-modified corn they feed their chickens or the antibiotics they give the chickens. It is all in the fine print. Without much effort, you can find information all over the Internet about the shocking practices of poultry farms. Birds are raised in tiny cages stacked on top of each other all their lives. They can barely sit down and they can never run free. Any reasonable person would cry to see the way they are treated.

Remember, all the drugs and growth hormones are embedded into the meat of the chicken. When you eat their flesh, whatever is in theirs is going to end up in yours.

A note about eggs: I try to only eat eggs at home, not when going out to eat. When you eat eggs in a restaurant the chickens have probably been treated with antibiotics for years. They have more than likely been feed food with growth hormones and pesticides. Am I telling you not to buy or eat eggs, NO, but if you don't want to buy the organic, choose the eggs labeled no hormone, no antibiotic given. Read the box VERY carefully to truly see what you are buying, they use the word natural, cage free, but that does not mean they have no antibiotics or growth hormones unless it is stated on the box.

As with meat, you have to look so closely at the carton to make sure what you are buying is truly organic. The farms are masters at making you think you are buying organic products when you are not. They pay a lot more to raise organic chickens, it will be plainly written all over the box.

Fish

Now, let's talk about fish. We think fish are swimming free in oceans and ponds, right? No. Fish are now raised in a fish farm environment. I could not believe it when I first heard it: fish farms. Massive tanks hold fish and they are raised on food doused with growth hormones to get them to grow faster so you can buy them sooner. You will be so surprised when you see this.

The food they are given is foreign to fish. Fish don't like corn! You should be wondering: *What happens to the fish in order to adapt to this food?* When you give an animal a food it is not used to it will change how the animal digests this food. So, if you think about it, the fish will become sick trying to deal with this.

Check out this article, "9 Things Everyone Should Know About Farmed Fish." It will freak you out.[3] The author tells us farmed fish have dubious nutritional value:

> "Here's a frustrating paradox for those who eat fish for their health: the nutritional benefits of fish are greatly decreased when it's farmed. Take omega-3 fatty acids. Wild fish get their omega-3's from aquatic

---

3 "9 Things Everyone Should Know About Farmed Fish," by David Robinson Simon, as posted on the mindbodygreen website. https://www.mindbodygreen.com/0-11561/9-things-everyone-should-know-about-farmed-fish.html.

plants. Farmed fish, however, are often fed corn, soy, or other feedstuffs that contain little or no omega-3's. This unnatural, high-corn diet also means some farmed fish accumulate unhealthy levels of the wrong fatty acids. Further, farmed fish are routinely dosed with antibiotics, which can cause antibiotic-resistant disease in humans."

When you buy fish, you need to make sure the fish has been caught in the wild. There are certain fish that are better than others for your body. All the fish I eat (and I eat a lot of fish) is freshly caught and I try to eat deep ocean fish.

Always look at the packaging to see where the fish truly comes from and where it is packaged. Was anything done to the fish to package it? You are looking for an indication that the fish was caught in the wild and then frozen. Some companies add preservatives before they freeze it. This is because they don't flash freeze it as soon as it is caught and cleaned.

I know this sounds so crazy; to obsess over eating like this. But isn't it worth staying alive? Once you know the brands that work for you, keep buying them. The recipe can change, but the source and quality of your products stay the same.

If you want to skip meat altogether I understand, but you still need proteins. Review my chapter on protein bars and shakes. You have to have the right amount of proteins into your diet. Without it your body can break down your muscles and affect your organs that are trying to get protein. This is NOT something you do without studying it all the way first. It is not just taking meat out of your diet, you HAVE to replace the protein with something. You have to count the grams of protein and make sure it is enough to maintain the body. It has to be easily digested by the body and absorbed in the intestines. In my years working in holistic centers, this was a huge subject the doctors worked with all the time. Am I telling you not to do it? Absolutely not; I was a vegetarian for 5 years but it was just so hard to do it right for me with all I was dealing with at the time. To stay alive, you need to know everything you are putting in your body is to help it heal and stay alive in the future.

I know it seems like a lot but it is not when you think of the alternative. Stay focused. Ask questions before you eat anything new that you haven't vetted. This is why I rarely eat out and when I do, I know exactly where I'm going and what I'm going to order.

Eating the wrong foods puts such a strain on the body. Sure, once in a while, splurge on something outside the guidelines. But daily? No. And believe me, once you start eating for your body, you will no longer crave or enjoy foods that are not supporting your body's mission to get you healthy and stay that way.

CHAPTER 25

Genetically Modified Organisms (GMOs)

WHAT EXACTLY IS GENETICALLY MODIFIED food anyway?

When I read the article, "What's really in a McDonald's hamburger?" I almost threw up.[1] I mean that. You have to see what you are eating. This report explains—with visuals—what growth hormones do to the body. Look half way down the web page and you will see what happens to a rat when growth hormones are added to its food. I did not get it until I saw for myself what they would do to my body. What could they do to a tumor in my body?

Why would companies put these things in our food? To make the crops grow bigger and faster, to make it resistant to bugs, and to preserve it from rotting on the shelf. All of these choices are to gain more money. They will continue the practice of growing and packaging our foods in ways that help their bottom line until we stop them.

I have to laugh at myself, because it's crazy: I still think of farms being like those I learned about when I was in grade school. I have a vision of big open fields, rows of crops growing in God's light, a soft breeze blowing the tops of the produce as it reaches for the sky in His perfect love.

Then I studied farms to stay alive and I was mortified to see how much it is not like that at all. Farming is *big business*. Most of us are clueless as to how they are run. Is this the best kept secret in the world or are we just too scared to look at it?

---

1 "What's really in a McDonald's hamburger?" by Robin Konie, as posted on the Thank Your Body website (updated 2019). https://www.thankyourbody.com/mcdonalds-hamburger.

Almost every product we touch now in the store has been modified in some way. I learned the most about this from my local organic grocery store when they started to pull any food from their shelves (food I thought was good for me—after all, it was coming from a health food store, right?) that had GMOs in the product.

I mean, I read the labels and there was no non-God ingredient that I could see, right? I was a label reader and I knew everything. Wrong.

There is no nationwide regulation that requires food be marked if it has been altered with GMOs. According to the article, "Restrictions on Genetically Modified Organisms: United States":[2]

> "There is no law in the US requiring that GMO foods or foods with GMO ingredients be labeled to so indicate. Proposed federal legislation, the Genetically Engineered Food Right-to-Know Act, which would mandate labeling of any GMO food or food with a genetically modified ingredient, has been introduced in the last several Congresses, but has never advanced beyond the committee stage in either chamber. At the state level, a 2012 California initiative mandating labeling of GMO foods, and a similar 2013 Washington State initiative, both failed."

What? Are you kidding me?

The thing that scared me the most is knowing that because GMOs make crops grow faster, they could also make anything in the body grow faster and bigger.

If you have tumors in your body right now, think about feeding them something with the ability to make them grow quicker than before.

Is it modifying God's work when it comes to breast tissue? When it changes this tissue, will it change it enough to cause cancer at a younger

---

2 "Restrictions on Genetically Modified Organisms: United States," as posted on the Library of Congress website (updated 2015). https://www.loc.gov/law/help/restrictions-on-gmos/usa.php#Research.

age in women? Why do other countries ban GMOs from being used but the United States allows it?

Health-conscience people in California and other states have been screaming about this for years, but we are going up against big business and the government.

In his article, "GMOs and Cancer," Jeffrey Smith's first point warns us:[3]

"The very process of creating a GMO creates side effects that can promote cancer. Monsanto's Roundup Ready corn, for example, has higher levels of putrescine and cadaverine. These are not only linked to cancer and allergies; they produce the foul smell of rotting dead bodies."

Here is a list of where you'll find some of the most common products that include GMOs.

Animal Products

Animals are fed the GMO corn and therefore, it's present in their bodies when we eat them. This is *not* an antibiotic, so when the label says there are no antibiotics, that does not mean there are no growth hormones. The label has to say "no growth hormones, no antibiotics" for it to be safer for you to eat. If you can afford it, buy organic meats and eggs which means that the food and what the animals have been fed are free of GMOs.

Corn, Soy, Aspartame, and Canola Oil

Corn. It is unbelievable how much corn is in the food we eat. You have no idea, trust me, unless you have studied this in-depth. Corn is everywhere. Farmers produce so much that they are now feeding it to farm-raised fish and cows as a filler. Why? Because the federal government is involved in agriculture and farmers receive

---

3 "GMOs and Cancer," by Jeffrey Smith, as posted on the Responsible Technology website (2017). https://responsibletechnology.org/gmos-and-cancer.

subsidies to grow it. This arrangement was set up decades ago and the practice continues. These animals can't digest corn correctly because God did not give their digestive systems the ability to digest it properly. But the growth hormone *is* digested anyway. So, farmers and the government allow feeding it to animals because it is cheap and helps them grow faster, not because it is good for us.

Soy. If your cancer is estrogen-based, soy products should not be consumed. Soy has been known to help cancer grow. Now, add a growth hormone to soy products and when your doctor tells you, "We are going to watch your tumor for a while," and you come back and it is twice the size you'll be thinking, *what the Hell?*

Aspartame. This is an artificial sweetener that is used as a sugar substitute. It is found in gum and many other food products and is made with genetically modified bacteria.

Canola Oil. This is in so many packaged foods and it's one of the most chemically-altered foods laced with growth hormones. I thought it was supposed to be better for you. No. Read the label. Once it's altered, it becomes toxic.

Did you know that canola is an oilseed crop created through plant crossbreeding? This article "Is Canola Oil healthy?" says most canola crops are genetically modified to improve oil quality and increase plant tolerance to herbicides. In fact, more than 90 percent of the canola crops grown in the United States have GMOs.[4]

One of the best oils is organic extra-virgin olive oil. It is rich in anti-inflammatory compounds, including polyphenol antioxidants, which may prevent heart disease and mental decline. Seed and nut oils, along with

---

4 "Is Canola Oil Healthy? All You Need to Know," by Jillian Kubala, MS, RD, as posted on the Healthline website (2019). https://www.healthline.com/nutrition/is-canola-oil-healthy.

coconut oils, have benefits but should be used in moderation. As always, do your research. You can find arguments for and against everything under the sun. Coconut oil was touted in recent years as being a wonder food. But Harvard professor Dr. Karin Michels described coconut oil as "pure poison" in his article.[5]

One of my personal favorite oils to use for cooking is avocado oil. There are so many health benefits of avocados that I gravitated towards the oil for cooking. Maybe I'm biased being from California, but I can't see a day without them.

The list goes on and on. Am I a purest? People ask me that all the time. No, I am not. I am not in a food bubble at all. I get cravings like everyone else. My last one was onion rings with ranch from Jack in the Box. I ate them twice a month when I went walking on the beach.

Here is how my thinking process goes. Okay. If I eat an Egg McMuffin meal from McDonald's right now, the chances of that egg having antibiotics, pesticides, and growth hormones are high. Not to mention what's in the meat and cheese. They then fry it on a grill with oil that has probably been modified. That potato thing that comes with the meal is deep-fried in modified GMO oil of some type. Not to mention the potato has a chemical that does not allow it to get growth sprouts—a chemical known to cause cancer. The cheese probably came from a rBGH-raised cow with growth hormones. The muffin has gluten and grains that have probably been altered.

So, when I think about it, how much in this meal is pure food from God at all? I would be eating a science experiment. Then, I am asking my body over and over again to cleanse itself of what I'm putting into it. The body has no defense from these attacks. See what happens?

---

5 "A Harvard professor said coconut oil isn't a superfood, calling it 'pure poison'," by Valentina Resetarits and Ruqayyah Moynihan, as posted on the Business Insider website (2018). https://www.businessinsider.com/harvard-speaker-busts-coconut-oil-health-myth-calling-it-pure-poison-2018-8.

Note to self: carry more healthy snacks, get up earlier to make a smoothie, fill your water bottle and drink your hunger away for right now. My life does depend on it. Every day, I need to think about how can I protect myself from what the government is allowing to kill me.

These foods are something to ban from your life now!

Ask the question to everything you put in your mouth: does this have GMOs in it? Read the label and if it does not say "non-GMO" think twice. A label can say "GMO-free" but if it's an animal product, did the animal eat GMOs in their food?

I hope you think of this for the rest of your life. That could be a tumor in your body, and I am trying to help you not give it a chance to grow.

CHAPTER 26

Organic Food

SOMETIMES I HAVE A HARD TIME writing this information down for you because I have been eating this way for so long, I naturally think (or maybe I desperately hope) that everyone eats this way. I forget I live in California in the "natural" capital of San Diego County. We are not the same as the normal person when it comes to eating or, for that matter, our lifestyles.

There are so many stores around me where I can get organic food now it is crazy. The closest is 10 minutes from my house. I can buy organics all year long with little effort. I think I take that for granted sometimes.

I want to explain to you in this chapter why it is worth the effort to go and get organic foods or have them delivered to you. There is a difference in organic foods and you should know about these before you buy them.

I know eating organic foods is one of the reasons I am alive today. I eat organic 90 percent of the time. I am asked by friends, "How can you afford this?" and then they look in my closet and see I had a very small wardrobe—maybe 20 pieces of clothes I wear over and over.

I have only taken one vacation with my daughter, and that was not until she was 25 years old. I am lucky to live in San Diego, so every day is a vacation. I always had bills I was paying off for surgeries, copays, and all the supplements insurance would not cover. But the one thing I knew would save me was what I was putting in my body to protect my body.

Here is why eating organic foods are so worth it! There are four different levels of organic you should know about:

	ORGANIC INGREDIENTS
100% ORGANIC All ingredients and processing aids must be certified organic. These foods may use the USDA organic seal as well as 100% organic claim.	**100%**
ORGANIC All agricultural ingredients must be certified organic, but product can contain up to 5% non-organic content. These foods may use the USDA organic seal.	AT LEAST **95%**
MADE WITH ORGANIC INGREDIENTS Contains at least 70% certified organic ingredients; remaining 30% not required to be certified organic, but may not be produced using excluded methods. These foods may not use the USDA organic seal.	AT LEAST **70%**
SPECIFIC ORGANIC INGREDIENTS Contains less than 70% certified organic ingredients. May list certified organic ingredients as organic in the ingredient list. These foods may not use the USDA organic seal.	LESS THAN **70%**

I know you are probably thinking, *there are levels to organic food? I thought all organic labels meant the same thing.*

No, they are not the same. Think of it as select and non-select organic produce. If you want to see a store manager flinch, ask them the level of organic food you are about to buy. They do not want you to know the level, or even that you know there is a level. They probably will not know the level.

Here are the questions I asked them: If you are paying for organic from a country that does not have the same strict laws we have in the United States, how do you know what you are getting? Are there laws in other countries for growing organic produce?

When I asked the organic store how they know this food is truly organic by United States standards when it comes from another country, I was told: "We go there at least once a year and check."

"Check the soil?" I asked? "You do a soil sample to see what is in the soil?"

No, they don't. And what is to stop that country from mixing in their regular produce with the organic to save money?

I know in the United States they will lose their license for five years and get a $11,000 fine per violation for doing that. So, I asked, "If the produce is coming from other countries, are there any penalties if they are caught?"

"I do not know how you would catch them," came the answer.

I asked this at one of the major organic chains I buy food from. Boy, was that an eye-opener. As I was having this discussion, other shoppers gathered around and said, "I never thought of that!"

One of the countries supplying them with organic food is Mexico. I asked more questions. Who in Mexico looks after the organic farms? What is the fine in Mexico for not following the standards from the United States? Wait! The question should be: What are the standards in Mexico? Do they have the same standards as the United States? Read the article, "Does America Have the World's Worst Food Quality & Safety?"[1]

When you export organic food from another country, what is the protocol followed so the consumer is not taken advantage of when buying it? How do I, as a consumer, know they are actually delivering organically-graded food? How do I know they did not mix in non-organic batches for higher profit margins?

This article opened my eyes. "USDA Failure: Organic Farmers Play Dirty."[2]

> "In 2012, the United States Department of Agriculture (USDA) published a study that found nearly 40 percent of food sold in the U.S. that was labeled "organic" tested positive for restricted pesticides.

---

1 "Does America Have the World's Worst Food Quality & Safety?" by Ty Bollinger, as posted on The Truth About Cancer website (2016). https://thetruthaboutcancer.com/america-worst-food-quality-safety.

2 "USDA Failure: Organic Farmers Play Dirty," by Charlene Bollinger, as posted on The Truth About Cancer website (2019). https://thetruthaboutcancer.com/organic-food-fraud.

"It's also important to note that much of the organic food sold in the U.S. is imported from abroad. According to reporter Anna Casey, about 75 percent of our organic soybeans and nearly half our organic corn is imported from other countries. Many of those crops are used to raise beef and poultry."

When the country of origin is so far away and the land itself is not governed well, how can we make sure we are truly buying organic? Here is information on identifying organic foods from the article, "Learn How to Tell When "Organic" on a Label is True."[3]

USDA Certification Foods that meet USDA organic standards are "certified organic," also sometimes called "USDA-certified organic." Organic food in the United States can be identified when the following conditions are met:

» The product bears the official USDA organic seal.

» The product has been certified organic.

» The product contains 95 percent or more organic ingredients.

The USDA's official organic seal is green and white, and some manufacturers and producers use a very similar, though different colored, seal. Such mislabeling can result in fines of up to $11,000 per violation. Also, a product does not have to contain 95 percent organic ingredients to be truly beneficial. The USDA allows those products with at least 70 percent organically produced ingredients to use the words "made with organic ingredients." However, those products cannot carry the green-and-white USDA seal.

Fruits and Vegetables

If you want to know if the fruits and vegetables, you're purchasing are truly organic, look at the Price Look Up (PLU) sticker. If the produce is organic, the code will contain five-digits beginning with the number 9. Nonorganic counterparts will have four digits. For example, organically grown bananas will be 94011, compared to

---

3 "Learn How to Tell When "Organic" on a Label is True," by Jennifer Chait, as posted on the Balance Small Business website (2019). https://www.thebalancesmb.com/when-is-organic-really-organic-2538312.

4011 for those treated with chemicals and pesticides. A five-digit PLU beginning with the number 8 means the item is genetically modified.

Farmers Markets

Organics may cost less at farmers markets because of lower shipping costs and no middlemen, but it can be hard to know what you're getting—especially when products lack PLU stickers. Under the USDA's National Organic Program, farmers who market their products as organic are supposed to have their wares certified by a USDA-accredited agent or face fines if they get caught. If the product is being touted as certified, you can ask to see a copy of the organic certification paperwork. Vendors are supposed to have it on hand whenever selling their wares.

Okay. Let's talk about how food gets to our shelves. We are programed to not think about this too much. It all just shows up somehow, right?

I watch people when I go to the grocery store. Most people carefully look over the produce to see if there are rotten spots because we all want to provide the best for our families. Food is such a large part of our expenses. We try very hard to bring the expenses down by shopping at big box stores, looking for deals on the foods we buy.

America is practically the only country with giant supermarkets in every community, and these companies are quickly expanding their footprint across the globe. Traditionally, other countries value fresh food more and people tend to buy their food at markets on a daily basis, selecting only the foods they intend to eat in the next day or two. Some of these fresh food markets are vast—usually the size of our big box stores—and vendors sell the best available in their specialty. And guess what? The populations are outliving Americans! It's a wonderful shopping experience when you have local farmers selling what they have grown themselves and you can ask questions as you purchase their food.

I want to help you see how to buy food that will actually heal your body. Every time food travels to get to you, it loses some of its ability to heal you. I am blessed to live in California so I can look through the food to find the "grown in the USA" labels. But many people want to buy produce that is not in season or fruit that is not grown in the United States.

We all imagine produce comes in on trucks from the farm to the store and then we put on our shelves at home. It used to work that way, but now it is so different. We import so much of our food and since people are used to seeing so many varieties displayed in the isles, they do not realize they are buying produce grown in a different country. Has it even crossed your mind to check the label when you are buying produce? Yes, check the label to see where the produce you are buying is coming from it. If you are not in the habit of doing this, it will shock you.

For example, if the produce is coming from Argentina, it has most likely been on a ship for months. They can not afford to ship produce on a plane so you have to ask yourself these questions. Do you know if it was shipped to the store by plane or ship? How long ago was it harvested? Trust me, it was picked way before God was done with it. This means the fruit or vegetable was not brought through its entire growing season. How could it be ripe when picked, and then travel on a boat for months and not be spoiled? What kind of effect does that have on the produce? They ripen it in the ship.

When you pick something before God is done with it, it does NOT feed the body the way it was intended to do. The nutrients are not in the produce designed to feed the body. The items can appear fresher, but the taste is flat. It may not be gross or smelly or look like it has been picked a long time ago. But aren't these the warning signs that we should not eat something? Now they have taken those obvious warning signs away so we do not truly know what we are buying. The fruit importers have figured out how to pick crops months before and then sell them to us.

This is going to shock you. Ready?

More than half of the fresh fruit and more than one third of the vegetables we consume in the United States today come from somewhere else; they are imported into our country.

Ninety percent of the fruits and vegetables I buy are grown in the United States. Does it get boring eating the same fruits and vegetables? Not if it means eating food that I do not know what has happened to it before it gets to me. Not when I cut all other expenditures to get it. If I have to cut my fun money to buy it, it better be true organic food.

I am doing an experiment on a potato from Mexico I bought at my health food store. It is supposed to be organic. It took over a month to form an eye and now *two months later* it has still not molded or broken down in any way. Was it really organic? I'll let you know the results and how many months it took to breakdown. Yes, try this at home and test your vegetables.

CHAPTER 27

Pesticides on Our Food

EUROPE HAS BANNED FIVE PESTICIDES from farm use due to the effects these chemicals have on the human body, yet the United States still allow the chemicals to be used on our food.

As I started to study this, I became increasingly upset. **There are chemicals used that we know cause cancer and yet we still use them.** The chemicals are to kill the bugs living around your produce.

Pesticides and fumigants include herbicides (such as Atrazine to control weeds and other plants), insecticides (such as Fipronil to control insects), fungicides (to control fungi or other plant pathogens), nematicides (to control parasitic worms), and rodenticides (to control rodents).

If you want to know what these are, and what farmers are allowed to use, it's easy to search for them. It will amaze you and scare you at the same time. Farmers are allowed to use these chemicals on our land, which we all know eventually leaches into our water supplies. They actually shoot these chemicals into the soil before they plant so the plant has these chemicals built right into them.

As I studied on the Internet, it amazed me to find so many articles about the pesticides that are still allowed in our food even if they are known to cause cancer. *Wait, what?* We are the United States of America, how can we allow this to happen to us? They know this and the studies stop without proof or they end without showing us the proof. We have all heard about the Roundup lawsuit and we think it has nothing to do with us if we did not buy it at our local store. I rationalized it myself. Thank God I did not use that at my house to kill my weeds, right?

It has nothing to do with personal use; they use it on the crops in the United States. **The United States has used 1.8 million tons of it on crops in the United States.**

I'm not a scientist; I am a cancer survivor trying to stay alive. When the food we eat to stay alive has chemicals that can cause cancer to what we are trying to heal, then we are in a vicious cycle.

Why is this a concern for you? Let's think about this. When they spray your food to keep the bugs off of it, we rationalize that the skin of the produce will not absorb it. We can wash it off before we eat it, right? But if it is introduced into the soil first, we all know from elementary school that when we grow plants, the plant pulls everything from the soil in order to grow, both good and bad properties.

The example that really explained it to me is a store-bought bouquet where they died the flowers a different color. They way they died them was food color in the water. It traveled up the stock and into the flowers so they became blue. When they started to die, the dye went in the water and when I cut the flowers the dye was on my hands. That is the same concept as the pesticides going up the stem to the vegetables and fruit, except it stays in the food and then we eat it.

If you still can't grasp what I am saying, think about the promises made by Miracle Grow fertilizers. The company's commercials show you how it helps your plants grow miraculously!

This is the same concept with pesticides. The growing properties enter the plants the same way; there is no way it does not get into the produce. If your produce sits in the chemicals as it grows, (think of produce with thin skins—strawberries, lettuce, potatoes, celery) the pesticides are absorbed through the skin.

I love to garden and there are always bugs everywhere. It was like I was a bug Lord. I went to the nursery to find something that would kill the bugs.

Wait, what? I have to wear gloves, protective clothing, not get it in my eyes or cuts on my hands, and I'm going to then put it around the food I am going to eat?

I asked myself what are other countries putting on their crops to kill the bugs? Are we monitoring what they are using before we allow their food in our country? If the answer is yes, how often are we taking soil samples? How do we know if the food is coming from the areas we have sampled?

I found the chemicals used in the United States to kill bugs, but I do not have the time to go through every country to see what they use. Do these other countries care about the effects on the body from these chemicals? If we only have the bandwidth to check our own farmers twice a year, I'm sure they know we will not be checking them anytime soon.

I will take one food to make my point: potatoes. Now think of every potato you eat. My addiction used to be French fries, not after reading this. The potatoes they use have so many chemicals on them you will not believe it. The main chemical is one that will not allow the potato to "eye" when stored for months—yes, months. It has been known to cause cancer. Not to mention the other drugs that are sprayed on them to keep them from growing fungus and so on.

There are up to six chemicals added to one vegetable so they can be sold looking fresh, but little do we know that means chemically fresh.[1]

If you are paying for organic produce from a country that does not have the same strict laws we have in the United States, do your research, and see if you can find out about that country's laws and restrictions. My new rule is to buy organic foods grown in the United States. When you are in doubt, ask. I know we think our hipster organic stores have done the research for us, but that shouldn't stop us from asking, "How safe are we?"

---

1 "The Health Risks of Eating Conventional Potatoes," by Max Goldberg, as posted on the Living Maxwell website (2013). https://livingmaxwell.com/health-risks-conventional-potatoes.

If food is going to keep me alive, I realized I better become versed in food and where it comes from. I really started to study the farming industry and it scared me. What we actually grow in the United States would surprise you. What the government pays farmers to grow (including food we don't eat) would boggle your mind. Research "corn exports" to see how much corn we sell to other countries. It's crazy.

I often wonder how much it would cost and how long it would take to change soil that has had pesticides sprayed on it for years so that it would be able to grow organic produce. I thought you would have to replace the soil entirely, which must cost millions of dollars.

One article I found said all you had to do is let the soil rest and not have any commercial pesticides on the land for three years. After that, you can start growing organic produce on it.

So, the commercial pesticides are gone after three years?[2]

That did not seem like enough time to me. A cancer-causing product is gone in only three years? Where does it go? Has it been proven it is not harmful to us anymore after three years? I could not find articles on it.

What I did find was all kinds of articles on organic farming. I learned a lot about what they go through to keep the food safe and now I understand why organic foods cost so much more in the store.[3]

Today, we have services that will deliver organic food. Farm Fresh to You is one company based in the United States that grows and ships organic fruits and vegetables fresh from their fields to your doorstep.[4]

---

2 "Guidelines for Organic Crop Certification," as posted on the USDA.gov website. https://www.ams.usda.gov/sites/default/files/media/Crop%20-%20Guidelines.pdf.

3 "Wait, Organic Farmers Use Pesticides?" as posted on the Rodale Institute website. https://rodaleinstitute.org/blog/wait-organic-farmers-use-pesticides.

4 Farm Fresh To You grows and ships organic produce. Find out more information on their website at https://www.farmfreshtoyou.com.

Remember, if you only have enough in your budget to buy a few organic things, it's better than none at all. I always think of this: *Who wants food that has been sitting in chemicals for months?* If the skin of the product is soft or thin, it has absorbed the chemicals. If the seed germinated in soil laced with chemicals, the produce lived in that soil as it grew.

If enough of us start buying food from companies like these, maybe the rest will get our point. You know the times are changing because all the major food stores now have organic sections. Believe me, they are fully aware of how much of it we buy, exactly what we buy, and how we divide our spending between organic and non-organic items.

As we join together, we send a powerful message to the growers that we are spending our money on this and not this. As we choose growers in the United States and not overseas, *we*—not the government—tell growers what to grow and what we will allow to be put on and in our food.

As we join together, we tell them loudly and clearly that we will not be behind other countries providing our food and we will tell local growers what we *don't* want to be put into our foods.

Be safe. Always know exactly what you are putting in your body!

CHAPTER 28

Fast Food and Eating Out

PEOPLE TEASE ME ALL THE TIME about the way I eat. They truly don't understand why I eat the way I do. We have been trained our whole that if we do anything in moderation that it will not affect our body. Okay, that sounds so good on paper, right? But what is moderation?

We live in a culture where time is a very valuable commodity. We believe everything needs to be done quickly, and that includes buying, preparing, and eating food. Everywhere we go, we will see a fast food place to eat.

I am not sure the public knows how hard it is to make money as a fast food chain. There is an extremely high overhead and high competition with another chain right across the street. Let's think about what this means because this is so important. Eating fast food truly affects your life.

The margin of profit is about 5 percent on what they sell you. If the margins are so low, how can they buy quality food to sell you? Think of it this way: if your burger costs you $2, and the profit is only 5 percent, they have only made 10 cents on that sale. What kind of meat can you buy for that?

Restaurants are the same. They have very low profits after they pay all of their bills. These are the restaurants we go to all the time, the ones we can afford to go to. According to this article, "What is the Average Restaurant Profit Margin?" the range for restaurant profit margin, "typically spans anywhere from 0–15 percent, but usually restaurants fall between a 3–5 percent average restaurant profit margin."[1]

---

1 "What is the Average Restaurant Profit Margin?" as posted on the Toast website (2019). https://pos.toasttab.com/blog/average-restaurant-profit-margin.

The high-dollar restaurants we go to on special occasions are different. They are forced to buy quality food to keep their reputations and that is why eating there costs so much.

Let's now talk about frozen dinners. There is no difference between buying these and eating in the local chain restaurant, as far as profit is concerned. They have to pay for the product, pay the store for shelf space and shelf position. The margin is around 10 percent profit to the company.

"Why are you telling me this, Karen," you ask. "Who cares?"

You should care a lot. Because they have to make a profit so costs come down. When costs come down, so does the quality of the product. It has to—or the company will go out of business. The *only* thing that can change is the product they are selling, and this time it is food.

If the building, the equipment and furniture, and all the employee costs stay the same or go up in cost the only thing they can cut corners on is the quality of the food. If they can get the food cheaper, they will in order to make more profit.

I call this food "air food." It fills you up, but does nothing for your body. Do I ever eat fast food? Yes. Hello? I am human! My favorite is the Mexican food at Del Taco. I love their red sauce. But I eat the vegetarian burrito when I go there. I choose what will have the least effect on my body. However, their fries are so good, I eat those, too, on occasion.

The most important thing is to select the fast food that is the least likely they will have to cut costs on. That includes vegetables, beans, rice, and grains. They will cut costs on all meats. I used to eat French fries at least once a month, they were my cheat food. The fries I use to love are cooked in oil modified to last a week, and even though the only ingredient is potatoes, they are not going to use organic potatoes. So, the fries I'm eating were grown with chemicals that stop them from forming eyes.

This chemical is maleic hydrazide which has been known to cause cancer when cooked. First introduced in 1950, it was evaluated for use in 1976. The chemical is initially introduced into the plant though its stock and then receives a second dose when its sprayed on the potato skin while it sits in storage—sometimes up to 6 months. **This chemical can stop a potato from eyeing for 6 months!** Warnings say not to eat the skin or wash it thoroughly before eating. What? The skin is the best part. Who peels potatoes before eating them anymore except at Thanksgiving? How does something like this go unnoticed?

Please think before you pull into the drive-thru window. And also think about what you are getting when you buy frozen meals.

You know frozen-food companies cannot afford to throw things away because they are running on such low profit margins. So, the food they select has to have a long shelf life. How can these meals stay on the shelf for so long? Because they use chemicals and preservatives that allow the food to survive. Do the food companies tell us what these chemicals will do to our bodies?

Of course, not. They'll tell us they are Food and Drug Administration (FDA) approved additives. The FDA can only make decisions based on the data they have at the time. Once a process has passed, they do not go back and check it unless there is some giant catastrophe. They do not keep checking it as the years pass. The only time they are brought back to look at the process is when enough people scream there is a problem linked to the product.

They do not use leach-proof containers to store the food in. If the product has been on the shelf for a long time, materials from the plastic container will break down and leach into the food. Then we use the containers again to cook the product in. We heat the meal in the oven or microwave and the container by-products are further released into the food. How could it not, right?

Americans eat $20 billion worth of this kind of food per year, and we wonder what is killing us.

We are killing us!

We now have organic frozen food meals made in paper containers so when you heat the meal, the product will not leach into the food. This is the only frozen food I buy, if I buy any at all.

When going to a restaurant, I only eat the food that will not be a danger to my body. I order vegetables, salads, and soups if they can confirm they are made fresh and not from cans. My daughter teases me all the time: "We are having salad with salad for dinner."

I try not to eat things that will be thrown into a microwave to heat up. When I am at a restaurant I always ask, "Is this fresh or frozen?" You can always ask if any food has been heated or prepared with a microwave. When you use drive-thru ordering, most of the food has been sitting under heat lamps, or they will pop it in the microwave to warm it up before giving it to you. Sometimes the food is so hot, I think, *Hello? Wrong setting on the microwave.*

The most important things to consider when fueling your body are:

» How can the body use this food for fuel?

» How hard does it need to work to convert it to healing, usable fuel?

» What other organs need to step in to help break it down and eliminate it?

» What is that doing to these organs as they try to get rid of what they can't use?

I think the difference between the United States and the rest of the world is the way we eat. There has to be a connection with the food we eat and cancer. The United States is rated 9th in the world for cancer. We are one of the strongest countries in the world yet we are dying from disease at an alarming rate, why?

Because we are programed to eat a certain way by the billions of dollars spent on commercials to train us that this food is good for us. When we can see on a menu the calories and fat content, we still eat it, why? Because we are programed to eat it. Our children are rewarded with prizes to eat it.

Please think before you eat. *Help your body keep you alive for years to come.*

CHAPTER 29

Herbs I Took During Surgery

BEFORE I START THIS CHAPTER, I want to state again that I am not a doctor. This is just my personal journey and what I choose to do with my body. I am not leading you to do what I did nor do I know that what I did will work with your body or cancer situation.

My treatments were done more than 25 years ago at a time when there was not as much research on supplements as there is now. There were also not as many companies trying to make money on cancer as a big business in both Eastern and Western medicine as there is today.

If I had a dollar for every company and person selling me something to cure cancer or to prevent it now, I would be a millionaire.

Please realize there are lots of predators who feed on fear when you are sick. We all want to stay alive for our loved ones and will try anything to do so. I get asked all the time, "How do you decide what to do?"

This is how I personally decide what to do:

1. If it is not made by God for His body, I don't do it.

2. I only take things that will support God's body and make it whole again or as strong as it was before I got cancer.

3. If it causes any stress on the body or forces the body to create a side effect to use it, I don't do it.

4. If it does not have a long clinical trial history, I don't do it. A long trial is 10 years or more. In my opinion, it takes at least 10 years for the trial to truly know the side effects.

When the world saw cancer survivors turning toward supplements and the holistic way of life, they saw that as a money-making opportunity. Some of the largest drug companies are now working as a silent partner, or under the umbrella, of the larger owners of supplement companies.

How do I choose what to buy to support my body in addition to all the things I eat and do? Remember, I worked with holistic centers for years so I was always on a program to keep healthy. I had just had my daughter two years before my diagnosis so I was keeping my body healthy before and while I was breast-feeding.

As you read in my story, I worked with an herbalist, Keith Stanton, who put me on his herb program. I did research him. My plastic surgeon had a cancer patient which the cancer spread to the bone marrow who was still alive years after she should have been who was using his program. Remember, this was in the mid-1990s when there were not many choices. I studied next to him and saw patients with him who all told me how they were better or became cancer-free because of his program.

I also worked with an acupuncturist named Mark Heck who gave me some oils to use. He rented an office from one of my chiropractors in Beverly Hills. He gave me some oils I used on acupuncture points which helped me heal faster. This is the program I used when I was first diagnosed with cancer. I did this program throughout my first year. I did not use Western medicine, just these herbs.

It is very important you understand herbs and how they work. They do not leave the body quickly. They are stored in the body tissue and compound as you take them. They are not to be taken without knowledge on what exactly you are doing. They are like a drug and should be treated as a drug. You can get *very* sick if not taken as you would a drug: with caution. Many herbs and supplements may cause you as many problems as taking drugs if used wrong.

If you use anything holistic or medical and it puts a strain on the body, the body will react. Please, please do not take just anything from anybody. Many, many people do not care what happens to you after they sell you their products. Your body is just that: your body and it may react totally differently than others to a non-study herb.

Nature's Sunshine is a long-standing herb company that has been in business for 48 years.1 They are the highest quality herbs on the market selling worldwide. They have their own labs and package their products to keep the standard they have been known by for years. I have trusted them with my life for years.

You can find direct links to these products from Nature's Sunshine (and receive a discount) on my website, twentyfiveyearsandcountingcancerfree.com.

Trigger Immune: Helps boost your immune system which helps you guard against infection and helps in healing. This is the most important herb to take.

THIM-J: Helps boost your thymus gland. This gland helps produce your white blood cell count, which helps your healing.

Spirulina: Helps create oxygen in your blood, which helps with healing.

Valerian Root: Helps repair your muscle and relaxes your muscles. It is a natural muscle relaxer and sleep aid. It is very strong and needs to be used with caution. You cannot use this product if you have any kind of ongoing breathing problems such as asthma as it relaxes all muscles of the body.

Vitamin C: This is a high-potency Vitamin C and helps to heal the body. Vitamin C is a water-soluble product so if the body does

---

1 Nature's Sunshine is one of the leading health and wellness companies in the world. Visit their website at https://www.naturessunshine.com.

not need it at the time it will be eliminated in the urine. I took it throughout the day to get the most benefit from it.

My doses back then were:

Trigger Immune: 3 pills, three time a day while healing. Then follow the bottle recommendations for maintenance.

THIM-J: 3 pills, 3 times a day.

Spirulina: 3 pills, 3 times a day.

Valerian Root: 3 pills, 3 times a day.

Vitamin C: 1000 mg, 3 times a day with the pills above.

At that time, I also took a product called Spir-r-teen in my protein shake every morning. I would not take it now because I now know that soy is not something I should take when dealing with an estrogen cancer like breast cancer. New research has shown soy is an estrogen-based product and may help tumors grow. But there are studies that it helps encapsulate tumors. Did eating soy help save me? I don't know, yet. I wish they would complete the studies.

The above doses are what I took when I was going through all my surgeries and I healed so quickly, no one could figure out how I was totally healed so fast. I remember when I went in to have them remove my stretching implants, they could not believe the amount of healing (scar tissue) in the implant sockets. They had to scrape it out as if the implants had been in for years instead of months.

Now, I do not take the immune system program every day. I do take it when I am feeling sick or run down. I do not take anything from doctors and avoid over-the-counter drugs if I feel sick. I *always* take herbs or oils and supplements. Read on to find out what I now take daily.

CHAPTER 30

Vitamins I Take Every Day and Why

YOUR DIGESTIVE SYSTEM has been off for hours repairing the body. So, when I wake up, I take a shot of Aloe Vera juice. I like to turn my system back on with a product that helps the liver and the colon. I wait about an hour as I am getting ready and then I drink a "green" drink.

There are lots of green drinks on the market and I have looked at most of them. I've probably tried at least 15 types through the years. The one thing is that they must be organic. You do not want the freeze-dried chemicals in your green drinks which will go right into your system.

Upon waking, I take a dose of Realfood Organics Aloe Vera Plus.[1] After about an hour, I drink a shake with Amazing Grass Green Superfood Chocolate.[2] I added a protein shake with this to give me a protein boost in the morning, it's Garden of Life Organic Plant Protein Smooth Chocolate Grain Free. When picking out a protein shake, make sure it is a plant-based protein. Mine is made with pea protein. Look at the sodium amounts, which have to be below 350 milligrams (we are not athletes). I do not drink anything hot with these products and until this has had a chance to digest first.

Many of my daily vitamins come from MegaFood. You will see why once you read about them on their website at megafood.com. They are amazing. Here are the vitamins I use, and many you can order from their site. You can see a list of what I take with links to each product on my website, twentyfiveyearsandcountingcancerfree.com.

---

1 Realfood Organics Aloe Vera Plus available on the Pure Formulas website. https://www.pureformulas.com/rfo-active-aloe-liquid-32-oz--country-life.html.

2 Amazing Grass Green Superfood Chocolate available on the Amazing Grass website. https://shop.amazinggrass.com/products/chocolate-green-superfood.

MegaFood Vitamin D3 2000 IU. I have taken Vitamin D for years, way before low levels were linked to breast cancer. I had to take it for years before it registered in my bloodstream. That was how depleted I was in vitamin D. I take 2,000 milligrams a day, every day. Again, made from food, not man, so the body can use it.

Country Life L-Arginine 500 mg. I take amino acids for two reasons. First, to help with my workouts. I do not eat a lot of meat, maybe once or twice a week tops, so I do not get amino acids easily. Amino acids help rebuild and maintain muscles. I like to work out, jog, walk, and lots of physical things so I need help to keep my body strong. Second, amino acids help my mental state. The neurotransmitter dopamine is made from the amino acid tyrosine, and the neurotransmitter serotonin is made from the amino acid tryptophan. Without these in sufficient levels, there will not be enough synthesis of the respective neurotransmitters, and the deficiency has been associated with low-mood or aggression-mood disorder. I was depressed when my support team died from cancer: my sister, my best friend, my mom. They tried to put me on drugs and I studied them. I found out that I probably had a lack of amino acids. I didn't take any drugs, I just added amino acids to help during my workouts and to keep balance in my life.

MegaFood Multi for Women 55+. Why do I take a multivitamin every day when I eat so well and I take so many other things? I do it to fill in the holes where I may not be getting what I need otherwise. There are so many areas the body needs help with because so many things are attacking the body on a daily basis. I probably don't know the extra thing my body needs to help it. So, why not cover all my bases?

<u>MegaFood Ultra C-400 mg</u>. Vitamin C helps the immune system and to help heal after surgery, I take this in the morning and before I go to sleep.

<u>Natural Factors Coenzyme Q10 100 mg</u>. Also called CoQ10 or ubiquinone, this is a natural substance essential to cellular energy production. It is also an antioxidant that scavenges free radicals throughout the body and is involved in maintaining normal heart function. I started taking this for heart health and for protection from free radicals which can cause cancer.

I am sure there are tons of supplements someone thinks I should be taking that I am not taking but this regimen works for me with the food I eat and my lifestyle. Please know you are entering a huge business that is not regulated by the government at all. Am I against supplements? Absolutely not. It is my life.

But be smart, research the company and know what you are being asked to take. You are not the test pilot for the company. Be safe!

CHAPTER 31

Probiotics

I'VE STARTED ADDING PROBIOTICS more recently because I am older and my digestive system can use some help. Probiotics are organisms which help with digestion, brain function, skin health, and your immune system. Ninety percent of your body is comprised of microbial organisms. For you to stay healthy, they need to stay happy as they help you digest.

You've probably heard the saying, "All diseases begin in the gut." Here are three secrets to making sure you are getting high-quality probiotics in your system.

The 3 Secrets of A High-Quality Probiotic[1]

1. It Lists its Sub-strains. The sub-strains listed next to each strain indicates that a specific probiotic strain has undergone clinical studies. Many probiotic formulations do not list their specific sub-strains. This is a huge red flag that suggests they may be using generic (and cheaper) sub-strains that have not been clinically studied.

2. It Contains Prebiotics. The latest research shows using fiber-based prebiotics (such as Nutra Flora Fiber) will help the probiotics populate and flourish in your gut. This will significantly increase the overall effectiveness of the probiotic.

3. It Doesn't Require Refrigeration. Refrigerated products can be damaged during shipping. Another note: you're not always going to have access to a refrigerator, so we suggest

---

1 "Which 2019 Probiotic Supplements Are the Most Effective?" as posted on Smarter Reviews website. https://smarter-reviews.com/lp/sr-probiotics.

choosing a probiotic that is well-formulated to withstand room temperature and does not require being refrigerated during periods of non-use.

I have been trying to find the correct probiotic for years and could not find one that really made a difference either way that I could feel after I took it. Then I came across a video from the doctor below.[2] I really learned a lot and for the first time in my life I bought a product from a video. Why? Because he made sense, he had scientific proof, he was a doctor using both worlds, Eastern and Western medicine. I think this is why we are so far behind the rest of the world—we do not take all medicine to cure people.

If you want to see the video I watched just search for his name online and there are numerous videos to watch. I watched the long one and I did not fall asleep.

I started taking his Synbiotic 365 and I can feel the difference in my body. I really think it is helping me lose weight and digest my food better. I was skeptical at first but I do feel a lot better.

I have been taking it for three months and I can say I am going to make it part of my routine from now on.

---

2 Dr. Pedre is a Certified Medical Doctor and Chief Wellness Officer at United Naturals. After graduating with honors from Cornell and receiving his degree at the University of Miami School of Medicine, he founded Pedre Integrative Health, where he takes a largely holistic approach to medicine. He believes that combining both Western and Eastern medicine to better address every patient's needs is the future of healthcare. https://app.unitednaturals.com/checkout/biotic?clear=1&source=probioticsorg&LANDING_PAGE_ROUTE=probioticsorg.

CHAPTER 32

Protein Bars and Shakes

I *HATE* **PROTEIN BARS.** I have not found one I can call my own or that I would eat all the time. I have spent thousands of dollars on them through the years, only to find they constipate me, don't taste good, or have ingredients in them I do not recognize as being from God. Which does not make sense since we are trying to clean the body, not give it things it does not recognize or know how to use. If you are hooked on protein bars (they *are* very convenient), read the ingredients carefully. Many have high-fructose sugar and high sodium levels.

I do not eat a lot of meat and I found out the hard way that without protein your body stores fat. I also found out how tired I would get. Everything I did became more difficult without the right amount of protein. Here is what I discovered: without enough protein, I crave things that give me a quick energy boost, like sugar or carbs, which then put weight on me.

I also found out that my body did not like it when I ate too much fish to increase protein levels. I do eat organic chicken and, on occasion, red meat (once a month, maybe). I know there is a lot of protein in beans, but I don't really have a taste for them. I eat organic eggs but they have been known to increase inflammation which doesn't help my lymphedema pain. So, why cause more problems? Nuts are high in protein but in large amounts they made my colon very upset and the fat-content in nuts is high.

Cheese is high in protein but organic cheese is so expensive. I also have my doubts if anything from a cow is good for me to eat.

So, plant-based protein shakes seem the best way for me to get enough protein. I finally found a shake I LOVE, yes LOVE. The shake I'm drinking now has all the things I'm looking for. To make it even better it tastes great with just water. It's Garden of Life's Organic Plant Protein Smooth Chocolate. The things I look for when selecting protein powders are:

1. The type of protein used. I do not use whey protein at all as it comes from cow milk. I do not use egg protein. I search for vegetable protein from peas or brown rice.

2. The amount of sodium. There was a shake I loved and then I looked at the sodium amounts. I guess there is so much sodium because they think we are athletes? Sodium levels should not be more than 250 milligrams (and even that is high).

3. The amount of sugar. There should be no sugar in your protein powder. Many are loaded with sugar. It's crazy.

4. The amount of carbohydrates. Since carbs are a form of sugar, the levels should be really low.

5. The number of calories per serving. Check this number carefully and see what is considered a serving. It will fill you up if you drink it with 8 ounces of fluid of any kind; just that much fluid will fill you up.

6. Digestive enzymes. I like powders with a digestive enzyme so the protein is easily absorbed by the body.

7. Gluten-free. I do not like gluten. I am not a freak about it, my body just does not do well with wheat, bread, pasta, and the like. These are special-occasion foods for me, and otherwise I try to stay away from gluten foods completely.

8. Grams of protein. I look for at least 15 grams of protein, which is like a portion of meat but easier on the body to digest.

9. Organic. The product has to be organic. The last thing I want to worry about is what a freeze-dried chemical is doing to my system.

I added to the shake mix Amazing Grass Green Superfood for my morning shake.[1] In my afternoon shake I add Amazing Grass Green Superfood Antioxidant. I know it does not say organic, but it is if you look at the website. They just change the status because they were a few ingredients short of the code for organic. Yes, I drink two shakes a day, the first one in the morning, early after my workout and the second before 1:00 in the afternoon. If I drink it later, I will not go to sleep. When my loved ones where sick I always made them drink shakes. When they could not get food down, I knew if I could get half of this down we were feeding their bodies. Mixing the two products gives the best of both worlds, protein and fruits and vegetables.

Digestion takes a lot out of the body. Your body needs white blood cells to help you digest. When healing, you want those cells to work on healing so the easier you can make it on the body, the better.

I have tried so many of these drinks, I could write a book about them! The protein in the shake is very important to make sure the body can break it down and use it. I am off sugar now, so after hours of going through every product on the shelf to find one product to mix the shake powder with, the *only* product I found without sugar was Elmhurst Unsweetened Milked Walnuts walnut milk and it tastes great. Please try to drink with just water, it costs less and you get a full 8-ounce glass of water to mark off your water for the day.

Again, I am not a doctor. This is just what works with my body. If you decide to start a diet program, study the program. Ask a lot of questions and know that even things designed to help may ultimately hurt you if not done correctly. Always remember you are a money source for a lot of people wanting to sell you "health" products, and they use your fear to do it. They use the word "natural" a lot to trick you into buying their products. Natural

---

1 Please see https://shop.amazinggrass.com.

is only a word and it means nothing unless you also see organic, GMO-free, no enhancements or hormones, and so on. Please read all labels.

Ask plenty of questions to anyone who wants to put you on a diet or supplement program. If you do not have the energy to figure it out yourself, assign someone you trust to do it for you. There will be many people telling you what to do. Please know that I am not one of them. These are only suggestions by telling you what I have done. I hope it encourages you to be curious and to find your own answers.

Nutrition is vital to healing and keeping healthy. This has become my way of thinking all the time. I have my bad days and my bad weeks; 25 years (and counting) is a long time to be this way when everyone around you doesn't seem to care. But I am not them, I am trying to be here for my daughter, I am trying to help people know the truth so they can focus on staying alive.

I have seen many people I love not make it and I would give anything if I could have helped them stay here. I want to honor them by helping you stay here as long as God wants me to help.

CHAPTER 33

Body Products

WHY DO A CHAPTER ON BODY PRODUCTS? Are they really that important? Why does it matter? Aren't all products pretty much the same? No. They are not all the same. I try not to put things in, or on, my body that will hurt my body.

Am I super-strict about all the body products I use? Not all, but pretty close. I do my research and keep makeup to a minimum. Let's go through some of the products we use daily.

Makeup

Some makeup products have cancer-causing chemicals. Are there laws to prevent them from using cancer products? The answer is easy, NO. We as consumers can send out a message by buying holistic products showing we want a change. Hit them where it counts—their income.

I do not use 100-percent-holistic makeup. It's expensive and I spend money where I think it will help my body the most and that is on healthy food.

For example, I use Cover Girl mascara because I like it more than any of the holistic mascaras I have tried. But I learned to be careful because some mascaras have metal in them, which can flake off and be ingested through the eyes.

I use Physicians Formula foundation and powder, under eye makeup, eye color, and many of their other products because they have fewer chemicals than other brands. I have not attempted to study or try all the holistic body products on the market, but I'd like to, and this is step one for me.

Hair Products

Fortunately, it's a rare day when someone doesn't comment on my hair and how beautiful and healthy it is. Is hair only about what shampoo you use on it? No, it has a lot to do with family genetics. But if your scalp is not healthy, where is the hair to grow?

As the first line of defense, I have a filter on my shower that removes chemicals in the water before I start to shampoo. In the chapter about chlorine in the water, I mentioned I use Rainshower's "Restore" filter, made in San Gabriel, California, that takes the chlorine out of the water for me.[1]

I use Giovanni 50/50 shampoo and Giovanni 50/50 cream rise. My hair products are holistic and have limited chemicals in them. Have you ever had a hair follicle get clogged so that it created a bump or an infection? So, thinking about it, your entire head of hair is formed from thousands of hair follicles. If there are harsh chemicals in your shampoos and conditioners (not to mention the leave-in conditioners) then that is affecting your follicles. The chemicals cause them to clog up and stay in your scalp so they cannot breathe and stay healthy.

Hair Dye

Do I use hair dye? Yes, I do. I get gray hair just around my temples. But I do not want to dye every hair on my entire head. I only use root touch-up dye on the sides of my face where gray hair can be seen, and I only do this about every three months.

This is funny, I accidentally started a trend because I used a darker color on the sides so the top of my hair was lighter, kind of an ombre look but on the sides of my head. It looks like the sun bleached the top of my head and not the sides. You can see it in my author picture. People have asked me who did it for me, I have to laugh and say I did and explain the whole thing. I

---

1 The Rainshower Restore filter can be found online at https://www.rainshower.com/new/restore.html.

know that's not a pro result, but this way, I use only a very small amount of dye on my scalp. When my hair starts to get gray all over my head, I will look for a holistic hair dye to color my entire head of hair.

If you have to have red hair or shades of red hair, I would go with a holistic red dye. You are always better safe than sorry. There are no clear-cut studies on any hair products.

I have researched to see if hair dye can cause cancer. There are mixed studies all over the place. An updated article posted on the American Cancer Society's website says the findings are still inconclusive.[2] The National Cancer Institute does not say either way.[3] One study found if you started using hair dyes in 1960 and continued, those dyes had much harsher chemicals. But it's unclear if the effects were accumulative or not. Today, many harmful dyes are either prohibited or no longer used, but there is still not enough research and we need continued studies.

Your scalp is one giant piece of skin. When you heat it up it the pores open to cool you down, right? I'm always considering something's effect on the entire body. The skin naturally opens up when it is heated, so when you apply hair dye and "activate" it under heat lamps or a hair dryer, could that process let chemicals pour in through the opened pores? I am always cautioning to be on the safe side! Your skin is the largest organ of your body and what you put on it is how it will react on a daily basis.

Deodorant

There is different data on deodorants. I err on the side of caution. The surgery I had involved removing a lot of my lymph nodes on my left, so why take a chance and make the other nodes upset?

---

2 "Cancer Causes: Hair Dyes," as posted on the American Cancer Society's website (updated 2019). https://www.cancer.org/cancer/cancer-causes/hair-dyes.html.

3 "Hair Dyes and Cancer Risk," as posted on the National Cancer Institute's website (2016). https://www.cancer.gov/about-cancer/causes-prevention/risk/myths/hair-dyes-fact-sheet.

There has been concern that people are using deodorants with aluminum. The armpit is directly in touch with the lymph nodes of the body. Aluminum has been linked to Alzheimer's disease. (As a side note, I do not cook food in aluminum foil.) Alzheimer's disease is one disease that really scares me so any study linking a product to it is a stay-away product for me.

I found articles that argued both sides of the issue. Some say that the skin is formed to protect the body and it would not let aluminum properties from deodorants into the lymph system. Others say the armpit location is unique because it mixes with sweat coming from the sweat glands in the armpit.

I say, do what it takes to protect the body. Considering trying the aluminum-free Unscented Long Lasting Deodorant from Tom's of Maine.[4]

Toothpaste

If your teeth and gums are not healthy, it can lead to stomach disease, sinus problems, headaches, heart problems, and overall fatigue.

I use Tom's Fluoride-Free Antiplaque & Whitening Toothpaste. Fluoride can prevent calcium absorption in the body. Again, I think:

Why take a chance?

The mouth is the fastest absorbing part of your body. That's why you are told to put an aspirin under your tongue if you are having a heart attack. That's the kind of absorption that gets fast results.

If you are putting chemicals in your mouth to brush your teeth, how fast are they being absorbed into your bloodstream? Think of how close your mouth is to your brain and your face. If you are using a bleaching tray for your teeth, bleach is absorbed into the bloodstream. There is no way around it. Is it worth it to have whiter teeth?

---

4 Tom's of Maine makes a variety of natural products. Visit their website at https://www. tomsofmaine.com.

The latest thing I use for white teeth about once a month is a product called "Dirt Don't Hurt" which is made from volcanic ash and other minerals. I also use a charcoal toothbrush with the Tom's toothpaste I mentioned and it works amazingly.

Lotion

As we know, the skin is the largest absorbing organ. The pores of the body open to cool the body when heated, producing sweat to cool the body faster. When the body is cold, it tries to create heat by giving you goosebumps, which triggers hair follicles into releasing heat.

Depending on the lotion you use, its properties can be absorbed by the body in mass amounts. If it has chemicals harmful to the body, your body is bringing those chemicals directly into the body.

My daily face cleansing and moisturizing routine is really simple. I believe my lack of wrinkles and beautiful skin is due to genetics, drinking water, and the products I use on my skin. I only use lotion on my face. Thanks to the soap I use and my shower's water filter, which removes chlorine, my skin does not really dry out.

I use:

ShiKai Moisturizing Coconut Shower Gel. I also use this to shave my legs.

Evrim Exfoliating Wash Cloth / Dual Texture. It is really rough on one side and I scrub my face with it every night and every morning with the gel above. I get these at Walmart.

Aveeno Daily Moisturizing Lotion with Oat for Dry Skin. I apply this after I scrub my face while it is hot from the shower. I do not use a body lotion unless I am showing bare legs and then I use this lotion on my legs.

My body soap is an all-natural oatmeal soap with tea tree oil. Tea tree oil is a natural antibiotic so it keeps everything clean and germ free.[5]

My mother had no wrinkles when she died and she was past 80. She scrubbed her face and put Vaseline on it, that was all. It surprised me to see Aveeno has petroleum in the product like Vaseline.

I hope this gives you enough information. Until we know exactly why we are all dying, we need to consider everything we are doing, especially what we are all doing alike. We need to see if the body products we are using have links to the cancer we are getting.

---

5 "11 benefits of tea tree oil," as posted on the Medical News Today website. https://www.medicalnewstoday.com/articles/262944.php.

Be Prepared, Get Organized, Know Your Rights

The information and reference materials contained in this book are intended solely for the general information of the reader. It is not to be used for treatment purposes, but rather for discussion with the reader's own medical professionals. The information presented here is not intended to diagnose health problems or to take the place of professional medical care. The information is neither intended to dictate what constitutes reasonable, appropriate, or best care for any given health issue, nor is it intended to be used as a substitute for the independent judgment of a physician. All content and opinions of the author are for general information purposes, only. If you have persistent health problems or if you have further questions, please consult your healthcare provider.

The recommendations put forth in this book do not establish a doctor-patient relationship. Individuals should consult a qualified healthcare provider for medical advice and answers to personal health questions.

The information presented is not to be considered medical advice and is not intended to replace consultation with a qualified medical professional. The primary responsibility of your disease management plan is with your treating physicians and you should only follow your treating physician's advice. DO NOT change or modify your disease management plan on your own without consulting your treating physicians.

Some research needs to be completed and it is our voice that will make them complete it. How can we make decisions without complete testing? It is our job together to make them finish it. Then, and only then, can we choose what to do with our bodies.

"Tell us why we're dying!"®

CHAPTER 34

Medical Records

WITH ALL THE NEW THINGS that are happening with healthcare it's becoming increasingly imperative that you keep your own records on file.

Note that any facility that has your records right now will **only keep your records for five-to-seven years.** A lot of facilities are going through their patient records because of new laws requiring paperless records. This means if you don't have copies of your records from seven years ago, they very well may have been destroyed.

They are not required to give you any type of notice that they're going to destroy your records. They could be gone without any warning. This is the part I truly don't understand. If those records were part of your care, for, let's say, cancer treatment, they will destroy them anyway. So, everything that was done for your care, the diagnosis, lab tests, everything that could help you in the future if you came down with the same disease, could be gone without any warning.

You think they're going to keep these records because they are such an imperative part of your life. How can they treat something in the future if they don't know how you were treated in the past? Well, I found out the hard way.

I have had ongoing treatments for cancer and other illnesses from the same hospital for 18 years. I have gone to other emergency hospitals closer to me. But for any complicated problem, and for all the cancer care, I have always gone to Scripps Memorial Hospital. When I thought I was dying I demanded they take me to this hospital because I trusted them.

So, I had an ongoing case with them that never stopped. I thought my records would stay open and, as an insurance consultant, I figured when a patient had ongoing care, their records were continually being added to. Why would a hospital record facility destroy your records if you're continuously going back to the same hospital as a patient for the same problem?

I discovered they had destroyed my records. I was shocked and appalled when I found this out. I didn't quite know what to do. I was scrambling trying to find out who might have copies of these records. Fortunately, my life insurance company had copies of all of my medical records.

I remembered when I was shopping for life insurance, they tried to get my medical records. It was amazing how many of my doctors didn't have my files up to date. They also misfile records and put other people's information into the wrong records, and this is one of the reasons why electronic medical records are required now. It's a great thing to have records as digital files because you can be in a different city on vacation and should something happen, that hospital or doctor can instantly get your medical history.

The bad thing about having electronic medical records is that they can be accessed by people you don't want to have them. Your records are not supposed to be opened by anyone that is not authorized. Your health information is not to be sold to drug companies so they can market their products to you. But it happens all the time. And it's very hard to trace the person who allowed your records to be accessed. The HIPAA law was passed because staff were selling the medical records of movie stars to magazines.[1] The law denies any medical personnel to sell or release your information without written notice from you allowing it to be released. Study your rights and get to know them. Do not disregard this as it is really important. If they do not follow this law, your information could be released to anyone.

---

1 "What Information is Protected Under HIPAA Law?" as posted on the HIPPA Journal website. https://www.hipaajournal.com/what-information-is-protected-under-hipaa-law.

It's really frustrating when you start getting all kinds of information. All it takes is one mention of you being a diabetic and you'll be bombarded with solicitations from insulin manufacturers trying to get your business.

Please note if you use "value" cards given to you by grocery stores and pharmacies, they know what you are buying and the stores "share" that "marketing" information with practically anyone willing to pay for it. If you use pharmacy value cards, you can ask them to not release or sell your information.

So, here's what I'm telling you to do. Start using your smartphone and a private server space in your provider's cloud or some other Internet-based repository. Make a file called "My Medical Records." Take pictures of every single lab report, x-rays files, and anything else. If you have paid for x-rays, you can ask for a copy of the digital file to be sent to you by email. And, you can ask if you can take a picture of the x-ray while your doctor is going over it with you. Same thing at the dentist. Ask for electronic copies of your x-rays. You've suffered the extra radiation, not to mention the hefty prices, it's the least they can do for you!

When you take pictures of everything tell the staff what you are doing to let them know you have your own file. Take pictures of your intake forms, so you have records of what you told them in the first place. When you see the doctor writing notes ask for copies of your file once a year so you can see what they wrote. It is amazing: when I had my life insurance copy my records there was so much misinformation that I supposedly told the doctor?

When my daughter was going to a college, she lived about seven hours from home. She had been seeing a chiropractor and she just had new x-rays taken. I had her take a picture of the x-rays and her chart notes with her smartphone, so when she went to a new chiropractor near her school, all she had to do was show the chiropractor the recent x-rays on her phone and she could be adjusted perfectly without having to take new x-rays.

When you carry your medical history with you, you can use it at any time to help yourself. Especially if you go to out-of-network, non-participating, or cash doctors. The people who normally share records are hospitals, but if your primary care doctor is a sole practitioner, they may not be hooked-up to the national records database. So, to get your records released, you will have to sign a form requesting them by law. That form has to be sent to the doctor that you're requesting x-rays from and then—depending on how busy that doctor is—eventually your records will be mailed to the doctor you want to see them. Sometimes this can be managed electronically, but that can still take time to coordinate.

When I was managing clinics, sometimes it would take us a week or two to get records out, not because we didn't want to help our patients, but because the doctors have to look over the records before they are released. And because doctors are really busy, the records sit there waiting for their attention. I have seen this happen when the staff changeover is constant and new staff is coming in all the time and they are not trained properly. The staff cover their tracks by throwing things away. Staff that do not want to do their job do it half way because they do not care and the doctor is always the last to know. The doctor relies on others to keep your records and then surprise: they are gone. It would amaze you how many reports written do not get to insurance companies. But if they see you doing all of this, they will make a mental note of who you are as a patient.

Your records can never be replaced once they are gone. Please, you have to help yourself in order to help your doctor in the future. It could save your life.

CHAPTER 35

Insurance Companies

I WANT TO EXPLAIN SOMETHING most people do not know about insurance companies. They do not make money selling insurance. "What are you talking about, Karen?" Insurance companies are short-term money lenders. They take your premiums and lend them out or invest them for profit.[1]

So, if they can make money by not paying, paying less for your procedure, or by holding off paying you or your doctors, they can make more money on your money. Now that you understand this, read on to find out how they do it.

I asked myself a question (are you surprised?): If PacifiCare is going to pay for three surgeries for me anyway, and I want to have all the surgeries done at the same time, then why not pay for them and have everything over in one shot? This saved them money and time in the hospital. As I explain in my story, I had to fight to make this happen.

What to Look for In Your Insurance Policy

Insurance policies can be daunting and some booklets are more than 100 pages long on purpose. That is so you will not read them, let alone understand them. They are counting on you just accepting what is happening and not taking the time or spending your energy to really know what you should be charged. I totally understand you are trying to stay alive, so you need to assign this task to someone who will take the time needed. It could save you

---

1 "How Do Insurance Companies Invest Money?" by Patrick Gleeson, Ph.D. as posted on Zacks website (updated 2019). https://finance.zacks.com/insurance-companies-invest-money-11120.html.

thousands of dollars and allow you more money for treatments. You don't have to look over the whole booklet just what pertains to you, okay?

First, look to see if they have benefits broken down by disease and if they have listed breast cancer and mastectomies separately. They usually do, but if not, don't get discouraged. Next, let's go over some of the things to look through the booklet for your case.

1. Hospital Stays. Look to see if it requires a doctor's report. I extended my stay because of my complications and my doctor wrote a report. Look at the days, amounts, your percentage, and the costs of having a private room compared to a semi-private one. You can pay for the difference if you want to move to a private room.

2. Anesthesiologists. This is the service that can cost a lot of money. Most anesthesiologists are not part of the hospital staff and work as independent contractors. What does that mean? They charge differently and may not be included in your policy. Find that out now so you can plan. If they are not, they are considered out of network providers, which means you pay a higher co-pay for them. You can request one on your plan if they are available but it might take longer to get your surgery. Dr. Night-Night was not on my plan but I would gladly pay more for him every time.

3. Test and X-rays. Yes, you need both of these to live, I agree. Here is what to look for: some doctors do not make the time or effort to see if another doctor has already ordered the tests they are now going to do again. If you have not started using a care book (see the care book chapter on this with my suggestions), start one now. Make sure there is an area for the copy of all the reports for x-rays, blood work, and anything they have done to you. If they are going to order it again, they need to write a report about why they need it again. Get a copy of the report

right now. You will need it and you should have it because you have to pay for it.

4. Plastic Surgery. Of course, this is a covered expense but know the rules. There are limits to what they will cover. If you have a lumpectomy how much repair will they cover? Will they cover changing the other chest to match the one they repair? If you have a single mastectomy, will they pay to enlarge or decrease the other side to match? You need to understand this selection all the way about what they will cover. NEVER assume. What would make sense to you will not necessarily be covered. I remember one of my implants popped and I had to fight to get them both repaired. I wanted them to match and have the same shelf life. I pushed and they covered it.

5. Physical Therapy. When they take out lymph nodes, you may need physical therapy to help with the scar tissue. Look it over and see what they will cover. If you do not understand what they will cover, call them and get it right. Ask for an email to be sent with what they quoted for your care book.

6. In-Home Care. This might be a covered expense if your husband, partner, parents, roommate or anyone helping you at home has to go back to work right away and if you are unable to stay safely at home by yourself. It may also be included if you live by yourself and are not able to do things on your own or have no family to help you. This will depend on a report from your doctor. Never feel bad about asking for what you need. Always ask. Don't assume your doctor's office will do anything automatically. They will not.

7. Products for Home Use. There are going to be things they say they will not cover, but with an understanding doctor writing reports it will help you get things through if they are within reason. Please do not bog down your doctor going after things that do not make sense, but for things you know will.

Print out all you can so you can reference it. If the company gives you any explanation for what they will cover ask for confirmation in an email. If they will not send it, always—and I mean always—ask for the name of the person, date, time, their ID number, supervisor's name, phone number, and extension. If you are talking to a person overseas you will never be able to prove what they said to you. Do not waste your time as it is a lost cause. You can try to ask to speak to someone in the United States but good luck. You are going to have to fight using the printed-out coverage.

Do not count on your doctor's office knowing anything about your insurance policy or helping you to find out what it covers. I was an insurance consultant for doctors' offices for more than 20 years. There is a big difference in billing practices between doctors and hospitals. Most billing companies for doctors are merely code specialists: they only know the codes for what happens during doctor visits (and half the time, they don't know those).

Based on my experience alone, I can confirm that *millions of dollars' worth of mistakes* are made by the billing "experts" employed by doctors. If you get paid no matter what you put out in billing will you really care what you are billing? The doctors do not have time to check over all billing as it goes out. Hospitals are probably worse when it comes to making sure billing is accurate. Unfortunately, this will have to be your job or the job of someone you designate to handle it. Always, and I do mean always, check the billing that has been submitted to the insurance company. One code submitted incorrectly can cost you hundreds, if not thousands, of dollars you do not owe.

Coding for Insurance Payments

This is one area that is rarely explained to patients, because if you truly understood how badly this is done you would lose your mind. As I stated above, if you get paid the same whether you put the codes in correctly or incorrectly, what is to motivate you to put them in correctly?

"What is a billing code, diagnosis, and how does it affect me?" I'm glad you asked. It is so important to know these things.

Diagnosis Coding: First, I will explain diagnosis. This is the code the doctor uses to explain what is wrong with you and why you need the service in the first place. Every diagnosis has an amount of money tied to it. The more diagnoses the doctor adds to their billing to explain why you need the money, the more money you might be able to receive

Okay, here is the tricky part: That area on the bill for the codes only allows for twelve diagnoses so if it takes more than that to explain what you need, the doctor has to write a report. Most doctors are really busy and they know on average 30 diagnosis codes. They use these codes over and over unless they have an incredible billing person who knows about other codes they can use to get more money. If the coding person puts in a diagnosis code that is wrong, guess what? They'll get less money. If they do not ask for the report from the doctor that means less money. If they pick codes from his long list he gives them to fit in the twelve spots and they are follow-up codes and not primary codes, it's less money. It is so amazing how twelve little numbers can do so much damage to payments.

The Coding for Services: Everything a doctor or hospital does to you has code to explain to the insurance company what was done. Each one of those codes has a price point associated with it. You can add other codes at the end to make the bill higher (worth more money). If you are a billing person and you are typing in codes, or if you are a doctor picking things off a list to bill, both can make mistakes all the time. Those mistakes can cost you money and here is how.

The wrong code is billed for a service and if it has a lower price point you pay the difference. If they code a service not covered in your insurance you owe for that code amount. It might have been covered but they billed the wrong code. I have seen so many diagnosis codes put in wrong and all the services were denied. I have seen codes for testing denied because they were run in the same year and you are only allowed one a year, otherwise you pay for it. Am I telling you not to get the testing? No. But do they really need it again or can they make an effort to get the last one? Or should you bring the report with you? Ask what they need and get it if it already exists. If the doctor gives you more time in the hospital, like they did with me, and the doctor said he would write a report to cover the costs, send an email right now to his office and tell them what he said so you don't forget.

When looking at your Explanation of Benefits (EOB) form, if you don't understand what the codes mean you'll need to call to find out. Start with the billing department and try to make a friend there who can help you if you need to call again (you will). But before you call the billing department, let's go over together exactly what you're being charged for. Because knowledge is power when you understand the insurance game.

How Insurance Companies Work

One basic thing you should understand about insurance companies is that they are not there to help you. I know that sounds harsh. But it's not a newsflash to you if you have had to deal with insurance companies. They are like any other for-profit business: they exist to make money. Even non-profit companies still need income to operate. Every single thing in the world that provides a service needs to be paid for that service.

I smile when I hear people vent their frustrations about insurance companies. This is what I hear: "I pay my monthly premium on time, I meet my deductibles, I pay my copays out of pocket for doctor visits, so I don't understand why they just can't pay my doctor bills. Why do they make me jump through so many hoops, can you just explain that to me?"

It's kind of easy to explain but it's probably going to make you mad. I will use myself as an example:

I pay $450 a month as a premium ($5,400 a year paid to the insurance company.) I also have a deductible of $5,000 a year which means they will not start paying anything to the doctors or hospitals until I reach that $5,000. Here is the crazy part: They only apply the percentage allowed by the insurance toward your deductible not dollar for dollar (I'll explain later).

So, you are asking, "Karen, if you put those together you have $10,400 to spend on your health care, right?" Two days in the hospital costs approximately $1,000 but that doesn't include any testing, blood work, x-rays, medication, physician care, surgeries, devices, medical supplies, and so on. This is just for spending the night in their uncomfortable bed. For even the simplest care, one night in a California non-profit hospital averages $3,833.[2] Doing the math, that's a minimum of $15,332 for my four-night stay. The insurance company can count on collecting a total of $10,400 from me for the entire year, but in the first four days, they've spent more than that. (They will collect another 20 percent or so after I've met my deductible, based on their coverage limits.)

So, it's easy to see that if something catastrophic happens and I run up a huge bill, the insurance company is never going to come out even. They are in the hole by insuring me, and they haven't even started to cover their general operating costs! This means they have to rely on insuring a large number of people who never get sick, or only get sick to the degree that the cost of their medical care is considerably less than the premiums and deductibles they collect from them. They also have another way to make money which I will go over later in the chapter.

Our new healthcare laws can't discriminate against me for a pre-existing condition, but there are caps on amounts for treatments to cancer patients like chemotherapy and radiation per year to try to get some money back. So, in order to stay liquid (have cash in the bank), they do what they can *not to pay* claims. By law in California, once you submit a claim to an insurance

---

2 "Average hospital expenses per inpatient day across 50 states," as posted on the Becker's Hospital Review website. https://www.beckershospitalreview.com/finance/average-hospital-expenses-per-inpatient-day-across-50-states.html.

company, they have 45 days to answer that claim. Most doctors' offices and hospitals don't submit their claims to insurance for at least 45 to 60 days. Then, the insurance company has 45 days to answer.

If the bill has been submitted with a charge for a service or procedure they can point to and use a loophole to get out of paying for it, they will run with it. If the bill was not filled out correctly, if something on the bill was deleted, or if the codes are wrong, all of these things give the insurance company ways to deny claims. They will hold that claim for 45 days, then send it back, pointing out the error and asking for a correction. The doctor or hospital takes another 30 days to correct the claim. When returned to the insurance company, they see this as a new claim with 45 days to either pay or decline it again. So, we are up to about four or five months before your bill gets paid or not.

That gives the insurance company four months' worth of investing your money for profit. Now, let's say we do this to thousands of patients and millions of dollars' worth of claims every month. That is where they make their money, don't forget.

Now, here's the bad part (okay, the worst part): depending on how much the insurance professional at the doctor's office or hospital is willing to fight for you, either they will try to get the error corrected or they will give up and just send you a bill for whatever the insurance company didn't pay. I was a collection expert, hired to collect back payments from insurance companies. My job (which became a passion) was to make the insurance companies pay for everything they were obligated to pay. My goals were to help patients avoid being stuck with bills they shouldn't be paying in the first place and to help professionals get paid what they were due.

When looking over your EBO paperwork, know that the doctor's office and hospital get an exact copy. Everyone can see what the insurance was asked to pay for and what they intend to pay. From this statement, you can see if the billing codes are right or wrong, and exactly what your policy says about covering the services. This means you (or your designated person) need to be super aware of what services and procedures you actually had, and it's a great idea to make a note of them right before or after they happen. In fact, you can ask the billing department at the hospital for a financial consultation to go over the codes before you agree to have anything done. Most hospitals do this before the operations but if they do not offer it, ask for it. This way, when the EOB arrives, you can make sure the doctor's office isn't charging you for something you didn't authorize! You can compare your list to what's being reported.

This happens all the time: a doctor's office will send you an invoice telling you it's to cover what your insurance wouldn't pay for. But did they even fight to get the insurance to pay for it? Probably not. If your doctors rely on outside billing companies to handle all of the insurance claims, you can bet they aren't interested in fighting for you. Unless your doctor has a person on staff who diligently reviews the EOB and compares it to your case, they will assume the insurance company is right. As a consultant, I would find procedures that were denied or only partially paid for when they should have been completely covered.

They know that most patients are eager to move beyond whatever health issue they've been dealing with and are more likely to pay a bill just to "get it out of their lives" than they are to question everything. They are not allowed to treat you differently because you have a balance due and the doctor can be cited if they do. But they are there to be paid for their service as we all are when we provide a service. It is so important to have a person who handles this for you.

Earlier, I mentioned calling your provider when you have questions. Another way the insurance companies make it harder for you to access their help is when you make that call. No doubt you found this out the hard way. Many insurance companies use call centers that are based outside of the United States using workers who are paid a very low wage. They must follow an exact script or risk being fired. Chances are, the first person you talk with is not the person who can help you. This is by design as management uses this as a barrier. This person is encouraged to stick to the script and get you off the phone as quickly as possible. For nearly every question you ask they will respond by asking if they can put you on a brief hold. This, of course, is after waiting 20 minutes in a queue and then spending 10 minutes to qualify you as insured with them, even though you just did that by answering the automated questions at the start of the call.

Putting you on hold is a great way to "make you go away." They want you to get tired or angry, or hang up because there are a million other more important things to deal with. Don't give in! Plan to call them while you can multi-task with reading or watching TV until you have someone's attention. I always ask for a name and write down who I spoke with and the date and time and then I repeat it to the person I am talking with and ask if I am correct. Then, go one step further and ask for their supervisor's name. Tell them you need it just in case this issue does not get resolved on the call. That is why they have a disclaimer at the beginning of each call; they need to cover themselves if the call doesn't result in giving you the information you called about. The way you can know if the information they give you is correct, and this is super important: **ask for a call confirmation number.** If they give you one, you may have a chance.

You can also ask to speak to a representative or supervisor who is based in an office nearest to you in the U.S. Once requested, unless the U.S. offices are closed when you call, they are obligated to transfer you. But what usually happens, is that once again, you are put on indefinite hold, or the call just dies. You're left staring at a disconnected phone. By any means necessary, the call center employees want to either resolve your issue themselves (which they never can) or end the call. They are told to never "elevate" calls to supervisors unless it is the rarest of circumstances. They would rather disconnect a call than switch you, because too many elevations and it could mean their job.

It used to be that you could threaten to report them to the insurance commissioner to get a transfer. Now, they couldn't care less what you say because the call center is out of the country and our laws mean nothing to them. If you were in their place, would you risk losing your job for a person in a country that has so much more than you have already?

But what's really behind this stall tactic? They don't want you questioning their billing practices. I wish insurance companies gave you an option to pay for elevated service. I'd gladly pay. Imagine the prompt at the beginning of your call: "If you'd like your call to be directed to a claims person in the United States, press one. You will be charged a minimum fee of $25 for this call or whatever is needed to resolve your issue. Please have your credit card ready." I would pay it every time! Of course, this will never happen because your call is costing them so much more in paid benefits.

Now that we've had a chat about insurance in general, remember that knowledge is power. The more you understand what's really going on, the better you can fight for what you want.

Joining Networks

There are five common types of health insurance plans and later in this chapter I talk about PPOs and HMOs in detail.

> » Preferred provider organizations (PPOs);
>
> » Health maintenance organizations (HMOs);
>
> » Exclusive provider organizations (EPOs);
>
> » Point-of-service plans (POS); and
>
> » High-deductible health plans (HDHPs).

Depending on the type of plan, when your doctor joins an insurance network, they signed a contract. In that contract, they exchange part of what they will be paid for the marketing of the insurance company. The insurance company then allows the doctor to be marketed to you. So, if your doctor wants to get direct marketing to you and the ability to bill the insurance company for you, they have to be a provider with your network. The insurance company "owns" your doctor, otherwise the doctor will turn into a cash doctor.

Once your doctor is part of the network, they will pretty much do anything they have to do to stay in that network. The network only allows a certain number of doctors in a designated area or town with your doctor's particular field of practice to become part of the network. There are doctors every day, every hour trying to become part of that network. Your doctor knows that, and is reminded of that, so this is the reason your doctor is not going to risk being kicked out of the network for your procedure.

Now, let me explain this in more depth. Remember: knowledge is power. **Do not skip reading this.**

If you are a doctor and you paid $250,000 to get your medical license, which insurance would you want to be a part of listed below? My personal opinion is to pay for the PPO insurance every time if you can afford it.

PPO Insurance Plans

If you are in a PPO, your doctor will be paid a higher percentage for each visit to his office. Why? Because you, as a consumer, are paying a higher premium for your insurance. Since you are paying a larger percentage, they are not asked to manage care, or pre-authorize what you want to do as a procedure. That is why it's always better, if you can afford it, to purchase a PPO insurance plan. When a doctor sees you have PPO insurance—even though they're not supposed to—they will treat you differently. These plans are less hassle for them and they make more money. There's also less stress for you, and you definitely will get more procedures pushed through the insurance system.

HMO Insurance Plans

With HMO plans, doctors are paid less. Before they even get paid, the doctor has to see you and decide at that time whether or not they should allow you to get the procedure. HMO doctors are scrutinized by the insurance company on whether they should have allowed the procedure at all. The doctor will have to write reports and prescriptions and submit those to your insurance company before you're allowed procedures or medications. So, your doctor is in a way, "begging" to let you have the healthcare they want for you.

But here's the bad part: if your doctor has asked for too many procedures, more than what the insurance company thinks you need, they can drop your doctor from the network. If they do, depending on the insurance company and how many patients that doctor has linked to their company, this will affect the doctor's income immensely. So, put yourself in your doctor's place. Is the procedure you're asking for worth losing income over? Maybe there is a cheaper way of helping you? Because, it all comes down to cost factors; exactly how much did it cost the insurance company and was it necessary? Most insurance companies aren't using doctors to look over the reports your doctor submits. They are likely using untrained insurance claims adjusters who have their own set of rules about allowing procedures or they will be docked. Some insurance companies use nurse practitioners to lower costs. Although many of these nurses are incredible at what they do, they are not doctors. So, if you have an HMO insurance plan, **get ready to fight!**

Now that you understand what your doctor has to do and why they do it, let's go over what you're going to do and why. "In-network" means you can go to doctors who have joined your plan. The following information is for in-network doctors.

In-Network Deductibles

Simply put, the deductible is what you have to pay before your insurance company will start paying. Let's say you have a $2,000 deductible. You have to hit that $2,000 of acceptable charges or your insurance company will not make any payments for anything you do medically until you do. Here's the unfair thing about deductibles. When your doctor's office sends in charges toward your deductible, your insurance company will only give you credit for the amount that they pay out to your doctor. If a procedure costs $100, but your doctor's contracted payment amount he can receive for that particular procedure is $50, you will only have $50 applied towards your $2,000 deductible. This is their way of making sure it takes a long time for you to even hit your deductible. They are hoping it will take an entire year before you hit your $2,000 deductible so they don't have to pay for anything.

Most deductibles are much higher than this, otherwise your premiums (monthly payment) will be unaffordable. If I know I'm not going to hit my deductible for routine services, I ask what the cash price is. Sometimes this can be 40 percent or more less than what the doctor will charge your insurance company. If I pay cash, I cannot bill my insurance company for that procedure. I have to weigh out which is more important: do I take a discount now, or run it through insurance in order to reach my deductible before the end of the year for more expensive treatments.

My last point about any deductibles is very important. While you're trying to hit your deductible, if you go to multiple doctors and pay them since you have not hit your deductible yet, here's what could happen. When your doctors call to see if you have hit your deductible, they could be told by the insurance company that you have not reached your deductible yet. Here's why they do this: it takes different doctors more time to bill your insurance company, so even though you've paid them, they may not have billed your insurance company yet, meaning you do not get credit toward your deductible even though you have paid towards it.

So, you continue to pay the next doctor and the next doctor, with no one watching the billing to tell the insurance company your deductible has a payment toward it. When all the billing goes in, it depends who bills last, and that is where your credit could be sitting. Do doctors send you a check for overpayment to reconcile this? It depends how good the staff is at applying the insurance checks.

The lesson is to keep track of every bill you've paid so *you know* exactly when you've hit your deductible. When you review your EOB statements, pay close attention to this because it's the ammo you'll need when going to appointments. You want to show them exactly when you hit your deductible. Take a picture with your phone. Have your EOBs ready to show what you've paid toward your deductible so you can tell your doctor you have so much left to go before hitting your deductible. Make sure all doctors know where you stand.

In-Network Copays

I think most people think they understand copays, but in reality, they don't. Copays are what you agreed to in a contract with the insurance company when you signed up for the plan. But depending on what you do with your insurance, the copays can change.

For a doctor's office visit, in some insurance plans, there is a flat-rate copay fee of $20 when you see a doctor. In other plans, the copay is a percentage of the amount the doctor contracted with the insurance company. This is not a percentage of the overall fee. Let me explain what that means because this is really important. Many patients pay more than what they need to pay because they don't understand this one point.

If your insurance says that you need to pay for 20 percent of the procedure, you are paying 20 percent of the contracted amount the doctor agreed to. For example, if the fee is $100 and the doctor agreed to accept $75 from the insurance company, the doctor adjusts their fee by $25. You now owe 20 percent of the $75, which would be $15.

Why is this so important? Because when you're dealing with percentages, the amount you owe for a large surgical procedure can be hundreds or thousands of dollars. Depending on the staff at the doctor's office, whether they will understand this concept and charge you the correct amount of money or not, it is up to you to check. It is also imperative that you look at the EOB carefully, not only to make sure that you paid the right amount for your copay, but that the procedures that were charged are for what actually happened to you. Mistakes can easily be made when loading procedures for a doctor because all it takes is inputting one code number incorrectly on the bill for the procedure to change dramatically.

I have had so many patients tell me they never had all this blood work done, they never had an EKG, they only had one x-ray taken, not two, and the list goes on and on. They owed their percentage for every one of those procedures that never took place. Don't be afraid to ask what each charge is about. Don't put your head in the sand and don't let the EOB statements pile up without pouring over them as soon as possible after they arrive.

Out-of-Network Doctors

Unfortunately for me, many of the doctors I see are out of my insurance network, or, as they like to call them, "cash" doctors. Cash doctors are doctors who have not joined your network. Your policy will spell out what out-of-network means, and you need to study that portion carefully. Otherwise, the insurance company may allow you to go out-of-network (see a doctor who has not joined their insurance network), you'll just have to pay higher fees. It is almost like seeing a cash doctor who accepts no insurance at all and does no billing. An out-of-network doctor is registered with the insurance company but has no reduced contract with them. To encourage you to stay with in-network doctors, the insurance company will take away the advantage of the deductions they have negotiated with the doctor. Your deductible can also change. If you stay in-network, the deductible is $2,000 but if you see out-of-network providers, the deductible could possibly go up to $4,000 or higher. This is another penalty for not staying inside their system.

When I was looking for doctors for the many procedures I needed, I didn't really care if they were in- or out-of-network. All I cared about was if they were the best at what they did. I know, not everyone can afford to do this, and it cost me a lot more money but, in the end, I think it helped me stay alive.

Make sure that when you see out-of-network doctors you get a "super bill" that you can submit to your insurance company in order for their charges to be credited towards your out-of-network deductible. Here's more about that.

Super Bills

Super bills are what you submit to your insurance company to go toward your out-of-network deductible, or to get reimbursed for once you've hit your out-of-network deductible. The following is what you have to have on your super bill in order for it to count:

» The doctor's tax ID number;

» The CPT code for the procedures you had;

» A diagnosis code which goes with the CPT code; and

» The total amount, which needs to match exactly what you paid to the doctor.

You'll need to file an insurance claim form that you'll get from your insurance company. Fill out the entire portion on the top of the form about you; don't leave anything blank. The bottom portion of the form is where you'll fill out what procedures were done.

Write in big letters: SEE ATTACHED SUPER BILL. Somewhere in the middle of the form, there will be a place where it says something like "assign the benefits." Write boldly in that section: PAY PATIENT.

Here are the next steps to take:

1. Make a copy of the bill or statement from the doctor. Ask for the bill to be marked "PAID" by the doctor, showing a zero balance.

2. Make sure this bill or statement lists out, line-by-line, the exact procedures you had done, with the billing codes that doctor's office uses. They should provide you with a detailed bill before you leave the office. Tell them you'll wait while they generate one for you. In my office, we created a bill like you send to the insurance company and we just changed it to say pay the patient, instead of assigning it to the doctor. I wrote in black marker pay the patient. All our patients where paid quicker for just 10 minutes of our time. Ask your office if they will do this for you.

3. Make a copy of the credit card receipt or your canceled check showing that you paid.

4. Make two copies of all this paperwork, including the claim form you completed. They will lose it at least once. If you can scan the paperwork and save a copy as a PDF file, do that, too.

5. Attach everything together, get a large envelope because it will be noticed if it is large and mail everything to the right address for claims. Please double check where claims are to be sent, it will be a different address then anywhere else, it is a processing center for claims. It is always better to get a person you can fax or email the claims to if you can and the follow up information of that person.

6. In addition to mailing the claim, ask for the billing department's fax number and fax the claim to them. By law, they have to keep a fax account of every fax they receive. They can't say it was lost because they have to verify and log every fax that comes in.

When submitting super bills, or any bills with a doctor or facility that is not a provider in-network, just know that you are going to have to fight. This will be whether you want them to apply the amount toward your deductible, or to get reimbursed for your cash outlay. A fun trick they might try is to keep returning the paperwork to you, saying it is missing a billing code, even though you have already given them the code three times. They want you to realize you will be rewarded for staying in-network and penalized for going out-of-network.

Personally, I have never followed the rules when it comes to insurance. I break the rules all the time; not because I want to cause problems or be a troublemaker and not because I like to fight. I like to fight because this is my body. What I allow to happen concerning my health is totally up to me and nobody else. If I know what's going to help my body to survive, and I allow the insurance company to divert me from what I think is right for me, I have no one to blame but myself. I would rather go into debt than to do something I didn't feel was right for my body.

I hope this chapter helps you to find your own courage to demand your rights. Learn all you can about your insurance benefits and codes. Codes are not hard at all to learn. Each has a detailed explanation and if that does not fit what happened, then be ready to prove it.

The next chapter is about creating a care book. When dealing with your insurance company, write down everything and keep copies of all your paperwork in your care book. Know your coverage so when they offer a procedure, you can quickly determine if it will be covered.

After doing your research, if you find a treatment—such as receiving extra fluids by IV—that will help you survive, always find a way to get it if insurance isn't going to pay. Find out the cost, work out a payment plan if needed, and say yes. If a treatment can extend your life for a year or two, think about that time with your family.

Insurance companies are not sympathetic when it comes to money due them. The fact that a loved one has passed away will not be an excuse. Collectors will come after your family for the balance and eat away at any savings you have left behind to pay for things. This amazes so many people. They believe when they die, any balance is forgiven. But if there is money to find, they will come for it. If you have a spouse, they will be responsible for paying the balance. Even if it takes years, eventually, the insurance company will collect in full.

Yes, you can claim bankruptcy, and try to charge off the debt. And unfortunately, many cancer patients and families have had to do just that. This ruins credit ratings for at least seven years, and becomes a public record. If you own property, they can attach a lien to the title. They will get their money. They may lessen the amount in negations, but they will not put themselves at risk to do it.

Many families have told me if they had known, they would have chosen a different path. When emotions are high, and grief is mixed in, things are not always thought through. There is nothing like living through cancer with the stress of bills to be paid back when you are done. Staying on top of all costs during your care is the best thing you can do for yourself and your loved ones!

CHAPTER 36

Your Care Book to Keep You Safe

IF YOU HAVE A GROUP that will be taking care of the loved one going through cancer it will be hard to remember what is going on from day to day. One mistake can cause a lot of problems. Doctor's, nurses and care givers can make mistakes they are human. To make care giving easier for the patient, between family and friends helping you need to make a family book. This book can easily be passed between caregivers.

This makes the care giving less scary for anyone helping out.

I have created pages you can download off my website twentyfiveyearsandcountingcancerfree.com to make the book. Please make sure to use it all the time or not at all.

If one person helping does not want to use it, it will be so hard because you will not know if it has been completed and it will make all other people fearful if they should rely on it.

You will be questioned by the doctors and the book takes the pressure off the person at the appointment or in the hospital with the patient.

It could **take hours** or **most of the time days** before you see the doctor again. It is a totally different world then when you call your personal medical doctor. Any specialist or surgeon you will not have a chance to call them back most **do not accept** phone calls.

You will have to ask the nurse who will tell the specialist then the nurse will relay it to you. Your primary doctor relies on reports and some conversation with the surgeon. They will have one point of contact which is you, to put it all together what they are saying is what happened. It is better to have the same person or people with you taking notes on what they said in the book. So when you talk to your primary doctor you can check if he is informed on what is going on with you.

When you write down things in front of anyone in the medical profession always ask these questions EVERY TIME , I mean EVERY TIME. What is the **date**? And lets see **what time** is it? I need to spell your name right it is and spell it off....

I used to call this in the medical management world a timeline of care. When the doctor comes to see you, he has to timeline his notes as to what he said to you day and time... they should match with what you have in the book, right? It depends when he has time to write his notes or should I say transcribe them to the tape recorder, most doctors now type as they examine you, but believe me they are short with no emotion in them.

Your emotion is just as important as the medical. The coping and the fear can hinder the healing and can cause medical problems in the colon. Not all side effects are easy to see. It truly depends what the patient is feeling as well and that is what they miss all the time. Your colon can be affected by your emotions. They will not ask if you drink water, ate a full meal, had a bowl moment, walked, only what is happening with what they did not how your body reacted to what they did. You have the care book to tell them what is truly going on. If they do not ask tell them to put it in their notes what you tell them.

Medications

Your care book is so important for keeping track of medications. Are you supposed to write every medication down? Yes, you can if you want to. I know, you are thinking, "They are the hospital, why should I have to?"

Because in my case, they tried to add or change my medications all the time. I refused a lot of it when I found out they were only giving it to me *in case* something happens. I kept insisting I didn't want to take certain meds because of the side effects. "Oh, it's okay," they'd tell me. "We always give it to people."

Yes, you can refuse to take it. Always ask what it is for and what are the side effects before taking any medications. This is not only to help your body, but remember, you will be paying for everything. Nothing is free or "included" in the cost of something else. You only have a set amount of insurance money so do not spend it on things that do not make sense for you.

I have seen hospitals try to give my loved ones meds.

"This is *in case* he gets constipated," they'd say.

"Wait," I'd challenge them. "He is not constipated."

"I know, just *in case*," came the reasoning.

"No, his body does not need one more drug to overcome," I'd insist. "Why are you trying to give that to him?"

"It makes it easier *on us* instead of having to deal with it later."

What?

Every, and I mean every, drug has a side effect to the body. If God did not design it to be included then it's foreign to the body. The body has to figure out how to get rid of it. As I started to ask questions, I found most of the drugs are not needed. Plus, if taken, I could have more problems to fix later.

Emotions

Your emotional state of mind is so important. How are you truly feeling? Not what you are just saying so as to not be a burden to the family.

"No, no. I'm fine. You can all leave me here alone for hours."

Is that truly what you want?

The time in the hospital has to be used for both physical and emotional healing. You know there is only a certain amount of time you can be away from the things your family needs from you. Use a video-chat app like

FaceTime to connect with them outside of visiting hours. This way, you can talk about how you are feeling and see what they are up to or need help with. This can be so helpful in making you feel you are still part of the family while you are in the hospital.

You can also assign your loved ones certain times to visit. The important times when you need someone for support are during doctor rounds, tests, meals, when nurses change shifts, at medication times... yes, all of these things are on a schedule in the hospital. Ask when they happen and be ready to make notes in your care book.

Elimination

Something to pay close attention to in your care book is what goes in and what comes out. If you are given fluids, that same amount of fluid should come out. If you are not urinating regularly, that is a problem.

If you are eating, you don't want to become constipated. Many patients become septic because they are not eliminating waste from their body often and regularly. If no one is keeping daily or hourly track, it can't become a problem after it's too late. Why don't they keep track? Because you were admitted for cancer surgery, not digestive problems. A one-time bowel movement is not a bowel movement if the colon has impacted the rest of the food. Think with common sense. If you eat for three days and you have one movement, where is the rest of the food in your colon? Do not let them send you home with a problem. They are primarily watching for complications from your breast surgery. Again, you have to speak up because they won't go on a fishing expedition.

Your body will tell you just about everything you need to know about how it works if you are paying attention. Stress can cause your colon to act differently and bind-up waste. Many heavy pain medications are also diuretics and they rob the body of fluids, causing all kinds of problems.

Just think of how many times you should go to the bathroom in a day. Think of babies and your animals. How often do they go? Adults should eliminate at least twice a day. Your body wants desperately to get rid of what it doesn't want and can't use. You want your cells to be cleaned and they need fluids to do that. This means drinking water throughout the day. If you can't drink it directly, consider asking for fluids to be administered by IV.

If the hospital room does not have a measuring tool in the toilet, they are not measuring your levels of the water coming out. If they just come and empty the hat, they are not watching it. I cannot tell you how many times a nurse would empty the hat without writing down the measurements. I would say, "Wait, don't you have to write that down?"

"Oh, I will later," they say.

"No, you will now because I'm keeping track and I want to know, too."

(Dirty look.)

Meals

One of the most important times to have someone at the hospital with you is during meals. If you are too tired or nauseous to eat, eventually they will take the food away. No one will be told you did not eat. Remember, you need nutrition to heal! The nurses do not have time to make you eat. What are they feeding you in the first place? Is it enough to give your body the strength it needs to heal? It doesn't make any sense to eat what I call "air food" with no nutrition.

You maybe craving an outside food for the taste but at what cost to your body? Is it going to be easy to digest and use for your healing of your body, or make it harder taking healing from your body to deal with it?

You need protein to have the strength to walk and move the body fluids. My husband brought me protein shakes. If asked they will give your loved one what they consider protein and supplements which is Ensure. All you have to do is read the back to see why you should not take it, it is a drug. There is nothing from God so how can it heal His body? The drink is very high in sodium—which raises your blood pressure—and it's full of sugar: an 8-ounce serving has about 6 teaspoons of added sugar.

Which brings me to picking food on the little menu they give you. There will be limited food that will heal you on the menu because of the what is purchased and how it is prepared. Always go to the easiest to digest for your body with the most nutrition you can find.

For protein, a non-red meat is easier to digest; salad (use olive oil and lemon for a dressing) is good to help you not get constipated; lightly steamed vegetables and rice is okay (brown rice is better); but no bread, no dairy, and no sugar. Select everything you can find that God has a digestive enzyme for to break it down. Try not to pick anything that is a processed food.

Work with your family and plan how you are going to have the best fighting chance to heal while you are in the hospital. Eat as much fresh, organic foods as you can. Ask if you can put a small refrigerator in the room. If they say no, just ask for help in bringing in fresh food every day. If anyone objects, ask to speak to the nutritionist on staff.

And don't forget to put all the diet information into your care book. This way, everyone knows your food plan and what you are eating so they can fill in the holes and give you the best chance to heal.

Walking

In order to get out of the hospital, you need to be sure that when you get home, you are safe. The sooner you get up out of bed and start walking, the sooner you will be home and able to walk to continue your recovery.

Use your care book to mark down your walks. Write down how much walking you need to do on your own as your exit-strategy for getting home.

Have a walking plan for when you do get home and assign someone to help you with your scheduled walks.

Nothing is more stressful than trying to manage your own care. Your loved ones want to help you and be part of your recovery plan. Just as with your food program, get a plan for your daily exercise and stick to it as best you can. Always remember just one step toward healing is all you need to do, then two steps just keep moving ahead everyday

Water

This shocked me, but 90 percent of the time, no one wrote down what I was drinking. How do they know if you are becoming toxic if they do not know how much water you are drinking? How do they expect your body to flush out the anesthesia drugs? How do they expect you to have a bowel movement when they are giving you pain medication if they do not know your water levels going in?

When I was visiting my sister as she was dying, she had been constipated for days. I knew she was in terrible pain from the waste build-up. I found a colonic clinic and took her there for treatment. Mounds of waste came out of her colon. She was out of pain, finally.

During a colonic, a small tube is inserted and warm water will flow in and flush your colon. They hold the water in as they massage your colon. When released, the water and the waste that has been stuck is removed. If you can stand to see it, it will amaze you. Please be sure to only see a licensed specialist in this field. Ask your doctor or hospital to make some recommendations and then do your research. Holistic centers are also a good place to start your search.

If you can't drink water, then find out how to get more water in your system using IV methods. This is so important to keep your bowels functioning. Your insurance and medical staff may tell you that it's not that important. But don't listen to them. If you are not having regular bowel movements or urinating equal to the water you are taking in, don't listen to them. Be able to point to your records so you can make an informed decision.

There are water IV clinics popping up all over to help with water intake. I would either pay the hospital or go to one of these clinics. Always investigate them thoroughly first to make sure they are clean and know how to properly insert an IV. I was in a hospital once and they inserted the IV wrong and my tissues filled with fluid. I was the one that brought it up to the nurses that I was not peeing. I had to stay in the hospital for three days on diuretics to get rid of the fluid.

Hiring a Caregiver

Here is the order of how staff takes care of you in the hospital: doctors work with registered nurses (RNs), who work with licensed vocational nurses (LVNs) who will take care of you in the hospital. LVNs report to the RNs. They are all human and make mistakes. If you don't see them putting something about your care in your medical record right after they do it, then it is up to them to remember to do it, or they'll tell someone else what you said or did. If you talked about it and they did not put it in the computer, *then was it said?* The LVNs do not have access to the computer and they are the ones getting the information from you because they are around you more than the RNs. Make sure to tell the RNs directly if you want it entered in your record. If you do not see them enter it into the computer, ask them to do it as your doctor checks the computer for updated information.

A Note to Families: When hiring a caregiver or notetaker, remember to go over this with them. So many people think this will automatically be done because they are in a hospital but that is not the case. This is a lot to put on the patient to do by themselves.

Let the patient know someone cares about them and if you can't be there when needed, arrange for someone to be there for you. Even if you have to pay for this, it will cost more later if something goes wrong. It will cost you the rest of your life if you should have been watching, but did not catch something. I have been an advocate for people sharing my hospital room when they had no one to help them. I think since no one was with them they were treated differently. The more watch dogs you have, the better.

Remember, everyone makes mistakes and there are many aspects to your loved one's care. Computer records are only as accurate as the information they are given by humans. Be active in your loved one's recovery and pay someone to keep the records updated and ask the questions needed. When something doesn't look right, speak up!

Wound Care

After surgery, how you take care of the wounds is a serious assignment and not something you should ever take lightly. Improper wound care can mean life or death. My father died of a leg wound that was not treated correctly by the family members who were watching him. They never told me about his wound until it was too late. I sadly found out they never gave him proper care.

After a mastectomy surgery, you'll be dealing with drain care and wrapping the chest. It is so important both are done correctly. All breast surgeries can lead to complications. The hospital is an infection waiting to happen. Everything you touch can have a germ on it. I used to clean my room when I was bored. It would make you sick to see the filth that came off. The IV pole was the worst, the bed rails were second, and the list goes on and on.

The drains go directly into the wound and can cause all kinds of infections if not emptied often. The drains work by suction and if they get too full, the suction lessons, so less fluid is being sucked from the wound which can build up in the chest.

You'll need your care book to keep exact records of the amounts coming out, including the date, time, amount, and fluid color so you have a log of the progress. If anything does not look right, take a picture, and send it to the doctor immediately and call the office to make sure they received it. Do not wait. If they do not call you, call them again—it is that serious.

When we have a written account of what's happening, it's the best way of keeping in straight. This way it's not hearsay or we think happened. If an emergency comes up, hand your care book to the EMT or the hospital staff so they can see at-a-glance what has been going on. This could be a lifesaver when minutes count.

Wound healing is the hardest part of any surgery. You need to look at the wound's recovery as a part of your entire recovery. The body has a lot to say to you. Are you listening? A good way to confirm what you are hearing is by keeping your care book updated at all times.

My plan for this book is to keep you safe and allow you to heal without stress and to help your loved ones feel safe when they are taking care of you. This is a way of you working together as a team when dealing with your care. You do the healing and they do the watching to make sure everything is being done correctly while you heal. **You can print a copy of my care book for yourself which is on my website,** twentyfiveyearsandcountingcancerfree.com.

Please make sure you totally understand the above and everyone commits to it all the time. There can be **no gaps** or people won't know if something is accurate or not. Make sure you add the date and time to everything and initial what you wrote so you know who wrote it. If questions come up, you can go to the source and ask.

Be safe, be prepared, take charge, and know it is always your right to ask questions of anyone.

Acknowledgments

ALWAYS REMEMBER when you are given a task you think is impossible, you are the one limiting yourself. The people you ask for advice will limit you to what *they* would do. Always base what you can do on *you* and surround yourself with people who share the dream that you can accomplish anything you want to do.

Stay on task and the Lord will do the rest.

So many people have helped me write this book. I never would have completed this book without you.

To my sister, Erin Artoff, a day does not go by that I do not think of you. I know if you were here you would be cheering me on like you did with so many other things in my life. I know I will see you again, I will make you proud helping other people know the truth. Love You So Much.

To my mom, Joanne Illsley, you showed cancer who is stronger by living years longer than what they thought. I know I will see you again, Love You.

My daughter Kasondra, thank you for believing in me. You are an amazing daughter; I am truly blessed by you. I love you.

To my many friends I have lost, we will fight to make sure you did not die in vain, we will find the truth. Love you.

Friends I Could Not Live Without, Thank You All

Peggy Bence, no wonder you're a great life coach and friend. Without you I would not have completed this book.

Becky, you kept the fun in my life, which gave me balance. Thank you for your kindness and friendship.

Luisa, for such fun distractions, support, and ALL your prayers.

Sandi, for your dinners of listening to me, supporting me.

The Life Groups at North Coast Church Carlsbad

Thank you. You never let me stop even when I wanted to. The accountability made me always move forward. I have truly been blessed by all of the groups. A special thank you to these amazing ladies who never questioned that God gave me a project. I was blessed by your encouraging words weekly. Delilah, Linda, Tobi, Kim, Dody, Sue, and so many more.

The Team Behind the Book:

To the team that was there through it all, you were amazing, and I consider myself blessed to have received both your book experience and knowledge. Thank you for your help, you are amazing. If you are interested in receiving professional guidance for book writing and cover creation, please go to my website twentyfiveyearsandcountingcancerfree.com for direct links to those who lead me on my book journey.

The True Power Behind This Book

The true credit for this book belongs to my Lord, Jesus Christ. Whenever I became stuck in the process of publishing this book, the Lord would introduce someone new to help me continue my journey; every time, and without fail. When the Lord leads you on a journey that challenges who you know yourself to be and what you may think you're capable of, don't stop. He will be there with you always…

Ultimately my prayer is that this book saves the lives of all women facing this disease, so that no family has to know the pain of losing someone to breast cancer.

About the Author

IN AUGUST 1994 AT THE AGE OF 35, Karen Campbell faced breast cancer with adversity all around her. She had to fight doctors, insurance companies, and family to get what she wanted. Why? Karen decided to do the opposite of what the normal protocol for breast cancer treatment was in the 1990s. Her fight saved her life. Before receiving her breast cancer diagnosis in 1994, Karen had managed holistic centers all over the country for more than 20 years and that knowledge paid off. She had watched the body heal itself for decades. She knew there must be a better way to help the body battle breast cancer—and she was right. Her doctors warned her she was putting her life at risk. Twenty-five years later she proved them wrong. As Karen began to tell the breast cancer community how she stayed cancer-free for more than 25 years, daily requests started coming in for a book to make it easier for them to follow.

In 2015, using the Internet, Karen began her quest researching the latest findings to add to her chapters on what she had personally done in the 1990s. What she found were studies and research that were not completed and other studies explaining what in the environment was thought to cause breast cancer. As she studied, she found research to improve the chances of not getting breast cancer again. Why was this not told to her, her sister, and other family members as she watched them lose the battle—along with countless other breast cancer survivors? The findings could have helped them to better their chances of staying cancer-free.

Karen's goal, by taking five years to write this book, using her vacation days and weekends, was to take these studies and make them easy to understand. Using these studies and her experience, her goal is to give you a fighting chance in your battle with breast cancer.

Karen's belief is with knowledge comes power, with power comes strength, and with strength comes your ability to fight breast cancer. Her book will give the information you need to find your inner strength to battle breast cancer.

Karen's mission is to bring the breast cancer community an understanding of why we need to stand together to find the truth of what in the environment is causing breast cancer.

If only 25% of breast cancer is genetic
then what in the environment is giving 75% of us cancer?®

Join the cause and sign the petition at telluswhyweredying.com.

Made in the USA
Las Vegas, NV
05 August 2021

27617891R00199